Daniel Lux

CAMDEN PARASITES

CAMDEN PARASITES

DANIEL LUX

Phoenix Press
London
2007

Published in 2007 by
Phoenix Press
PO Box 824
London
N1 9DL

ISBN 978-0-948984-36-5

Cover illustrations by Laura Norder
Design and DTP by Jayne Clementson

Printed and bound in the UK by Polestar Wheatons, Exeter

CHAPTER ONE

I won't bother you overmuch with details of family life; a quick sketch of my circumstances being sufficient. Anglo-Irish, born in Islington, London, 1958. Fortune never smiled upon me. Our family occupied an unenviable space somewhere bottom of the social and economic pyramid. Bad housing, chronic overcrowding, appalling diet, shoddy clothing, indifferent education, every physical and psychological disadvantage imaginable. When you're a kid, it's noticeable through having no money or the things that money can buy. The other kids have sweets, comics, new toys, and a degree of self esteem derived from a limited spending power. Relying upon fickle generosity and handouts from those other kids gives a sense of impotence that stamps you from an early age. So the choice is simple, resign yourself, or do something about it.

Shops were stacked high with unobtainable goodies, so it became a case of go without or steal. After all, I figured, it doesn't make any difference if one or two things disappear from the groaning pile. Getting a belting from the old man if caught didn't mean much. I'd be on the receiving end if he'd been boozing anyway. So if the nicking opportunity presented itself, I'd take advantage.

Sufficient to say that by age fourteen, I nicked on a regular basis. My school, a Catholic institution off Brick Lane, stood far from my Holloway home. This meant employing various circuitous routes back home to distant Holloway, taking me through parts of the nearby City. Invariably I'd be accompanied by my classmate Stan, who also lived in my faraway part of the world. Stan was taller, thinner, more gangling than myself, with his lank dark hair. I was of average height, well combed black Paddy barnet, flawless face, complimented by baby blues. A portrait of youthful innocence, supplemented by a pair of glasses when necessary, although these were only produced for complicated shoplifting scenarios. Usually, a couple of hangers on would join us homeward bound, hoping for a share in the booty.

Me and Stan had nerve and daring. He drew the attention of the assistant while I got down to work. I didn't bother just helping myself to a couple of chocolate bars, feeling that if you were going to take something it might as well be a lot. After all, the penalties were the same, whatever you took. So I'd have a whole display box away, sometimes from behind the counter, off in a flash with the goodies.

We started going further afield to maximise opportunities, a chemist near Liverpool Street mainline station became another target of wandering fingers, helping ourselves to sunglasses, plucking them from the rack, then flogging them to Messenger boys or young office workers for a couple of bob. A church stood near the chemist, so sometimes we'd nip in, pay our devotions, then rifle the charity boxes. If we struck lucky, we'd come out a couple of quid richer.

Our attention was now drawn to a nearby musical enterprise, situated in an arcade, more corridor than shop. The owner seated at the back, behind piles of sheet music and old 78s, instruments stacked haphazard. The man himself blended with the musty atmosphere. Mid fifties, he reminded me of a teacher, fading jacket, patched leather elbows, sex offender type. When you're fourteen, someone that age appears truly antediluvian, a pushover for quick wits. We'd employ the decoy strategy, the favourite ruse being to ask him for sheet music from the charts. While he searched, we plundered.

By now myself, Stan and a promising recruit Lingy were naturals at this thieving lark. This Lingy was another tall stringy specimen. bit of a freak, abnormally long legs, squat body, bristling acne. The three of us haunted this musical shop. taking anything that struck our fancy. Soon, we became more daring. a box of expensive German harmonicas went astray because I liked the illustration on the box label. A violin found its way out under my blazer. Again, as always, we'd end up distributing our haul as gifts or keeping them for ourselves – not that we had any use for these things. One fact I'd always noticed, even at this early stage of my career. I'd never known anyone turn something down because they knew it to be stolen.

But sooner or later, all things come to an end, the bloke must have twigged it, for we found ourselves caught in a trap.

Maybe, due to inexperience, we were getting complacent, returning to the same place, not allowing for a breathing space. Whatever the cause our guard dropped. The same light fingered trio returned, but the man seemed alert for once, darting eyes, stepping from behind the piles of sheet music. We didn't indulge our usual purloining, apart from a tambourine tucked under my blazer. Soon as we walked outside two men grabbed me and Stan, Lingy scuttling off.

Alright for him; not us though. These were plainclothes police, attired in early seventies casual style, the one who nabbed me having longish ginger hair, brown leather jacket, flares. He didn't waste time on formalities, firing questions in rapid succession.

"Right lad, what are you doing? Where are you going? What's this? Where did you get it?"

Stan being clean, they took his lying particulars, sending him off, flea in the ear. The geezer ran out of the shop in a state of extreme agitation.

"That's the one! He's the thief!"

Leather jacket held my arm, no real force employed as I'd bowed to the inevitable, I didn't resist. They had me, that was that. The other cop took custody of the tambourine, patting my back as they loaded me into a nearby patrol car.

"Don't worry son, you'll only get a ticking off, unless you've been in trouble before, then it'll be the high jump."

I went quiet, in a state of combined disbelief and shock, none of this breaking down crying, I want my mum. A short drive took us to City police station. Taken in, I wasn't charged. Instead they deposited me in an empty office, searching my pockets thoroughly. The pitiful schoolboy contents arousing a degree of sympathy on one copper's face. Bubblegum, glasses, elastic bands, snot-rags. I needed a piss, so one of them accompanied me, standing there, watching. I remembered some of the stories I'd heard from other kids.

"They'll search you, take everything from your pockets. One'll come along, take a butcher's at you 'aving a slash."

Having extracted the required information they left me alone to ponder my situation. I heard a lone typewriter clatter away in the distance and thought about Stan and Lingy tucking into dinner at home. The door swung open, another officer, this time in uniform. He looked pretty strange to me, dark hair, balding on top, long sideboards. The uniform smiled, making out he liked me, giving out with some chat.

"Well, Daniel, I've just called your mother on the 'phone ... She didn't sound very pleased ... She's coming down to collect you."

God, I thought, it'll take an hour, she'll be well narked. Uniform sat behind a desk, me surprised to see him light up a cigarette. Leaning back on the chair, looking important, he opened a drawer, producing a piece of apparatus.

"Do you know what this is Daniel?"

I'd seen a breathalyser on the telly but played along. "Is it a balloon?"

He looked pleased, this obviously being part of some well worn routine. "You know Daniel, you're not far wrong there."

Like a presenter on kiddies telly, he droned on about the breathalyser, demonstrating its uses for my benefit. I pretended to listen but had other things on my mind, wondering if my old dear had told the old man. I snapped out of it when he popped the vital question.

"Why did you take that tambourine Daniel?"

"Don't know,"

"Well ..."

He drew back, then after some hesitation, continued along this track. "What would you do, how would you feel, if you had something and someone stole it from you?"

Had the answer to that one, no point in playing it too thick. "But I haven't got anything worth stealing."

That particular avenue of questioning blocked, he began another approach.

"What do you want to do when you leave school Daniel?" I must admit, he had me there.

"I don't know."

He rolled his eyes, fumbling around in the drawer, jangling keys, looking occupied. He sprung one on me.

"Have you ever considered joining the police?"

Honestly stuck for a reply, even a sarcastic one, I stayed silent. Getting no reaction, he returned to shufflling. I wasn't daft, having heard what the police were like, knowing how to behave if collared. So I kept my trap shut, said nothing.

After an eternity mum showed up. She didn't mess about, gave me a clip around the ear, pulling the punch though. The uniform had a word with her, me receiving the predictable bollocking. It felt all a bit unreal.

During the journey home I had to ensure mum didn't tell Pigface so I cracked her up, making her laugh. Every now and again she'd be amused, then slip back into disapproval. On the upswing, I broached the subject.

"We'll see."

Landed it. Knew I'd be okay. Not charged, that would be the end of this episode. After moaning about the time and expense, she asked me one question.

"What on earth did you want with a tambourine?"

I fancied saying something about joining the Salvation Army but on reflection, thought better of it. I promised the old dear I'd return home using a different route, avoiding further trouble.

All went without incident until the end of the week, Friday. Kids are always more lively that afternoon, glad school's finished for a couple of days. It all happened without warning as we walked along, fucking about. O'Connell, the meanest kid in the bunch, a hardnut, initiated the action. O'Connell fascinated me, not so much his dullard personality, but the prematurely thinning hair on his old man face. Passing a block of gloomy council houses O'Connell, followed by the rest of the pack, rushed over to a nearby pile of roadworks rubble, scooping up stones and fragments. O'Connell bellowed, spit flying.

"Get the Paki cunts!"

The others chorused. "Paki bastards! Paki cunts!"

Straight away they heaved munitions. Ground floor windows smashed. I saw the intended victims in their houses. The whole thing seemed strange, like slow motion. An old man sitting on a chair holding a baby, other figures, partially obscured by net curtains, diving like shadows to avoid injury. I ran off with the pack, heart pounding. Within a minute's breathing space, all strolled along as if nothing had transpired out of the ordinary, talking about football. They broke off to go back to their respective homes, leaving me alone with O'Connell who snarled in my direction, making it clear he wasn't pleased.

"Never saw you fucking pick anything up."

After he'd lumbered off growling, I resolved there and then to get back with Stan and Lingy. No more sitting on the substitute's bench for me, first thing Monday afternoon, I'd resume the journey home around the more picturesque detours of the City.

Once nicked, you tend to be more cautious for a couple of weeks but it didn't take too long to get back into the swing of things. Thieving mania grabbed me, I started thinking of striking further afield, taking note of shops as I travelled home, making observations from the top deck of the bus.

By now, I'd steal anything I could get my greasy mitts on. It was not as if I derived any financial advantage from my wrongdoings, it just boiled down to the thrill of taking what I couldn't buy in normal circumstances. Most of the stuff I gave away at school which enhanced my reputation to the extent I wasn't shoved about by the hard cases, who admired someone with a touch of nerve.

Outside school hours amusement came from meeting young lads with interest in the thieving line. The kids in my street were thickos, losers with impressive probation records and tramline scars. Their main interest in life consisted in loafing on street corners and the odd ritual punch-up. Wit and conversation that strayed beyond their narrow horizons seemed to be lost on them. As for myself, if I had any personal interests it was the movies, to which I bunked in regular ... and nicking.

Stan told me about a place nearby our homes called The Factory. So being of an open mind, I paid a visit. It wasn't up to much, no table tennis, five-a-side football or many other activities associated with youth clubs. The place resembled nothing more than a glorified hut, dimly lit, decorated with cheap, badly painted murals. Hits of the day thumped out from a creaking speaker, the older kids not throwing their weight about as they spent most of the time engaged in the equally futile pursuit of chatting up the girls. Gregarious as ever, I mixed with everyone, shyness had never affected me to any degree. The more adventurous lads from my street attended, hut I steered clear, knowing what was on offer. Some of the older lads took the odd sly puff from a joint in the corner. As for me, I had no time for anything except nicking. Finally, patience paid off as I met a couple of lads I found interesting. One was American, named Davis Seaburg, an outgoing type like myself.

My curiosity was aroused as I'd only seen Yanks in movies and on the telly. Despite Davis being resident for six years, he retained a trace of accent, he was a thief on the side, as indeed were all the kids I mixed with. An acquaintance of his also sulked in the corners, a lad named Redd, squat, ginger hair, square face, bulging eyes, giving him an embryonic appearance. Redd glorified in his reputation as a brawler, the older kids never messed him about as Redd wouldn't hesitate to front out a grown geezer. With this duo, plus the crew from school, we were in the process of building up a team.

The formalities of introduction concluded, we had ourselves a functioning gang of thieves. We lacked an operational base but that wasn't long in coming. Curious to check out where Davis lived, as I'd heard from Redd his parents weren't short of a bob or two, I wangled myself an invite. Even from the street outside I could see straight away this was a million miles removed from what the rest of the crew were forced to endure as living conditions. The Seaburgs lived together in a splendid Georgian terraced residence. This place stood several storeys high, overlooking a narrow park, close to the Angel tube. Inside was a revelation, another world. I was overwhelmed by the sheer size of the house, the number of rooms and endless staircases.

Goodies lay all around the show, antiques, Persian rugs, the works. Everything here seemed comfortable, not off-putting in a hands-to-yourself sense. I wandered about in a daze, exploring. Paintings, full length bathroom mirror. This family also possessed all the modern conveniences of life, central heating, electric toothbrushes, stereo and wonder of wonders, a colour telly, plus thousands of record albums. As I'd just started to appreciate music, this collection resembled a treasure trove, a never-ending source of experimentation. I found myself wondering how comes the four Seaburgs had such good fortune to occupy so much space while my family of five were crammed into a damp patch, a fifth of the size? A bohemian atmosphere prevailed in the house. The parents, Roach and Edy, lived what is described as an open relationship. But I wasn't there to criticise, far from it, I wanted to learn, gain every possible advantage. The house usually contained guests, people staying over for indeterminate periods. Roach and Edy constantly popped out to attend exhibitions and other such edifying experiences and were friends with celebrities although, to confess my ignorance, I'd never heard of any of them. All I knew was stealing but I fancied developing fresh talents, maybe something in the musical field.

It didn't take long before the crew were meeting up at the Seaburgs, sometimes after school but mostly during weekends. Centrally located, having plenty of space away from prying eyes, this place became our base of operations. Roach and Edy didn't have a clue what was going down. I guess they were just pleased Davis had some friends of his own age.

Myself, Stan and Lingy started departing early from school on a regular basis. No one seemed to notice these vanishing acts, or care, as they don't put themselves out when you're festering away in a lower fourth year form. It's only a case of marking time until you're cast out on to the shrinking jobs market.

We started travelling around the underground system, bunking fares, picking out destinations at random. Occasionally, we'd find ourselves frustrated, stranded in a rural area, no shops, the day wasted.

I thought it was about time that I got myself some decent clothes, as befitting an up-and-coming lad going places, so we started afternoon visits to Carnaby Street and Kensington. Stealing clothes is difficult at first, but I learnt quickly enough. Apart from mental preparation, a degree of physical readiness is required, wearing clothes bigger than your actual size, or donning that old favourite, the mac, with little underneath. Menswear shops with their over-anxious assistants were avoided. Instead we'd haunt boutiques. If trousers were required, the trick was to inspect the rack, remove two pairs, giving the illusion only one had been taken. Without waiting for a nosey assistant, I'd walk straight into the changing booth. Making haste, I'd slip off my own trousers, dive into the desired pair, then squeeze my original pants over them. Once the wrinkles were smoothed out, I'd stroll out nonchalantly, replace the other pair back on the rack, making a big display, indicating I had no desire to purchase. The same performance applied to jumpers and jackets. Sometimes I might get a touch greedy, so it would look like someone in loose clothing, possibly in need of a meal walking in and later a chubby hunchback emerging into the street.

We graduated to big stores in Kensington and Oxford Street. Carnaby Street and Kensington Market were more for trinkets, although sometimes we'd strike lucky with a classy bit of merchandise. Oxford Street though, soon became a no-go zone, the police were alert, always on the lookout for kids like us bunking off school. We made regular visits to a large trendy store in Kensington, the famous Biba's. And we weren't the only ones. I noticed some lads from Holloway and Finsbury Park busy lifting gear. We'd acknowledge each other with knowing glances, winks, sly grins, then return to our respective plunderings. Usually, we'd be better dressed for this store, trying to look like spoilt rich kids, me wearing a stolen fake snakeskin jacket. Security was lax, to say the least.

Those involved on our expeditions would be from school plus Davis and Redd at weekends. Everything stolen got shared out at the end of the day, the booty carried around in a large carrier bag with the Harrods motif. Ordinary bags aroused suspicion. By this time, I had a nicking coat, a mac with false pockets and lining, could even have albums away in it, handy, since I'd already purloined a stereo.

No doubt about one thing, Biba's had become our favourite lifting spot. They sold fashionable clothes and had a swanky restaurant on the top floor. Biba's was so easy to plunder that at first we didn't believe it, suspecting a sophisticated trap designed to ensnare thieves like ourselves. But this wasn't the case, as we discovered to our delight. Biba's had all the features of a big store, huge staircase, extensive floorspace with plenty of nooks and crannies plus hiding places, pillars handily placed near the shelves, making it possible to blatantly line up clothes, nip behind the column, hide the goodies on the person as the others kept watch. I always enjoyed the thrill of lifting rather than keeping dog, more scope for individual initiative, plus the buzz factor. We rarely came out empty handed, our hauls including such delights as my velvet snakeskin jacket, leopard patterned trousers, the best silk and cotton shirts, sweaters with hand knitted designs, more jackets of all descriptions. Rock stars purchased gear here, everything being outrageously expensive, far beyond the pockets of even the hardest working man. All the stuff was of excellent quality, well ahead of its time in the fashion stakes.

Apart from stealing I cultivated other interests. The crew started attending big rock gigs at the premier venues. Naturally no financial transactions were forthcoming with even the fares bunked. We dressed for the occasions, wearing Biba's finest, Stan and Davis the most enthusiastic music fans, along with my good self. I found gigs easy meat, bearing a strong resemblance to bunking into the cinema, flashing bits of paper masquerading as tickets, sneaking through exits. So we had the opportunity to catch the star acts of the day perform. But we weren't merely satisfied with sitting on empty guest seats or swiping albums, posters and memorabilia from the promotional stalls. We discovered methods to get backstage, such as waiting for a bouncer to stray from guarding an entrance as most skived off, or had their limited attention span diverted. Once backstage, we mingled. There always being plenty of people hanging about, groupies, guests, numerous liggers. We played it straight, not allowing ourselves to get impressed by the here today, gone tomorrow celebrities, no rushing over for autographs or gawping open mouthed. No reserve was shown, however, when it came to tucking into the big spreads. At the most, the stars got a restrained hello off us.

With my burgeoning record collection, stereo attendance at rock gigs, interest in things musical reached the degree where the next logical step was to obtain instruments, learn to play, form a band. Then, just maybe, the ultimate. Success in capital letters. Everything else had gone so smoothly, why not this?At age fifteen, I felt myself to be going somewhere fast. And it wasn't a young offenders' institution.

The first golden opportunity presented itself near the Seaburgs' house as we strolled through Camden Passage antiques market, closed up for the evening. An older lad, Scobie, teamed up with us after we'd met him at a gig. From Belfast, willing to take a chance and, most importantly for us, able to drive, having use of a van. Redd noticed a partly-opened door during the stroll and as we puzzled about whether or not to enter, Davis ventured the information that music lessons were held in the building. Stan and Scobie's eyes lit up.

"Come on, what are we waiting for? Let's have a look!"

Straight in, along a corridor, checking locked doors, then downstairs. Here another door stood alone in the basement, unlocked. A surprise greeted us once we opened it. Nothing in the room apart from a fully rigged up drum kit. Scobie knew all about drums. Under his expert guidance we dismantled the set in a jiffy. We soon had the entire set snug and safe over at the Seaburgs. Once the euphoria wore off we piled it up into Scobie's van, driving over to his squat.

We pulled up at Scobie's place with ourselves and the haul jumbled up in the back of the van. This was our first visit to a squat and although curious, me, Redd and Stan thought the place a touch on the dingy side, mattresses, sleeping bags liberally strewn throughout the rooms. A fire blazed away in the lounge, spewing out toxic fumes from the bits of broken furniture burning in the grate. Light bulbs hung bare, sheets of tatty cloth draped the windows, adding to the scruffy surroundings. Scobie had a girlfriend in residence. The other squat inhabitants were a collection of life's losers: a couple of Northerners and a junkie in the basement. We weren't treated to a fixing exhibition, but he came wandering into the lounge, beard, long hair, cadaverous. After taking one look at us three lads, he left. One of the Northerners tried out some shock value on us innocent young fellows.

"He's a junkie, boys."

I'd never seen a junkie before, apart from on the telly. He, like this basement dweller, didn't look in a healthy state.

"He's on a Turkey lads."

"What's that?"

The Northerners glanced at each other, then at me.

"He's sick."

As we left, a warning sight greeted us – Redd pointing down to the basement. Through the window grime, I saw the junkie sitting huddled next to an electric fire, blanket draped over his shoulders.

What with the lifestyle, schooling took a firm back-seat. When you fester in a lower fourth form, the authorities only go through the minimal basic motions, not seeming to care, which was alright by me. Most of the other kids, those outside the crew, found my stories rather difficult to swallow, being so dense. As I attempted to convey the world of high powered nicking, rock gigs, meeting stars, some of the more primitive elements became aggressive, calling me a fucking liar. Soon, however, the doubters changed their minds when I became a star of television myself.

When you get into nicking in a big way the tendency is to talk shop. New methods, places to visit, security, layout. For relaxation we discussed music, listened to it, laid plans to play, enter that world, make our fortunes. Watching *Top of the Pops* on telly one evening, we started talking about bunking in. It didn't take long to discover when and where the programme was recorded, so next week we bunked the tube to White City and the BBC Studios. Me, Stan, Redd and Davis climbed over a wall, into the grounds, security being a joke. Once inside in the complex, we located the studio entrance, asking one of the bemedalled commissionaires which floor *Top of the Pops* was recording. We reached the appropriate floor, bursting into the studio, straight into the crowd. It wasn't a bit like the telly programme, but the studio appeared larger than imagined. The cameras seemed enormous, and you had to move out of the way pronto as they zoomed by. The songs were all mimed, clapping on speakers. Most of the audience came from youth clubs, the high point in many of their lives as they stood in dazed wonderment before the stars. We returned for six consecutive weeks.

The day after recording they screened the programme, us getting quite a thrill, sitting around next evening watching it. Friday, the kids as school would be all over the crew members, firing off questions. They believed me now.

"How did you get in?"

"What's it like?"

We ventured the information but none had the nerve to try their luck. At least my stories didn't sound far fetched anymore. It's strange how people get recognised after a television appearance, Redd getting laid on the strength of it. As for myself, I got waylaid by the rival school. Instead of a kicking, I too found myself recognised by one of the more observant. Plied with questions as opposed to getting rolled, I span a web of tales about how to sneak in, seeing the stars, that I'd wandered around some of the other studios, been inside the Tardis. The *Top of the Pops* craze only lasted a couple of months, us getting bored. We decided to concentrate efforts upon obtaining instruments, forming our own band.

CHAPTER TWO

Bunking off from school one afternoon, me and Stan headed up West in order to try out guitars in the music shops, the idea being to handle them, pluck a few strings, get the feel. Neither of us could play a note, but you've got to start somewhere. After attendance at gigs we were interested in electric instruments, so upon entering the first music shop, we attempted playing on a display model, plugging it into an amplifier. After creating an awful noise, the assistants moved us on.

"Come on lads, you've had your fun."

Straight into the next shop. Here, the guitars were hung up on a special rack. One of the assistants, obviously a budding star, demonstrated his virtuosity to a would-be customer, with the remaining assistant stood lost in conversation, chatting up a young woman who conveniently obscured his view from behind the counter. I reached up to the rack nearest the door, removing a flash looking guitar, then pretended to strum. No one noticed. Stan opened the door, me quickly zipping out, still strumming, doing the duckwalk. The tube journey back home felt unreal, underground lighting showing the quality of the instrument, a six stringed semi acoustic Hofner with gold machine heads and pickups plus Mother of Pearl inlay. Lingy could play a few notes so I flogged it to him for the knockdown price of a tenner. Plenty more where that came from.

Me and Stan then discovered a classy music store in Regent Street. An employee sat behind a desk close to the door, the rest of the store unattended, open planned. Various instruments were displayed in glass cabinets, the few guitars close to the door. Wearing our school uniforms, we explored. Near to the sheet music section a stairway led off to a corridor downstairs, so, ignoring the no entry signs, we dived down to take a peek, arriving at a repair workshop. Doors were closed but that didn't matter as I'd noticed a xylophone and glockenspiel parked outside, both handily cased. We had to steal something while the chance presented itself, so we picked them up, making our way upstairs, simply walking out. The man behind the desk sat reading a book, his mind elsewhere. Had he bothered to look up, he'd probably have mistaken us in our uniforms for schoolboy prodigies. Even as we strode out the door I planned a return visit, us holding the act together until we'd progressed further down the street, finally allowing ourselves the luxury of cracking up laughing.

Two days later, we returned. Straight past the sheet music, downstairs to the repair room workshop. This time our haul consisted of two alto saxophones, a top make, Selma. We traded them in, a task rendered easy as Scobie had by now obtained a job working in a music shop. He arranged the deal without the knowledge of his bosses. In exchange we received two practice combos, a bass guitar and electric six string. Now the proposed band could begin to take shape. I fancied learning to play the flute, figuring if I could master this, the saxophone, oboe and other such related instruments would follow as a matter of course. So two of us strolled in, out of uniform, well dressed but nothing flashy, Lingy had a coat slung casually over the shoulders as we wandered around gazing at the cabinets. A couple were unlocked, presenting an open invitation. Inside the flutes stood to attention, begging to be snatched. Lingy dipped his bony hand in, lifted a flute from the display rack, tucking it under his coat. Not wanting to leave empty handed, I made off with a piccolo, plucked from another cabinet, fitting it neatly into my inner top pocket. Within minutes we were out riding on a bus, scrutinising the day's doings, congratulating ourselves.

By this time the 'Davis lent it to me' story wore a bit thin. The bedroom crammed with a stereo, two hundred albums, a wardrobe full of expensive clothes, saxophones, xylophone and an acoustic guitar. My old dear hardly bothered to venture inside Aladdin's Cave anymore, knowing something serious to be amiss, but with the pressures of work and keeping the family together she had little time to do or say anything about it. I'd become virtually unapproachable, in a world of my own, always a thousand excuses or explanations at the ready. In any case, she seldom caught a glimpse of me as the Seaburgs' place had become a second home.

Having stolen a plethora of instruments and equipment between us we'd started trying to play something. Scobie had moved out of his squat, getting himself a small flat together in the Caledonian Road, living above a barbers, one of those trendy long-haired parlours. The bloke who ran it allowed us to set up in his basement. Progress on the musical front came tortuously slow, us succeeding in mastering a few chords. Sometimes, we'd draft in someone who played adequately, helping us sound a whole lot better, especially if they played lead guitar. Stan sounded good enough to be passable, while Davis turned out to be utterly useless, Scobie struggling away on bass, me providing vocals, harmonica blowing and tooting a couple of notes from a flute. Energy and enthusiasm were there in abundance. Soon we did begin to sound like something approaching a band of sorts. Redd and Lingy often turned up to provide moral support despite having no desire to be in a band. I started thinking that these humble beginnings could represent the first faltering footsteps on the road to fame and fortune. And why not? Everything else had gone smoothly enough so far.

Like most young lads of a heterosexual inclination, I'd become interested in girls. So far however, all my passion and energy had been invested in stealing, learning to play music and becoming a star. Not having a girlfriend caused no worry, knowing my time would come, that I'd get around to it sooner or later. I'd seen plenty of nice looking girls at gigs but, just turned sixteen, I regarded myself as on the young side, looking two years less than my actual age, and the girls themselves always appeared much older than me. Some girls Davis knew heard about the bunking into gigs, wanted to come along. Show-off to the end, only too happy to oblige, I helped get them in. They were suitably impressed, particularly since after the gig finished, I introduced them to the star of the show, topping off the evening by grabbing a couple of champagne bottles as we departed.

We started hanging around with some of these girls, eventually gaining access to their homes – big houses in fashionable areas. These were middle class offspring, wealthy backgrounds, that other world I'd glimpsed at the Seaburgs. The mothers, mostly divorced or separated, were usually neurotic actresses, university lecturers, writers of various descriptions, their other kids wild, smoking, growing dope plants in the greenhouse at the tender age of twelve. I'd never given the slightest consideration to going out with girls from my own background as they regarded me as mad while I knew they were all thick. Possibly both sides were correct in their assessment, but I'd discovered from experience, very much to my embarrassment, that any one of these twelve year old middle class children seemed more articulate, intelligent, better company than girls from my street of my own age or even older. At least these twelve year olds knew the name of the planet they lived on. Most of their houses were enormous by any standards, larger even than the Seaburg residence. The poorest girl from this gilded set lived in a ground floor Victorian flat near Parliament Hill. This still represented more than double the space in my home, with less people.

I wouldn't say I'd started getting big-headed, but I thought myself to be leader of the crew, nothing going wrong bar the occasional hiccup. Apart from being the best thief, biggest mouth, most confident, quickest wit, I was singer in the band. Sure I'd cultivated a huge swollen ego, but didn't suffer overmuch from this. Besides bunking in to gigs and band practice, I spent every other night at the girls' houses, feeling I wasn't doing too bad so far. I started paying attention to the best-looking girl among the new crowd, Louise. For a laugh, to show her something different, I took Louise along to a football international at Wembley, England versus Poland. We bunked in to see the home team putting up their usual dismal performance but, on the strength of that night, I got an invite up to her house, more importantly, unaccompanied by the others.

I travelled from the miserable, dismal Holloway to St John's Wood, dressed to the nines. On the escalator I thought myself to be rising in the world in more than one way, despite empty pockets. Louise's place stood like a fortress, detached with a decorative battlement arrangement, the only features missing were portcullis, moat and drawbridge. Louise ushered me in. Immediately I started checking the place out. It wasn't comfortable in a bohemian sense but nevertheless exceedingly plush, plenty of big airy rooms. Before introducing me to the parents, Louise drew me aside.

"Danny, please, if they ask what you want to do when you leave school, tell them that you want to go to college and mention nothing about wanting to be a pop star."

I shrugged. "Okay."

Louise then formally introduced me to the parents who were in their late forties or early fifties. The dad ran a Harley Street medical practice, mother worked as a shrink. Both were thrown by my accent, contact with the lower orders having been restricted to delivery men. They were uncomfortable, lost for conversation. Over dinner, as predicted, they broached the subject of my future. Failing to mention pop stardom, I handled the show with ease, careful to avoid bolting the food. The whole episode seemed awkward for them, but they were polite, so I spun a yarn pleasing to their ears about how I planned to study English and music at college. The parents allowed Louise to do as she wished in her life, trying not to pry. My relationship with Louise was no cause for concern, being childish, no sex, innocent. Maybe though, as regards such matters, I wasn't all that innocent because I'd been screwing Stan's girlfriend on the side, him unaware of the hanky panky. Sex was okay, another feather in the cap, but it didn't obsess me, not being all it was cracked up to be. I found sex the perfect way to unwind after a gruelling day of nicking, music and gigs, that's all.

Our favourite shop facility, Biba's, had a garden roof restaurant where they held night time gigs for the select wealthy few. We tried to crash one but security was red hot, impassable, so we found ourselves excluded, sitting dejected on the stairs, a couple of floors below the action. We all felt cheesed off, lounging about thinking of a way to gain access. Stan was leaning on the handwheel that controlled the shutters, having a smoke, fiddling with it. I noticed the shutters moving, then simultaneously we realised a golden opportunity had presented itself as light shone from underneath.

"Try it out Stan."

"Move it some more."

Stan succeeded in moving the shutter up a couple of feet while I kicked the door behind. To our amazement and joy it swung open. Quick as a flash we slid underneath, leaving Stan to wind down the shutter, sit on the stairs awaiting the knock. Inside, we walked to the entrance of the menswear department. The lights were switched on already and piped music played, no one in sight. It felt like being a robber band breaking into a Pharaoh's tomb. We dashed around in a state of near ecstasy mixed with slight panic, pure adrenaline rush, snatching clothes from racks, overcoats, silk shirts, sweaters. Once loaded up, we headed for the shutters, gave the knock and were away, swearing we'd be back mob handed for a repeat performance.

The following week, me, Lingy, Stan and Redd returned for a far more methodical plunder, not even bothering to check out the upstairs restaurant and gig. Stan remained behind to manipulate the shutters after presenting us with a detailed shopping list. Once inside, we rushed over to a table containing a selection of fancy leather holdalls and bags. Soon, we were stuffing them full of goodies like there'd be no tomorrow. Silk monogrammed pyjamas, mackintoshes of impeccable design, the ubiquitous silk shirts and leopardskin trousers, white cotton strides, cricket jumpers, skiing jackets. Patent leather shoes were scooped from boxes and racks while I lifted bundles of socks, bow ties and silk handkerchiefs. We moved to the next section of the department, helping ourselves to men's perfume and toiletries, art nouveau lighters and numerous other trinkets. When Stan got the knock, rolling up the shutter on cue, an endless stream of grossly inflated leather bags crammed with booty disgorged underneath, followed by the team. We loaded up, struggling downstairs, Redd kitted up like a Himalayan porter, two holdalls draped over each shoulder, a bag in each hand. The rest of us were modestly equipped, but it still presented a mammoth task, negotiating the stairs. Downstairs, outside, Redd hailed a taxi, then sped away, the rest of us taking the tube. As usual, we had no cash spare, so despite the wealth of material goods we bunked the fare. First stop Lingy's. His old man wept tears of joy as we piled the gear on him. Me and Stan then split, going home our respective ways. A couple of days later, I popped over to Lingy and Redd's homes. Lingy's old man wore one of the silk shirts and a pair of the white cotton strides, while Redd's dad wore just about everything except the leopardskin trousers. I thought it looked weird, old geezers dressed up like rock stars but I kept such observations to myself.

One Saturday saw me, Davis and Redd visiting a star studded open air concert at Crystal Palace. Heavy security, but we gained access, heading backstage. Soon tiring of that, we stepped out into the throng, Davis eager to prove himself, having previously failed to materialise for the great Biba's raid. Us lads from humble origin had made all the running, so Davis felt obliged to turn in a performance. Prowling by the catering tents, Davis lifted a flap at the rear and noticed the cash being placed in a bag behind a makeshift counter. We stood watching Davis stretching out, succeeding in grabbing the money bag without detection, me and Redd open mouthed in amazement. We all slipped off to the outside, splitting off in different directions prior to a meet up shortly after. From nowhere, long-haired plainclothes pounced on Davis. I simply slunk away, drawing a deep breath. One of the cops grabbed Redd who was nothing if not a slippery character. After a derisory scuffle, the cop fell to the ground doubled up, Redd's knee having found it's mark. The two of us met as arranged, creeping back to join the crowd, watching Davis being slung into the back of a meatwagon, handcuffed. He looked worried as the doors slammed shut. We couldn't do anything about it, just one of those things. Once you've been nabbed, that's it, it's all down to you to keep your gob shut, nothing more, nothing less.

It's strange how you tend to forget about someone once they've been nicked. Me and Redd went on to enjoy the rest of the afternoon and early evening. Return journey, I did some late night shopping at a trendy shop, having a fancy mirror away. Back home, while fixing it to the wall of Aladdin's Cave, both parents arrived back from the boozer, me thinking nothing of it until they burst into the room.

"Where did you get that?"

The old dear had spotted the mirror.

Out came the dog eared explanation that Davis lent it to me. She wasn't having any of it.

"Oh no he hasn't! Don't lie to me! The police were on the 'phone this afternoon, you've got to report to them. What's all this about you and Davis stealing?"

"I don't know what you're talking about. Davis must have got into trouble on his own. Mum, he's rich, he don't have to steal anything,"

The drunken old man, wearing one of the silk shirts and ties, threw in his penny's worth.

"The police know everything, you think the police are stupid, but they know more than you do, they've got walkie-talkies ..."

And so on. I'd heard this tired refrain before, knew it off by heart. Luckily I was a bigger boy, so he couldn't do anything about it physically. I switched off, allowing him to splutter into drunken exhaustion before closing the door in his face.

Monday, I went to the police station to be identified by the arresting officers. Scobie meanwhile had got a legal aid man on the case. This fellow was ace, no idiot. During my interview he passed slips of paper to me bearing such messages as 'Say no' or 'Don't answer that'. I'd spoken to the legal aid man before the interview, finding him interested in all the bands I'd seen. What with me able to quote chapter and verse regarding the contemporary musical world, everything became relaxed. They released me without charge, so I shot off to celebrate by bunking into another gig later that evening.

It later emerged that Roach had grassed me up, because the morning in question, he'd seen me in company with his snow white son. But Davis had been caught with the money, not me. My old dear gave him an ear roasting over the 'phone, so Roach must have suffered the pangs of guilt, fingering an innocent person. As a consequence, I still frequented my second home. One thing I couldn't quite understand. Unlike others I could mention, Davis didn't get probation, didn't even have to see a shrink, merely getting a stern reprimand from the bench. Maybe it had something to do with his impeccable background or behind scenes string pulling.

Towards the end of the fifth school year came the inevitable careers officer interview. The man looked bored stiff, me having no intention wasting my life working, aware that the wages on offer were next to nothing. People like the Seaburgs never did anything that remotely approached work yet always seemed to be loaded, lived in a nice house, so why should I toil away at a dead-end job for a reward not worth considering? I told the man how I wanted to get a band together. It must have been obvious that I didn't want to work. He tried to steer me off dreams of stardom by asking what my interests were.

"Music."

He found it difficult to pigeonhole me, line up suitable slave labour. I must have been a tough customer but he came up with a useful suggestion. Why didn't I try getting into a college of further education, study music? Now that sounded alright to me so I agreed to an entrance interview. He indicated that he'd make a special representation on my behalf and for that I was grateful.

Thanks to the efforts of the career officer I had an interview set up for Kingsway College. As an Institute of Further Education, it meant I didn't require any examination results. The college building, located near Kings Cross, seemed, in comparison to my school, to be ultra modern like a heliport. The students were predominantly white but there were a sprinkling of darker faces. Girls looked nice to my roving eye, like young women. As regards clothing and appearance, there was a heavy hippy hangover. I must admit, though, my hair had started to get a touch on the long side. But I wanted to be a star so such things were to be expected.

The interview was conducted in front of a panel. The woman looked like an older version of the students I'd seen in the building. She wore baggy mauve corduroy flares, sandals, a black woollen turtle neck sweater matching her long dark hair. One of the men was small with grey hair, knee length patch-pocketed leather jacket, Hush Puppies. The other fellow looked a bit of a scruffbag, older, I guess he suffered from a drink problem. As for me, I'd kitted myself up in the best gear, nothing too outrageous. After all, one thing I could remember from school, always dress well for interviews. They asked me what I wanted to study so I didn't waste any time beating about the bush.

"Music. English. Art. Drama."

I explained there were no facilities for such activities at my school. The scruffbag wanted to know why didn't I stay on at my school for another year, get some exams? Stumped, I came out with the first thing that came into my head, telling them how distressing school in the East End was.

"What do you mean?"

I noticed the young woman shudder as I piled it on. Most of the kids at my school were members of the National Front, dissidents supported the Klan. Three heads tilted in unison. The truth of the matter was the kids were too dense to understand anything about political parties. I felt things were going my way, I had their sympathy.

"Who is your favourite author, Daniel?"

"Steinbeck."

Like most of my contemporaries, I'd never read through a whole book in my life. I remembered a set book at school, *Of Mice and Men*, claiming this to be my favourite book. The woman questioned me further.

"What is it you like about his work?"

Lucky I'd also remembered a teacher telling us that you'd always find characters in a Steinbeck novel were invariably trapped in their circumstances and situations. So I parroted that line. Heads nodded in agreement as I strung them along. They asked me about other authors. As I'd seen *War of the Worlds* at the cinema only a week previously, I said H.G. Wells. They thought I'd read the book. I said nothing to shatter that illusion as I poured on the charm. They lapped it up, me telling them of my musical interests, practising in a rock band, wanting to play the flute. After a while, they asked me if I wouldn't mind stepping outside for a moment. Of course not. As I stood outside, straining my ears, I couldn't catch anything drifting from the other side. The door opened, scruff smiling.

"Would you come in please?"

I walked in. I'd landed it, enrolling later that month. Stan, Redd and Davis applied after my success but didn't even get an interview. Roach seemed puzzled.

"I can't understand why Davis didn't get in."

The answer to that question was that Davis was only one step above that of moron, but I kept the obvious to myself, not wishing to court eviction from my second home.

CHAPTER THREE

I became a college boy. Me and Lingy, the only person in the crew genuinely pleased at my extended role in the educational world, set about obtaining the necessaries I'd require. Piles of stationery, sets of pens, music paper. We could have done this blindfolded. Apart from bookshops, stationers are the easiest targets when it comes to theft. At Kingsway I'd already enrolled for all the artistic things, in other words everything I guessed to be a doddle, with minimum written work. Music, drama, film and media studies. Most of the posher students did arts like me, as they weren't much good for anything else. I'd already clocked the predominance of middle class accents. Had they hailed from my background they'd be out working in a factory, doing a life sentence. The atmosphere felt relaxed, laid back, unlike anything I'd imagined a place of education to be. I'd already discovered the common room, full of comfy armchairs. According to the rules, teachers and other staff were forbidden to enter. This was something novel, worth checking out once I'd become more familiarised with the surroundings. Not that this task took long. After an hour or so, I'd become everybody's friend, humorous, salt of the earth. Most people are shy, irrespective of social background and I had the knack of helping them feel at ease, wanted. By now I'd picked up enough information to ensure my stay would be a happy one. Mixed classes. Teachers who insisted on being addressed by their first names.

I attended some of the afternoon lessons. Owing to my outgoing perhaps somewhat manic nature, some of the students asked me if I took drugs, in particular, did I smoke dope. I lied to be hip, saying yes. I found myself drawn to the wonderful common room, this certainly being the most interesting place in the building. I had the feeling that there were some real extra curricular lessons to be learned there. So I checked it out. Some black dudes were playing cards, smoking spliffs, thumping the table whenever a good hand presented itself. The middle class group were automatically identifiable through their accents. Some attended my classes and they lolled around smoking joints, talking about that most boring of subjects, politics. One of their number had detached himself from the stimulating conversation and sat strumming a guitar, playing *Stairway to Heaven*, a cluster of admiring girls gazed at him. I just couldn't resist the urge to have a go, so after he'd finished his party number, I strode over.

"Give us a go, mate."

Before permission was forthcoming, I already had the guitar in my lap. Without hesitation, I belted out a few chords, shouting the lyrics to a half remembered

Beatles song. The previous guy didn't sing and I must say that I always found it remarkable that although a lot of these types could play, they were inhibited when it came to exercising the vocal chords. The ceiling shook as I bashed out my rendition, everybody sat up, taking notice, even though I hardly qualified as a brilliant player. It didn't matter, as the vocals muffled the fluffed notes. Everyone broke into broad smiles, a good response. I even threw in a trick I'd mastered in band rehearsal, twisting the guitar, throwing it, then catching it again to play on. All the common room were hooked by now, even some of the black guys peered over, managing a grin. Finally I handed the instrument back to the stunned musician. Now everybody wanted to know me there and then, asking if I knew so and so, what bands I'd seen. I'd cracked the scene. Someone handed me a joint, I passed it on without taking a puff. This would certainly be the place to hang around. These hippies, as I labelled them for want of a better term, came from Hampstead and Highgate. Thoughts of parties, getting laid, visiting more palatial homes raced through my head. The hippies must have been of the opinion that, owing to my behaviour, I was stoned out of my crust all the time.

By this time Louise and me had drifted apart. She'd gone her own separate way, mixing with chinless Hampstead guys a couple of years older than her. A pub scene, something that required what I didn't have: money. So, not wishing to compete with the chinless ones who were always loaded, I called it a day. Not that any of this represented a dent to my confidence. I had many things going for me, including a new girlfriend, Sally.

Sally was a couple of years younger than me and attended trendy Camden Girls School. Most of the young girls in this Hampstead scene seemed to go out with slightly older blokes, nothing unusual in that. I'd met Sally during the summer, having marked her out as a bit different from her friends, whose parents were the by-now-familiar collection of writers, actors and lecturers who lived in big houses. Although Sally went to Camden Girls she wasn't from the same background as her friends. She lived in a council house, a nice one though, situated in Hampstead. Dad was a Tory-voting train driver. Sally was yet another piano player, the parents wanting her to get on in the world. Despite this relatively humble home environment, Sally mixed easily enough in the exalted company, possibly explaining the mutual attraction. Sally reminded me of Louise in one important way – she refused to let me have sex with her. But again, this prohibition didn't worry me, as I busied myself screwing some of her less-inhibited friends instead.

Back at college I discovered the courses were far more relaxed than the classes I once endured at school. Learning here appeared to be more pleasure than burden. Teachers introduced me to the world of literature. The favourite lessons though, as to be expected, were music classes, one of which turned out to be the theory of music. Here I learned to read music, write it, the principles of orchestration. Encountering difficulties, I persevered, studying music from baroque through to classical. During this time, I was also in the process of mastering the flute with my own individual tutor.

On the social side I'd become a now familiar figure in the common room. The hippy crowd were friendly and my act went down well, talking about my favourite topic of conversation, the band. They passed me a joint again. Having told everyone I indulged I had to smoke it or stand exposed as a bullshitter of the first order. I couldn't get away with passing it on forever, so I took the plunge. I did it like an old hand, inhaling the smoke. A massive drag, straight down deep into the lungs. After holding the smoke down, I exhaled smoothly. Throat and lungs burned but I concealed this without bursting into a violent cough. At first the sensation felt like being glued to the floor, the inside of my head spinning as it tilted backward, then forward, finally coming to rest in my lap. I screamed at the top of my voice.

"Fucking hell!"

People started laughing, thinking me to be messing about. But this was for real. I passed the joint on without appearing to be a gibbering heap. After the reeling sensation, which wore off quickly, I now felt stoned, in a great mood. Elated, even better than usual. I could only compare it to what I'd imagined being merrily drunk might be like. Time for a song, I grabbed the guitar, making with the song and strumming. Then I broke down laughing, cracking up, just couldn't hold it together, bending double on the floor, clutching the guitar. My laughter became infectious, jollity spread all around. After ten long minutes the effect wore off, leaving a pleasant glow. I knew I'd be trying this out before long again. By afternoon's end, I was making enquiries as to where I could score.

Going out with Sally I became a regular attender of parties on the Hampstead and Highgate circuit. Her friends threw them almost every weekend. I didn't forget my friends either, with Lingy, Stan and Redd being true enthusiasts. My observations also continued. We were hardly ever formally invited, so I kept ears and eyes open to discover when one of the Camillas or Ruperts were holding one if Sally hadn't got an invite. The rest was easy, us always gaining access, usually by the simple expedient of talking our way past the door, dropping a few names here or there. Girls' parties were the best, owing to the higher ratio of female to male.

Once access had been gained we made for the spread, eat our fill, then look for someone from college, Camden Girls or other bastions of educational privilege. Curious as always, once I'd dispensed with formalities I'd check the other rooms out, in particular those that were forbidden as they represented the greatest temptation. Not that I harboured evil intent. I just wanted to see how the other half lived. It felt like exploring an unknown country, which in a manner of speaking is what it was. We adopted the ploy of attaching ourselves to anybody with dope, nine times out of ten cadging a blim or walking off with the joint. As the males of the species were freaked out by our accents they hardly ever objected to us taking liberties, fearing aggravation of the physical variety. The parties where the parents were present I found personally embarrassing as I watched them trying to blend in, acting young. They reminded me of the teachers at college and I had the suspicion they were keeping a beady eye on things despite their dope-smoking facade.

But all this aside, should the temptation to wander exert itself, the parents, if present would be looking over your shoulders. This was because of our accents. No matter how liberal or progressive they were, they distrusted and feared the lower orders, yet attempted to conceal it with patronising smiles and gushings. But I wasn't fooled. If the parents had been away for the evening but arrived back early, everything would be fine until their ears picked up our accents. Panic would set in. They'd scan the rooms, check to see if anything had gone missing then beam us some phoney grins.

At these parties I liked chatting up the girls, strumming any spare guitar, making people laugh. The girls seemed interested. After all, I had a band. Girls from my own background were certainly more repressed so I never had sex or other fun with them. These Hampstead girls were completely different in their outlook. All were on the pill, most into getting laid. They were also good conversationalists, the only minus being their habit of hitting you up with useless facts and information. But even this could be utilised, regurgitated to impress when chatting up at other parties. No doubt, the best parties were those where the parents were absent throughout proceedings. Mummy and Daddy might be staying in their cottage in Norfolk or the South of France. Their children were allowed to do more or less what they wanted, usually supplied with the cash to do so. When the parents were away, lots more dope was in evidence, plus screwing in the bedrooms, and music would be loud. These people had everything and more.

Most of the guys were slightly older than us intruders but we took the piss without mercy as we simultaneously scrounged their dope. Starting out on the moderately polite side, it didn't take long before the blow took effect. Then we'd cast aside any inhibitions and let rip. Threatened by our gruff mannerisms, accents and general demeanour, they'd allow us to get away with it. Being scared, they didn't know how to handle us. The more we excelled ourselves, the more we discovered that we could get away with it. We always hijacked the stereo sounds, playing music we preferred while making ourselves at home raiding the well-stocked fridges. By this time, I'd also started drinking, usually sticking to wine, always freely available at these shindigs. I quite enjoyed moderate tipples of booze as this tuned me up. I never drank too much, wanting to be in control, just merry enough to have my fun. If it became too late to catch bus or tube, then maybe the odd pushbike went missing from the hallway. Better still was staying overnight. This meant you'd get laid. With plenty of rooms, beds and willing girls, getting fixed up hardly presented a problem if I felt in the mood. I went for the soft comfortable roomy beds with sidelights, enjoying taking the mickey, putting on Daddy's night-gown, puffing a cigar, pouring a drink from the cabinet, gazing upon the floodlit garden below. I'd polish this off with a joint from the parents' stash and free phonecalls. I amused the girls by doing imitations of the posh accents I'd taken note of during the party, flicking cigar ash on to the oriental rugs, making remarks.

"Bottom's fallen out of the market darling."

It gave intense pleasure, laying there in the morning, surrounded by luxury and comfort. These places reeked of mostly inherited wealth, craftily masquerading as money earned from the pursuit of liberal professions. But I knew different. I'd been keeping my eyes open, not allowing myself to be overwhelmed or over-impressed. I learned daily as I progressed further into the centre of this new world. I'd had a good time for sure if I was still on the premises on Monday morning. By this time I'd have shifted the telly into the bedroom along with the remote control panel. Plus breakfast in bed with a tray. The life for me.

With the social side of things taking off I felt so busy that I didn't have many spare moments for college learning. Some subjects lost their novelty interest so I jettisoned English, concentrating on film studies. This meant doing little more than watching two or three movies a week. Alright by me. I persevered with the musical side, thinking that if not fame and fortune, at least a living could be had from it. My individual flute tutor turned out to be a small woman in her late thirties, straight-laced from her clothing down to her personality. The lessons consisted mostly of me standing in front of a mirror, keeping my body still while playing simple notations. When we finally got on to music, it proved to be a disappointment, being of a descant recorder level. *Pease Pudding Hot* or *God Save the Queen*. This charade dragged on for about three weeks, I felt myself learning nothing. At home I'd listened to a jazz flute record, slowing the speed down and changing the key on the instrument, I taught myself a two minute lick. Next lesson I attended, I played her the passage, giving a perfect rendition. Straight-laced looked stunned, venturing the opinion that I had an amazing technique. Then she put the dampeners on it.

"You really have to learn this way."

Out came the *Pease Pudding Hot* sheet music. I wasn't interested in these Noddy tunes, let alone playing them. I didn't intend wasting any more time with her.

By now the band had accumulated enough practice time and equipment to be a viable entity. Me, Stan and Scobie were the backbone of the group and we decided to place an advertisement in a music paper for a drummer. We finally settled with a fellow named Spider. He turned out to be a couple of years older than us, but what with him being a small time dope dealer, we drafted him into the band.

Now, we practised on a more regular basis, writing our own songs and lyrics. A local grammar school band had hired Hampstead Town Hall and we knew their drummer. We arranged to play as support band, me telling Sally to bring all her mates from Camden Girls.

On the big night in question, setting everything up, I couldn't believe how good it sounded once plugged in and amplified. Something akin to the big gigs I'd been to. We watched the punters roll in until they numbered about fifty. Most were about our age or a couple of years younger, the boys having long hair and Hush Puppy boots. Stan produced a bottle of Cinzano to work up Dutch courage. We both downed it quick, which for me represented a severe mistake, leaving my legs wobbly. Should have stuck to dope. The audience waited and, like I'd seen numerous times before, the band tuned up with me, the vocalist, in the wings. Then came my entrance. Warbling into the microphone, I couldn't hear a word of the lyrics. The sound bounced back off the wall a fraction of a second later like a long distance telephone call. A minute into the act I wished it was all over and done with. Between spasms of performance, I peered down into the audience, unable to distinguish anything, what with my short-sightedness and the hall being dark. At the back I managed to catch a glimpse of people walking out to the stairs. Unable to handle this, I walked off prematurely to the wings. Here I watched the band perform a couple of instrumental numbers, vowing never again to die on-stage.

The grammar school band sounded polished, result of constant practice. They could play, no mistake, but were boring and played other people's music. Observing this from the sidelines, I concluded that to be a first rate band, you'd have to get the whole audience on its feet strutting their stuff. We had a long way to go.

More than a term had passed at Kingsway. I'd rearranged my lessons so music and art became the dominant factor. Instead of Steinbeck I made clay pots and smoked more dope. In fact I couldn't get enough of it, always on the lookout for supplies. Stan and Redd developed a habit of popping over during the lunch hour, so I introduced them to the common room regulars where I still remained a number one hit. It ended up with them being mistaken for genuine students. They mixed well, having learned how to deal with these types at the parties on our Hampstead circuit.

After complaints at the barber's shop, we were forced to change our rehearsal venue. I'd done some homework chatting up a local priest, explaining that I had attended the primary school next to his church, in the very street where the Seaburgs' lived. I dropped a few names of teachers to prove the point. Father Mac was well respected locally for doing good in the community, running a youth club and helping kids in trouble with the law. Father Mac liked me, said I had the gift of the gab, allowing us to rehearse in one of the church towers. We could store our equipment on the premises. The sound of our band could be heard in the street below, but this time no one complained. We'd always be stoned at rehearsals, Spider the drummer still into his sideline of dealing. Curious, we asked him if he had anything else apart from dope.

"I've got some Mandies and Valium."

Spider quoted prices but I managed to ponce four Mandrax. Next day, I gave two to Redd, taking two for myself. We swigged them down with a Coca Cola, taking a walk along the canal towpath near the Angel. After half an hour, I got a tremendous headrush like a dizzy spell plus a tingling sensation down to my toes. Then a feeling of no inhibition. I wanted to do everything. Climb walls, jump from great heights. So we both started clowning, deliberately bouncing off walls, tumbling over on the towpath. Pain or injury was of no consequence. Redd felt expressive.

"Fucking hell Dan, this is great!"

These pills were hypnotics. Later, after forking out for chips which tasted marvellous, we didn't notice we were eating. The cup of tea that washed the chips down seemed exceptional, best I've ever drunk. Time passed quickly, with mental blocks where we couldn't remember what we'd been up to half an hour previously, leading to intense discussion about nothing. Later, recollection of the period under the Mandie influence only came back in fragments, if at all.

The Mandies became a once a week treat for me and Redd. With the fizzy drink starter, he called it doing a shandy. As usual, during a rehearsal, I hit Spider up for Mandies but much to my disappointment, he'd run out. Nevertheless salvation was close.

"I've got some Valium if you'd like to try them out."

"What do they do Spider?"

"They're like Mandies, only weaker."

Ten on approval. I always looked forward to seeing Spider at rehearsals. Me and Redd went swimming the following day, dropping five each. Redd was in the process of teaching me to swim as I'd never bothered to learn at school. We were in the water as the Valium started to take effect. Relaxed, my muscles went loose, an experience I found intensely pleasing. I wasn't a very accomplished swimmer, in spite of Redd's tuition, but now I felt I could swim an ocean and in a better style than my dog paddle. Swimming out into the middle of the deep end, I discovered that I could progress no further. Panicking I sunk below the surface. Redd swam over, somehow pulling me to the side, where I grasped the rail, spluttering, coughing out warm water from my lungs, sound and light from the pool blended into a mess of confusion then another massive headrush. Soon as I'd slithered out on to the poolside, I jumped back in again. I recovered, diving off the top board, a real sensation and a half, like flying, the near drowning accident soon forgotten. Afterwards, dinner. By now, I'd started to enjoy this drug business.

I continued to avail myself of Seaburg hospitality, earning my keep playing guitar, entertaining Roach and his guests. After the grassing incident I didn't trust Roach, knowing what a two-faced creep he was. I even began to suspect Roach harboured a touch of jealousy as I pulled the birds, often turning up with a different one in tow. Roach knew I'd edged useless Davis out of the band, but that didn't matter as he'd managed to get his own band together. The Seaburgs were on a macrobiotic diet and all cheated separately on it. Davis liked going over to Chapel Market to munch his way through a couple of burgers. A muckro diet held no attraction for the likes of me. Even though I regarded Roach as a slimebag, I retained a soft spot for the Seaburgs, or rather their house as this had presented me with the first opportunity to study the comfortable well-off classes and their pretensions. Roach bought himself an alternative status symbol, an old American schoolbus. Inside the vehicle, mattresses and a quadraphonic sound system. When Roach took it on the road, he fully believed himself to be an urban gypsy. These people never worked. Everything they did represented nothing more than glorified hobbies. Some years ago Edy, his wife, had penned a couple of hits, using, I later discovered, a rhyming dictionary. From personal experience I was aware that song writing is hardly the most physically or mentally demanding of labours. But this creative song writing happened to be nothing more than a blinder to somehow justify themselves. By another of those remarkable coincidences, Edy was the daughter of a millionaire, so no way did she earn a penny of the family wealth. Nor did the other drone, Roach. Edy also took drugs while, like many of her ilk, deploring the lower orders for doing the same thing. Me and her son Davis raided her speed and dope stash. Living in a cushioned dream world, Edy never noticed the shrinking stock.

Meanwhile back at my parental home the family was in the throes of disintegration. My lengthy absences went by unnoticed or uncared about. I returned on occasion to immerse myself in Aladdin's Cave, the nearest thing I had to any form of stability. Having little or no money still represented no handicap, everything being free, down to fares. My only expenses were pills and dope. Even then, much of that was on credit from Spider. I felt great, better than working, a world to win, things going my way.

CHAPTER FOUR

I asked Father Mac could we play a gig in the school hall? Alright by him. This gig was more of a sell-out, the local youth club, a contingent from Camden Girls, more friends and Redd. I made sure to be straight for the performance, saving the excesses for later. A touch of professionalism had crept in. We'd added more equipment including monitors, so we could hear ourselves. Nothing was going to get in my way this time. No support band, we were to carry the whole show. I'd mastered the sound system by now, for good measure bringing along some personal instruments, a tambourine, harmonica and the flute. My singing seemed polished and, although no one danced, we had their undivided attention throughout. No one walked out, we were on to a winner.

We asked a vicar up in Hampstead if we could play his church hall, taking care to drop Father Mac's name. So everything was set, with Redd taking money at the door. Confident all would go well, I got stoned prior to our performance. Onstage we hauled out some props discovered in an alcove. A stage tree and life-size crib figures, were spread around to decorate the act. Being no nearby youth club to boost numbers, only fifty people showed up, but this turned out to be the best yet. In the excitement, we all got carried away towards the end of the set, trying to create the atmosphere we'd seen at big-time gigs. We'd already done various costume changes, worn make-up, used a strobe light – and so for the grand finale I threw the baby Jesus into the audience, followed by a lamb. The remaining statues were booted over, after which I lit a match, setting the tree ablaze. Scobie put out the fire with an extinguisher, leading to billowing smoke filling the hall. Redd and Lingy loaded up the equipment pronto.

As we sneaked out, the vicar harangued the remnants of the audience, the hall filled with smoke, a broken sheep's head at his feet. The vicar became emotional, almost shrieking.

"Who did this? Who's responsible?"

Hearing an approaching fire engine, sirens wailing, we disappeared never to return. Word would travel, resulting in more people next time.

Throughout this time, party madness ruled, with me carrying on my performance off-stage, living the part. The new found fondness for pills led to bathroom cabinets and bedside tables. By now I'd discovered Mogadon. If we unearthed a whole bottle, me and Redd went fifty-fifty. Moggies made everything go faster, racing pace. You spoke to everyone, visited all the rooms on the double, then ate your way through the kitchen. Redd usually ended up walking about pigging himself on a tub of fancy flavoured ice cream. We certainly started getting about on this scene, sometimes doing two or three a night at weekends. Most of the geezers I'd met at these parties were about our age, the vast majority smug, snide know-it-alls, their fashion, long army overcoats and boots. If by any remote chance some real lads like ourselves crashed the party these smuggos were always scared.

If I paid a visit to one of the girls during the afternoon, I made sure to be on best behaviour. I enjoyed nosing around the homes, flicking through the album pile to judge musical taste. Sometimes I'd detect the odd mistake in the collection, the parent might have bought their daughter for her birthday something like an orchestrated greatest Beatles hits played by the BBC Philharmonic. The usual staple of a collection was Vivaldi, some might contain a sprinkling of blues and a couple of Simon and Garfunkels. Art featured prominently in the form of books or hangings on the wall, with occasionally the parents or children's work displayed. By now I felt able to distinguish between Victorian or Georgian houses. Some contained bare floorboards sanded and polished to gleam and real open fireplaces. All had antiques plus latest mod-cons. I thought one day I'll have this stuff and more, thanks to success with the band. If the parents were home during the afternoon, they were polite, making some effort at conversation. Sometimes a dad might knock out a tune on the piano for my entertainment. Quick off the mark as always, I dropped the names of composers, taking care to mention those in the album stash. They lent their heads forward on cue.

"Oh, you like classical?"

To which I'd point out the difference between romantic and baroque, information gleaned during Kingsway lessons. Sometimes after an introduction, the girls mentioned how much daddy liked me. Only rarely did I find myself bunged out by a neurotic parent.

I kept busy observing some changes in the entourage. Stan had a girlfriend whose father encouraged him in an arty direction. So he started to paint. The result was pitiful, sub-infantile. Five year olds in the big houses could have done better blindfolded. Stan accumulated art books, crayons, paper and a camera. Unread Dostoyevsky novels joined the recently acquired props. Stan didn't go to the extreme of altering his accent. Instead he used long words without knowing their meaning. Redd, meanwhile had been given a battered old sports car by his dad, who'd got it for the knockdown price of a hundred quid. And he grew a wispy beard. This wasn't the most obvious transformation because Redd now modified his accent, talking slower, trying to pronounce words correctly, making him sound a cross between a Red Indian and Barney Rubble. Redd was tangled up in a contradiction, despite being impressed by these rich kids he maintained a healthy disrespect towards them. Redd tried extra hard as he hadn't scored with this class of girl. French words such as *objet d'art* and *hors d'oeuvres* crept into conversations. Redd felt inferior as all these rich kids could speak foreign languages, little realising this had nothing to do with intellect, more to do with background, daddy owning property abroad, numerous lengthy foreign holidays and the best education money can buy plus individual tutoring. Both Redd and, to a lesser extent, Stan were hung up about their origins. Unlike Stan and Redd I didn't suffer from any of these inferiority complexes and I wasn't exactly helping the situation by taking the piss. Soon everyone was doing imitations of my mimicry of Redd's new routine. I led Stan into traps during conversation, showing him up in front of the girls, many of whom liked the way he looked, skinny, the look of the day.

Back at college I'd more or less dropped out of everything apart from joints in the common room, listening for parties, talking about the band. I sincerely believed success was just lurking around the corner. Money was no concern, I assumed that once I'd made it, we'd be rolling in the stuff. Summer approached, hence the end of a full year at college. I didn't bother showing up for many exams. Those I did, resulted in failure. So I had the choice of resitting the year or getting a job. No contest, another year at Kingsway wouldn't hurt.

The biggest gig yet came next at a squatted theatre in Camden. Connections, including Roach, introduced us to the hipoids who ran the place. All was arranged, us charging the usual fifty pence on the door. That evening, Spider was late, this causing a few anxious moments because we had a full house, mostly older people I'd never seen before. Roach turned up with his sycophantic hangers-on, a small condition applied, the Davis band played support. Spider finally arrived after the Davis lot started their nondescript performance. Spider gave out the apologies, explaining he'd been out of his head the previous night.

"What on?"

I asked this question, wondering if any samples might be forthcoming.

"Smack."

Spider also added that he enjoyed it, right through to and including the puking up. I felt a bit shocked at this revelation, the smack buzz being strictly taboo as far as we were all concerned. I remembered the junkie in Scobie's squat, the blankets, electric fire. I'd been hoping Spider had been taking acid, as I'd been reading and talking to people about it including Stan's girlfriend's cool dad, Hadji. Just before our entrance, Scobie sprung a surprise out of the blue. He was emigrating to Australia where he'd lined up a roadie's job. I pushed this to the back of my mind – everybody's replaceable after all. But for a parting shot I dared Scobie to go onstage naked, taunting him for lacking bottle. On we went to play our best session yet, adding new songs, sounding professional. Scobie came out bollock naked at the end of the set, adding to the now electric atmosphere. Afterwards, I bathed in the appreciative glow, people coming up congratulating us on our performance.

The smell of impending success more pungent than ever, immediate thoughts were about playing up the West End, the next rung on that ladder to fame and fortune. My sights were set big, gigging in clubs instead of glorified squats or youth clubs. We'd also put together a demo tape which had been recorded in a house out in the sticks on an eight track mixer. We sounded slightly better than alright but upon honest reflection, my voice sounded immature. I didn't worry, it would break soon enough.

Hadji was a dope-smoking, acid-dropping computer lecturer. Not exactly filthy rich compared to some of the other parents I'd met, but certainly comfortable enough, able to afford the bohemian lifestyle. Hadji lived near Kilburn with a garden full of dope plants, looking cool with his shaved head, tinted glasses and Israeli accent. Daughter Sharon, Stan's girlfriend, threw a party, so we utilised the occasion to swipe the dope crop. To his credit, Hadji's only complaint was that the harvesters hadn't even left enough for a couple of joints. More importantly though, I'd heard Hadji advocated the use of acid, so one night, me and Redd popped him the question.

"What's acid like then?"

During the course of the explanation, Hadji came out with some weird descriptions.

"You can become a lamppost if you want."

Redd gave me the what's all that about look. I asked Hadji what were, if any, the best time and circumstances to take it.

"You only take acid when you want to take acid."

"I'd like some now:"

Maybe I'd been a little quick off the mark but after a long rap he agreed to arrange a session.

"Are you free on Thursday morning?"

I was free anytime, so me and Redd went over to Kilburn after a light breakfast. Hadji brewed up some tea, then removed the samples from the box. Here, before us, lay a real collection. Hadji telling us the various brand names. Purple Haze, Californian Sunshine, Cones, plus today's fare, Microdots. Hadji took one, then we followed up, dropping ours, no real idea of what to expect. On this warm sunny day, the logical thing to do was go out into the garden, which we did, throwing a ball around. After twenty minutes Redd started looking like a garden gnome, a mile away. The ball kept changing size. Soon I'd forgotten how to walk, let alone catch. Hadji suggested going back indoors, listen to some music, so we ended up with a pair of headphones each plugged into the stereo. The music felt magnified many times over, my body functioning. I gripped the headphones, the body no longer existed apart from head and hands. Redd looked worried. This wasn't the sort of drug you took for a buzz, more like the nearest you could get to experiencing madness. What if I found myself stuck in this state permanently? Wisely, I didn't dwell on this possibility. Hadji was able to handle everything in this state, answer the phone, then the door to a tall Israeli geezer who stepped inside. They chatted in Hebrew. Redd looked confused.

"Who's this bloke?"

"Don't know, must be a mate of Hadji."

Hadji detected Redd's worries, reassuring him.

"It's okay, he's only a friend of mine. He understands, he's taken acid before."

Out into the garden again. Three hours elapsed since blast off, I was lost out there, in space. The tall geezer started taking the piss.

"Why don't you eat the grass? Looks nice." Together enough, I managed a reply.

"Eat it yourself, you look hungry enough."

After this exchange, we all piled into the motor, Hadji driving on acid, Redd worried again. Hadji drove at a crawl.

"Why's everybody in such a hurry?"

Arriving at Regents Park, colours seemed at full play. Trees and sky infinite. Hadji gave us another rap as we mellowed out.

After awhile, he departed.

"I've got to get home, wife and daughter will be waiting now:"

Even though I'd been wary of the changes Redd was undergoing and taken the piss, we were still great mates. I preferred his company when experimenting with drugs – the likes of Stan were more reluctant to dabble. My once fantastic nicking career wound down for other priorities although we still never paid for anything, pulling off the odd stroke whenever opportunity presented itself.

With the departure of Scobie we were presented with a '*fait accompli*' as Redd might say. The band had been riding the crest of a wave, I'd assumed automatically that everything would continue on the untrammelled road to success. What with all the parties, sex, drugs, rock and roll I hadn't the time or inclination to map out the future beyond dreams. But that niggling sensation kept coming on. So after Scobie departed the rot set in. Over half the equipment took a walk. Scobie had sold it behind our backs for the fare to Australia. We didn't mind him flogging some of the gear but we were surprised to discover he'd cleaned us out. Overnight we'd been reduced to a microphone, mike stand, guitar and combo plus my own equipment in Aladdin's Cave. Scobie also got things done, arranging gigs, driving us to venues, storing the most valuable equipment. Now we were effectively grounded, the band on hold. I collected what remained from Father Mac's, thanking him for the use of the tower. Plenty of the stuff Scobie filched belonged to me but could be replaced by the usual methods. I was of the opinion this all amounted to nothing more than a minor setback. However, it all seemed to melt away. Spider the drummer quit to devote himself to the more lucrative racket of drug dealing. Me and Stan were now always trying to arrange rehearsals, hiring a hall or studio but nothing clicked. The social side exerted a strong diverting role. Parties, drugs, getting laid. Maybe we'd peaked too soon. Me and Stan rehearsed, wrote songs together. Using acoustic guitars only, we sounded like an unintentional folk duo. As with so many other of our new musical projects, it failed to get off the ground.

Apart from the band, my family also split up leaving me alone with a drunken old man. Life continued as always though, with me and Redd going up to Hampstead to booze, listen out for party info. The two of us notched up a few more trips together, all enjoyable. Hadji wasn't the only person with abundant acid, it now circulated all around Hampstead, almost as easy to obtain as dope. Bored one evening we ended up buying a couple of tabs for fifty pence, green ones. The dealer gave us what we believed to be mere sales talk, how strong these were, nothing like them in the known universe. Being late evening, we decided to drop them next day, after all you couldn't treat tabs like jelly babies. Meeting up at a rich kid's home near the Heath, we swallowed them, awaiting the trip. The rich kid, Tobias, didn't exactly approve of us using his place as a launchpad but in order to retain his cool front he was forced to acquiesce. After half an hour it started coming on strong.

I began to get annoyed with Tobias. Then, confusion. The Hampstead hippy trenchcoat brigade arrived in force, Tobias beaming as they tramped in. With them I noticed a black geezer called Malcolm who I'd seen hanging about on the fringes of parties, having him figured for a bit of a Redd character. Putting on the accent, making with the big words. On acid, it was simple to see straight through his act. Malcolm, though, experienced in the acid field, must have regarded me and Redd as unwanted competition in the Hampstead scene. Seeing we were both tripping, he laid a bummer on me.

"Have you seen my Hunter watch?"

Malcolm produced it, me gazing at the object, which had become transparent. I saw the innermost parts ticking away. Now he played mind games.

"Have you got the time?"

I didn't bother to engage him. Instead, feeling the effects of this steadily mounting trip, I moved off in search of Redd, who I located in the mother's bedroom, standing in front of her mirror tears running down his cheeks.

"Strong innit, Redd."

Both shaking with laughter, we decided to adjourn over to the Heath. Much to our annoyance the Hampstead hippies decided to tag along. Truth was we only wanted to be together without this excess baggage, us tripping, them straight. I noticed some squirrels up a tree, eating nuts, illuminated by rays of the orange sun in the background. A Disney cartoon.

"Look at that, Redd."

Tobias, not tripping himself, could afford to be sarcastic.

"They're only squirrels for God's sake. We get them here all the time."

I felt like telling all the poshoes to clear off but couldn't get it together. We stood on top of Parliament Hill. Below the city, a technicolour film set. Malcolm strolled up.

"Have you got my watch?"

I said no, confused, having to momentarily check myself just to make sure this was for real. While doing this, another stronger acid wave came on. The sky turned crimson. One of the trench coats drew me aside.

"It's only a pill, man. It's all in your head."

Mind now tossed out of orbit, the guy became ugly beyond description like something out of a horror movie. Yellowheads covered his face. I braced myself to look straight at him, preparing to issue marching orders, pester someone else. Now the yellowheads hung from his long face, wriggling like green pus-filled worms with bloody heads. His eyes turned purple, hair into curly straw; I didn't need to hang about so I took off, running down the hill, screaming at the top of my voice. I thought I'd started flying, skimming over the grass.

Arriving back home, I dashed up the stairs to empty rooms above. Each flight mounted felt as if I'd just run up it a couple of seconds previously. Same sensation carried on into the deserted kitchen and living room. Everything seemed untidy, I had to go out again after difficulty trying to sit on pygmy furniture. In the street the world seemed impressive, gigantic, like being a three year old again, more room to breathe. Now the sky loomed, overcast, blackish. I thought I spotted Sally, yelling out.

"Sally! Where are you going?"

She ignored me, walking on. I crossed the road, shouting. "Oi! Sally!"

Now she walked faster but I caught up, grabbing her by the shoulder.

"Sally, wait ... where are you going ... it's Dan."

The woman wasn't impressed.

"You're fucking mad! Get out of it!"

I clung on with both hands, imploring.

"Please Sally ... don't turn away, I love you."

At this, she struck me over the head with a folded short umbrella. Each following blow magnified, bringing me back to reality for a split second. A small crowd gathered on the opposite side of the road, talking, pointing at the unfolding drama. I took off home again. Climbing into bed I tried to sleep it off. Impossible.

The walls were breathing asthmatically, floors liquid. I remembered a valium stash, swallowing the lot. Within an hour, I was partially down, the hallucinations still playing their tricks. Walls whispering, but at least things were slightly more rational. The phone rang, Redd at the other end. He hadn't enjoyed his trip either. According to him, everybody was concerned after my take-off into unknown parts. Redd managed it home, me telling him I'd had one hell of a bummer with everything under control, more or less. Later, the phone rang again, this time Sally at the other end. Word had travelled. After some words of reassurance, I hung up. Now I returned to bed, grabbing a few hours sleep, waking up early morning still tripping. The sensation wasn't strong but I had to think in advance to function. I rang up Hadji, him telling me to come over. The clock said early morning as I explained the situation over the phone. With Hadji claiming to be interested in people's bad trips, I made the journey out to Kilburn. On the tube, commuters looked pale, worried, dirt, grime and litter more noticeable than usual. Walking to Hadji's from the station, buildings leaned at a tilt, reminding, mocking me over the bad trip. People walked past like speeded up movie film, in a hurry to get to work on time. Hadji brewed up tea as I attempted to relive the whole story. He told me about a friend of his who'd had a bummer. She believed herself to be falling into a bottomless pit, the sensation persisting for seven years with her ending up resident of a mental hospital, committed for an indefinite period. At least I knew I'd recover, be back to my old self in a couple of days. Hadji analysed my trip, saying that with the breakdown of the family and the band, I'd obviously taken the acid at the wrong time, being in a disturbed emotional state of mind. Sally, he claimed, represented my mother, with me wanting her to come back, to reconstitute the family. Not totally in agreement but with the remnant of the acid still playing out, I didn't bother to argue the toss, just nodding. Hadji promised we'd do another trip together in the near future. This would help sort me out, a good idea, that soon came to pass, no further trouble ensuing. Back on the track.

The only person from Kingsway who I saw now on a regular basis was a fellow named Antonio, who had the hippy image, long hair through to the best patched jeans and pillowcase shoulder-bag. Like myself, Antonio wasn't from a rich family, but neither did he spring from dire poverty. His girlfriends, though, were carefully selected from the wealthiest backgrounds, so that meant I got to visit even bigger houses. Older than me, Antonio hung around with the sixth form girls in Hampstead and Camden, while Sally was a mere fourth former. In these houses with Antonio, after initial exploration, we'd fix ourselves up something to eat, play with new dishes then get stoned. After food, dope, thumbing through the record collections, we'd usually depart early evening. On the way home, Antonio always popped the question, asking me if I liked the girl.

"Oh, she's alright I guess."

In truth, I fancied girls a couple of years younger. Antonio would then triumphantly announce he'd already screwed the girl we'd visited. I must admit though what really impressed me happened to be the fact that some of these places contained indoor swimming pools. In spite of his showing off, Antonio seemed more together than me in his ability to manipulate these rich girls. Besides, he always carried dope and enjoyed listening to me playing the guitar.

To earn some cash, I'd been cleaning the home of some rich old woman near Belsize Park. First thing I discovered, to my great pleasure, an endless supply of Mogadon stashed. I enjoyed visiting this place, doing a token amount of work fuelled by a couple of her Moggies down the hatch. Moggies are what I'd call a 'have a nice day' drug. I soon found myself scooping them up by the pocketful. The woman never noticed, having a large jar of them. Blessed with moderate success in other endeavours, I still remained skint. No rich parents to lavish dough on me, I had no choice but to try earning some along the lines of my Belsize Park job. Stan had a job working for an agency, cleaning houses in Golders Green. I took a couple on. These were nothing like the big houses in nearby Hampstead, more like large suburban numbers. The interiors were always spotlessly clean when I arrived, so I spent most of the time gazing at the mismatched kitsch. I sprayed furniture polish into the rooms, making it smell like I'd been working furiously on the woodwork. The carpets got a once over. These places were stacked with plentiful Valium so I'd help myself. Sometimes I'd go through the drawers, searching for spare cash, wised up on whether to take money or not. If the notes came to a round number such as twenty quid, I'd leave it be, because people usually remember such a sum. But if the money came to an odd number such as thirty seven pounds, I'd skim off part. It helped ease what little conscience remained as these people treated you like you didn't exist, looking down their noses with contempt. Helping myself became a touch of instant vengeance. I'd swipe the odd shirt if I fancied one that was sealed in a wrapper. Jewellery sometimes lay glittering in the drawers but I only looked at it, preferring drugs, money, anything immediately disposable. Not just being bossed about, unable to handle it or see why me or anyone else should put up with it, I finally jacked the cleaning in. Also, I didn't like polishing the photos of their kids mounted in gold frames on the mantelpiece, straight-looking, residing in private boarding schools, fat like little piglets.

During my second spell at Kingsway, I heard some tragic news. My first girlfriend Louise had died. She'd been going out with blokes a few years older than me, rich kids into motorbikes. Getting a lift home from a party by one of these guys, Louise wore an ill-fitting helmet. Trying to impress, he'd been speeding when losing control taking a corner, Louise sent flying. The helmet came off and her face smashed headlong into a stationary builder's skip. Instant death. I heard the guy had been drinking, had no licence or insurance. I'd also heard strings were pulled behind the scenes, negotiations entered into, resulting in him walking out of court scot free. I couldn't help but wonder if I'd have ended up in court charged with nicking the flash bike, that it would be a different story altogether, with me serving time.

Unlike the Kingsway crowd, I'd been overlooked when it came to funeral invites but I went along to the church anyway. I also made sure to be well stoned for the occasion. Her father, the doctor, mounted the podium, then started reciting extracts from her school poems. Stuff about the sky and sea. Beneath, a white coffin, sealed with the lid on to hide the terrible injuries. Halfway through a stanza, he faltered, then broke down, rushing down to the coffin screaming.

"I love you Louise!"

He clung on to the coffin, had to be escorted out. Even I thought this a bit on the heavy side. A week later I heard the dad had committed suicide, taking his life with an overdose of Mandrax, one of my favourite drugs.

CHAPTER FIVE

The lessons at Kingsway turned out to be more boring than the previous year. Most of the Hampstead hippies started to knuckle under, so I'd never see them in the common room where a fresh younger batch of recruits took command. Kingsway for me only consisted of getting stoned, watching movies and photography, which meant I went out most of the time with a camera. Stan and Redd turned up but nothing much happened here anymore. For me the place had died.

By Easter, I was informed that regretfully, they were unable to keep me on at Kingsway, because I'd missed two terms work to say nothing of the previous year. I didn't argue. They had a youth centre on the premises so I paid a visit. The woman gave out details. Warehouse work, factory production lines, other stuff with no appeal whatever. She started getting frustrated.

"Do you fancy working with antiques then?"

This sounded more promising so I got an interview at a shop near Euston. During the interview their representative asked me if I had any interest in the world of antiques, so I just reeled off something from my music lessons.

"I like the baroque period."

I lied, telling them I had a couple of O Levels, thereby ending up with a five days a week nine-to-five number.

The job consisted of working in an antiques hire-shop. The firm rented out antiques for use in films and television, mainly. silverware. My tasks included cleaning the antiques with toothbrushes, cloth, Silvo and Brasso, so they shined and looked good. Riveting stuff. Other tasks were packing and addressing the boxes. I wore a white coat. This was about all there was to the job but they'd promised to teach me about hallmarks. All I got from that angle could have been gleaned from a beginner's handbook in an hour. Never one to pass by an opportunity or add a touch of glitter to Aladdin's Cave, I started swiping small objects such as pewter salt-shakers, silver spoons, the odd Mother-of-Pearl cut throat razor set. As a lot of this gear wasn't correctly numbered, they never missed it. An old geezer named Nick worked alongside me. Nick must have been knocking on about seventy, taking his time while I whizzed through the jobs. They'd always be finding something for you to do, should you finish quickly. The whole experience became tedious.

Outside, a glorious summer. How I longed to be elsewhere. So I started saving money out of the pittance for a holiday abroad also skipping the odd day arriving back with a doctor's note. I resented the fact that they wouldn't let me read newspapers, even listen to the radio during slack periods. It didn't take long before the only thing on my mind at work was leaving to go abroad, planning the departure.

Soon as I'd saved enough for my needs, I handed in my notice. Now they played a different tune. The boss took me aside, indicating that old Nick would be retiring. If I stayed, I'd be getting his salary. I told him I fancied living abroad.

"How will you live? What will you do for money?"

I spun a yarn about going to live in Spain for a while.

"But what will you live on?"

I mumbled something about the fat of the land. Despite his concern for my finances I had trouble extracting my holiday money settlement. This short work experience once again convinced me of the utter futility of employment. A feeling of total confinement, being told what to do, going nowhere slowly, skint by Monday. At least time was your own, the odd spot of fun cropping up if you weren't working.

Hadji spun me some tales about the island of Formentera off the coast of Spain. This place had a reputation as an acid paradise, populated by a sizeable contingent of acidheads and other drug freaks. This gave me the idea for the holiday. I'd never been abroad before, so I'd started to make plans within a week of starting work, I'd tired of the place that much. The prospective holiday was the sole reason for persisting with the job. The whole gang was to be transplanted. Redd, Stan, Sharon and Sally after the foundations for the trip had been laid. We hired a house from a friend of Hadji's for a month. An informal arrangement, we agreed to pay the bulk of cash after the holiday. Knowing me and Redd this amounted to a sure-fire impossibility. All except us two purchased air tickets, so we decided to hitch in order to save money. I handed Sally most of my dough plus the bulk of my luggage, telling her me and Redd were getting an early start, a few days ahead of the others.

As tradition dictated we bunked the tube down to Victoria Station, travelling light, a shoulder bag between us, a couple of towels and, concealed in a bottle, trips and blow. Bunking the train to Dover presented no problems. Once there, we hung around the Hoverport, sitting in the canteen, pondering our next move. Buying a ticket was out of the question owing to limited funds. We watched a hovercraft lowering the boarding ramp, then looked at each other.

"Let's go!"

We nipped around the terminal, through a building site, thereby avoiding ticket inspection and customs, joining the queue of people lining up for the hovercraft, edging towards a school party. Once we'd ascended the top of the ramp a stewardess asked for our tickets. We surmounted that obstacle by claiming to be with the school party. Without further questioning or demands for tickets we were soon speeding across the channel. Arriving in France, instead of hitching, we took the lazy option, stepping out of the port on to a train heading for Paris. Once there, Redd bought some cheese and a French loaf. He even looked the part, loaf tucked under his arm and newly acquired lad's earring. We slept rough overnight on some hospital steps. From what I saw of Paris, it looked interesting but we hardly had any cash and the goal was Spain. After being thrown off the motorway by police for hitching, we headed back into the centre of Paris, bunked another train, this time to Marseilles.

Kipping overnight at the station, Redd awoke to purchase yet more cheese and bread along with a bottle of wine. We bunked the train again, destination Barcelona.

In Barcelona we visited the Port area. Here Redd had a shave, removing his beard. Next, off came the barnet. I hadn't seen much of Redd's features for ages, now he looked like a fifties juvenile delinquent. Our only real expense turned out to be the ferry tickets to Formentera, a fiver each. Upon arrival at our holiday destination, we'd got there first, the others hadn't flown out yet, so we picked up keys to the house from neighbours who showed us the rooms, cooker and water supply obtained from a well.

Later next day as we waited for the others to show up, we spent some time nicking from local shops. Later, under my expert supervision, Stan took his first trip, which he enjoyed immensely. This was the first real holiday of my life, we all tripped, smoked dope, drank and went swimming everyday at a place named acid beach. We made friends with a couple of French geezers who also knew the locations of parties going down on the island. As I'd come to expect by now, they both came from wealthy backgrounds. But what interested me was that they claimed to prefer heroin to dope. Further curiosity aroused, me and Redd said we wouldn't mind meeting them in Paris on the return journey home. They said they'd be over in London in October, so we settled for that. I'd heard one of them shot up gear with a needle but if they had any smack available we didn't see it. After a couple of weeks here I'd never felt so healthy, my teeth pearly white, body bronzed. When time came to return home, me and Redd splashed out on coach tickets for the journey back. Driving into London, I felt depressed. The streets looked grey and dirty, people miserable, ill, badly dressed.

I moved up to a council flat in Archway with my old man after a relocation came through. At least it would be a handy base for parties in nearby Hampstead. Meanwhile, I had to get another job. Stan left home, sharing a small flat up in Hampstead with an Australian geezer, working in a betting shop. The Aussie returned home, leaving his hotel job, so I took the initiative, applying at the place as an experienced handyman, mentioning his name by way of reference. I got the job, starting Monday. Wages were good, the work a doddle. I wore blue overalls, spending most of the time changing lightbulbs. The hotel itself was located in the heart of town, near Green Park. Here I got the liking for foreign money, especially the dollar. I'd always visit the expensive top suites, searching cabinets, drawers, under beds. American travellers and their wives usually packed Qualudes, so this became another job perk, dropping them during work hours. I'd always look for the rolled-up wads of money, dollars, yen, francs or marks, do a touch of skimming, dash over to the foreign currency unit of a nearby bank every other day. With all this money coming in, I treated myself to shoes, clothes and drugs. In a couple of weeks, I had the whole place sussed, helping myself to shirts, after shaves, even socks.

One day, I hit the jackpot, finding a shoebox tucked under a bed. This room looked lived in, must have been a permanent guest. Opening the shoebox, I found it crammed full of watches, gold and silver Hunters and Half Hunters. Looking at the hallmarks, my antique job had paid a dividend eventually, knowing they were worth a few bob. I left them for the time being, talking later to Redd about the stash. He thought the hoard to be undeclared for tax purposes. Even though I didn't quite grasp the complexities of this, it gave me some sort of justification. Besides, if I took a few the owner wouldn't be any the wiser. So I returned, swiped six gold and silver. No questions or worries forthcoming, I hid them at home, investment for leaner times.

As promised, come October, the French geezers arrived, staying at a hotel in Kensington. They had money and wanted smack. Redd volunteered to score some. He knew a Hampstead dabbler who'd put him in touch with a dealer. Redd came back after a few hours with a gram, for which he'd paid thirty-five quid. Instant recognition from the Frenchies, Thai gear. Four lines were spread out, us snorting one each. It came on full strength after about ten minutes. The strangest buzz yet, me feeling wiped out, laying on the floor. I didn't utter a word, nor did the others. Later we smoked some in a joint. I lay back again, waves of sheer contentment rolled above and under me. Time lost meaning, cares and worries dissolved. We didn't allow it to wear off, more lines were forthcoming. We all floated to the bogs for a puke, I'd heard about this phenomenon before. However, I enjoyed it, feeling rejuvenated. Me and Redd went home together, both of us rating it, with Redd wondering if they wanted more. The gram lasted them a couple of days, so he made a return trip and we all had some more. This time however, I felt mobile, able to go on to work that evening. Looking into a mirror in the washroom, my pupils were like tiny specks in a mass of baby blue. I hardly knew anybody who did smack but word got around the Hampstead scene that I'd tried it, transforming me into a bigger hero than when I had the band.

The French geezers went home. By now I knew at least two places where I could score smack, both in Camden. Before they departed, Sally and a friend named Crispin plus some other daring souls had been turned on to gear in the hotel room. Stan didn't want to know. Smack now became the weekend treat, sometimes shading over into the week. By now me and Sally had drifted apart, but it didn't bother me, having other things on my mind like moving out from the Archway, getting my own place. Rented accommodation being prohibitive owing to soaring rents and me not fancying a landlord hassling, snooping about, I had no choice but to squat. This would be easy enough, I'd heard.

Back at the hotel, rumours of impending lay-off, investigations of theft. I took the hint, deciding to quit when ahead. On my final day, I got an income tax rebate. For the first time ever I felt loaded, two hundred and fifty quid. Off to the pub, getting roaring drunk. Next day, nursing a hangover, I went to a job interview at a bookies. Stan put me on to it, so I mentioned his name. Another Monday start, the only inconvenience was working Saturday, the busy day. With the rebate, I splashed out on two grams of Chinese rocks, a superior brand of heroin. Me and Crispin took most of it, with Redd getting a look in. As Stan couldn't afford his flat anymore, I suggested that me, him and Crispin should squat together. Seemed like a good idea.

Stan found an empty house near the Angel, a Georgian terrace in Gibson Square. It stood in this Square almost next to Crispin's girlfriend who lived with her parents, which could be useful in the future. Our tools for the cracking job were a hacksaw, screwdriver and a replacement barrel Yale lock. Stan got a lift up to the balcony, slipping through a window, letting us in through the front door. Both gas and electricity were in working order. Once we'd changed barrels, we were in officially as squatters, the law couldn't touch us. Getting together some old mattresses, me, Stan and Crispin colonised one room between us. I left the bulk of Aladdin's Cave at Archway, a mattress, clothes, the watches and trusty guitar. We obtained a second-hand cooker but never bothered with culinary diversions owing to prior drug commitments. We borrowed a record player from Lenny, brother of Crispin's girlfriend. Their dad Joe was a Jewish self-made man, a surveyor, and the family didn't object to us nipping over for social calls. Joe Gold quite liked my happy-go-lucky nature, thinking me salt-of-the-earth, the son he'd never had.

My place of employment became a bookies at Parliament Hill. Here I wiped down the board with a damp cloth, penning results as they crackled in over the blower. For entertainment during working hours I started picking out horses but the gambling bug hadn't hit me so I didn't place money on selections. This bookies was peaceful, only the odd drunk reeling in now and again, kicking up some noise, then drifting off. I'd taken a drop in salary but this didn't cause concern as I now enjoyed plenty of free time, lying in, owing to the late start. The manager, an obliging chap, allowed me an early finish before the end of the final dog meeting. In spite of squatting I still measured up in the sartorial elegance stakes with Cuban heeled shoes, leather jeans, an old but presentable black leather jacket plus short barnet combed, slicked back. I worked with Stan for a week, going pinned, puking in the bogs, raising his eyebrows as our Stan disapproved of gear. Back at the Square, we finally moved into separate rooms.

Punk started coming in as fashion and lifestyle, us following the trend, going to gigs. Impressed with the amount of drugs available, such as speed, Mandies or dope, we never came across any solvent abuse Going smacked out, everyone just assumed we'd been a touch excessive on the blow. Punks then weren't into smack, regarding it to be beyond the pale, heroin still being the connoisseur drug. On the musical front, me and Stan jammed together in the squat, believing ourselves far superior to anything we'd heard on the emergent punk scene. We talked about forming a new band, capitalising on this new trend.

The Gold household was indeed handily located. Should we desire to watch telly, take a bath or shower, or, if we felt hungry, we'd wait for the parents to leave then go over. Their kids reciprocated our visits, coming over to the squat, smoking dope. The parents knew of our squatter status but owing to Crispin going out with their daughter they put this aside, knowing nothing about the drug aspect. Now we'd become a local novelty as punkification took hold, dying our hair, wearing second-hand clothes. We furnished the squat with stuff nicked from the big houses during parties. Duvets thrown from windows, radios, alarm clocks, lamps, toiletries, collected later on the way back home. We didn't get around to shifting furniture, relying on skip pickings. During the cold of encroaching winter, we nicked bags of coal from the nearby hospital's stocks. Redd came over to indulge in the odd snort of gear. I quit the bookies. Having such a good time, work interfered with my flow. I signed on for the first time, collecting the princely sum of six pounds a week.

A French girl named Brigette came over to join us, friend of the two geezers who'd introduced us to smack. She eventually shacked up with me. Brigette fixed up gear, arriving armed with a full battery of syringes, long French ones, slimlined models. Brigette immediately asked me to score so I duly obliged, taking her over to a dealer named Baz in Camden Town. Like most heroin dealers, Baz himself had a habit, in this case, a gram a day. Back at the squat we all decided to give the needle a try, except for our clean living Stan who'd begun to freak at the growing scag consumption. Brigette divided the gear into little piles. Owing to the powder being pure white, it didn't need heating up she explained, placing the smack on a spoon filled with water, stirring, the gear mixing clear into the water. Brigette smiled, sucking up the liquid into the syringe. Before this operation, she'd broken the filter from a cigarette, placing the fibres into the mixture in order to absorb impurities. Brigette removed a silk scarf she wore around her neck, wrapping it around her bared arm, drawing tight, stretching her fingers. The veins stood up. I wasn't disturbed by any of this, just awaiting my turn for the ultimate experience in the drug world, shooting up. Brigette blew on her vein as she slid the needle into her forearm, pulling the plunger back until it filled with blood. She'd hit the vein, bang on target. Leaving the syringe in place, Brigette removed her tourniquet, shoving the whole contents into her arm, finally easing the needle out. She looked radiant.

"Ah yes, this is good."

I champed at the bit.

"Me next!"

I constricted my blood flow with the scarf while she cleaned out the works. Brigette came over to me, everything at the ready, patting the arm to bring up the vein, rubbing some perfume on it. She placed her finger on the anointed channel, running the needle in under her thumb. Brigette was a real pro, hitting the target first time, pushing the junk into the vein as I loosed the scarf. Afterwards I held a dab of cotton wool to the puncture mark, pressing down to prevent tell-tale bruising. Now I soared, it hit me with the violence of a cosh, the strongest physical buzz yet, forbidden fruit too good to be allowed, a rush like an electric surge. A small audience observed the spectacle, someone breaking in over the hush with a comment.

"Well Dan, it's downhill from now on."

The gear coursed through my entire system.

"I don't give a shit!"

For a couple of weeks solid, this performance became a nightly event, usually in front of a fresh audience of thrill seekers from the party scene or the girl's schools of Hampstead. Some even paid an admission fee as we ponced money to buy more gear, or sold blow to raise funds. And I had my paws in Joe's old drawers, taking the odd tenner – that's what we had to raise each day to support the binge. A couple of the watches went to a shop in Camden Passage. The owner must have known they were stolen but eventually fixed the price. Twenty quid a silver, forty for gold. An unexpected bonus for me was that on smack, sex went on for hours on end. Immensely pleasurable.

Lenny had use of a garage opposite the squat. This belonged to a well-heeled resident of the Square, one of the Gold's friends. Containing a motorbike, some furniture, heater and record player, we spilled out from the squat, creating a scene where we hung out in the warmer weather. We all lived day to day. Soon as cash was forthcoming from whatever source we'd spend it on drugs. My old shoplifting skills came in handy, favourite foods being bacon, cooked chicken, cold meats and the odd bottle of wine to wash things down, with that old faithful, a bag of chips providing the main staple. I'd also kept my contacts from the pre-squat period who were useful for dope or fridge contents. I still popped over to see Hadji, paying the occasional visit to the Seaburgs, making the odd bob or two scoring for Edy. We also commuted to another Square in Camden on scoring expeditions. Here, some of the older Hampstead lot had become squatters. We'd usually borrow Lenny's motorbike on these occasions, not wanting to be pulled by the police on foot. I became unstuck one day on slippery roads, having a skid which ended with me scraped along the deck. No broken bones, the bike only suffered minor damage. As convenience would have it, Baz happened to be knocking out morphine that day, which I'd heard acted as a first rate pain killer. In powder form, we wasted no time in snorting it up. The morphine wasn't as strong as the smack, physically I underwent a tingling sensation, aches and pains departed, leaving me comfortable.

Back at the Square, most nights we had visitors, with Camden Girls coming over for cheap thrills. As they still lived at home, this came to be the place to hang out, smoking joints in the front room. From our vantage point, we started knocking out measures of blow as Baz was willing to lay stuff on us. Brigette had long departed back to France but with the influx of Camden Girls and hangers-on we had no difficulty getting laid. The squat certainly became a major attraction. With the never-ending flow of drugs I adopted yet another habit, the use of barbiturates. Tuinal, Nembutal, Seconal. They reminded me of Mandies but without the hypnotic edge. Exercising a rare degree of caution, I steered clear of booze when taking them. Since the variation and supply of drugs seemed ever-flowing I didn't develop a smack habit. Not that I'd given the subject much time for consideration in the whirl of frantic activity. I only bothered to eat now when the munchies came on, regular meals ceased to exist. My dress sense evolved into a curious blend of permanent black leather trousers, scuffed Cuban heels and some of the diminishing stock from the cave. On occasion, I'd wear Doc Martens, combining this with the odd velvet jacket but mostly the leather top. I'd long abandoned the regular teenage occupation of watching the telly, only catching snatches of programmes when visiting or staying overnight. Still I bunked into the cinema, gigs, parties, after all I'd finished with the work ethic, swapping it for one of leisure and there wasn't much point sitting home at the squat doing nothing.

Owing to emergent publicity for the punk thing and our matching image, many people on the street took alarm at our appearance, thinking us to be crazed glue sniffers. Shopkeepers, passers-by questioned us like we'd become the local celebrities.

"What are you lot into?"

"What do you want out of life?"

"What bands do you like?"

Or usually asking something concerning a facet arising from a newspaper article or telly programme. All suffered from solvent abuse preconceptions but didn't know the half of it. Others thought this new rage meant anarchy, decadence and licentiousness. Always stared at on the streets, we didn't care being off our heads.

"You've been on the glue, haven't you son?"

A nutter turned up on the scene. Lenny was on good terms with a geezer called Duke, who'd tuned his bike, a sixties BSA 250. In spite of Lenny being obviously middle class, he'd cultivated a watered down teddy boy image, raising him to respectability with Duke. I met this Duke at the garage hangout one afternoon, he heard me mention something about our squat. Duke spat out a remark.

"Squatters? They don't wash or work."

I replied lying.

"I work"

Duke apologised, laughing, then talked some bike jargon. Soon I'd persuaded him to fix up a friend's machine. Duke looked it over, wanted to haul it back to his place in Upper Holloway, patch it up. I'd heard some rumour of Duke being a bit extreme politically in a right wing direction. But I ignored this, thinking that Duke couldn't be that bad if Lenny had his bike over at Upper Holloway. So me and Crispin went over on a social visit. Duke had a nice looking missus who'd shacked up with him in the early days when he'd ridden in a bike gang, leader of the pack. The house turned out to be a ramshackle dump, vans parked outside, bike parts strewn around inside. Duke's missus showed us upstairs. Picking our way over the wreckage, I couldn't help wondering about the irony of Duke's complains about dirty squatters. Opening the door upstairs, we both nearly suffered a heart attack.

"Hello lads, how are you doing?"

There sat Duke, dressed in a nazi uniform, plus iron cross. A large poster of Hitler dominated the wall behind him as he perched behind a pile of motorbike parts on his desk. A teddy boy lounged on a sofa. I whispered to Crispin.

"I can't believe this."

We tried to ignore the steely gaze of the Führer, diverting our attention to the flickering picture on the telly. Something sparked Duke off, with him pointing at a presenter, gesticulating violently.

"He's fucking queer for a start!"

Duke swung in our direction.

"You know what? These queers are fucking strong. Just try holding one down."

The missus came in with tea and biscuits. After supping we hurriedly departed. I drew up a mental picture of Duke foaming at the mouth, trying to throttle one of those 'fucking queers'. Mentioning to Lenny I'd been over to Duke's, describing his indoor dress sense, the wall-hangings of the inner sanctum. He just shrugged.

"Yeah, but he's doing my bike up for nothing."

Redd in the meantime purchased a BSA to help keep in the scene. Seeing the job Duke had done on Lenny's machine, Redd took his over to Holloway, persuaded him to do some work on it. Weeks passed, nothing further heard about Redd's bike, resulting in him going over to remonstrate. the whole episode ended with Redd thrown down the stairs by an irate Duke.

One thing I learnt from squatting, no security. You never feel relaxed, always aware that you'll be moving on at short notice. If there's space, someone always wants to move in or stay for an indefinite period. Squats are prey to burglaries, visits from the police, gifts such as bricks through windows, kind regards of local brain-damaged louts. On the plus side, you can throw parties, play loud music, have girls over without anybody like a landlord sticking their snouts in. After a court order we knew our days in the Square were numbered. We'd have to move out. Stan did his homework, spotting an empty property in another nearby Square. We gave it a look over, pleased at what we saw. Mock gothic, little turrets, curbed castle type windows. Once access had been gained over the back garden we discovered the interior to be in excellent condition, the only drawback being the place was too big for the three of us. Huge rooms with juice in full working order persuaded us to move in double quick. After transporting our belongings, we moved in more people, some punkettes who'd formed an all girl band. Their equipment, housed in the roomy basement, started to be used by me and Stan until we seriously thought about forming a band, milking the punk thing.

The smack habit took a back seat as I started piling into booze in a big way. There was plenty of alcohol on the punk scene at parties and gigs, our squat itself becoming part of the set-up. We threw parties at the weekends with the punkoid names of the day and future showing up. These raves usually lasted two days, with groupie types abounding, make up, leather clothing, aggressive looking, though of course nothing more than a pose. Drugs, as always, were in abundance. Some punks took speed by shooting it up. I tried it but the buzz only lasted a short time before more was required to maintain the high. A party treat became a smack and coke mixture shot up, the effect making you feel excitable, that you could do anything and more. No edgy sensation came on, so I regarded it as a good balance, smoothing any fringes of the buzz. They called this mixture speedballs.

The all-girl, all ex-public school band padded the basement with mattresses to soundproof the room, prevent complaints from irate neighbours in this posh area. The girl band were absolutely appalling, as were most punk outfits. The lyrics were shit, the sort of thing in demand at the time. Again the majority of these people came from comfortable middle class suburbia. Or were hippies who'd jumped on the bandwagon after cutting their hair and discarding sixties accoutrements. My personal music tastes differed radically as I now listened to early Dub, introduced to me by Hadji, who I still popped over to see with Stan for food, dope, the odd tab of acid and a place to rest up. Hadji didn't understand the developing smack craze.

"But it's only a physical sensation."

Very much to my surprise, some of the punk bands started to land record contracts, get radio airplay, with others going on tour. The bandwagon gained momentum. At gigs, fat cat representatives of the music industry were ever-present. Images changed overnight, people who wore straight jackets ripped them to shreds, flares were binned. As for myself, I wore jumble sale clothing with leather jacket and trousers. Hair styles changed also, multiple dollops of black dye, short combed black barnets, some spikes, even beehives for the girls. Others, from more opulent backgrounds bought the new image from expensive designer shops. My own barnet, in keeping with surroundings, became extra greased, longer and spiky.

Appearances aside, I wasn't keen on playing punk music but this looked to be the future direction, so we acquiesced to the prevailing trend with Crispin getting into the basement sessions playing bass badly. I did vocals putting out word that we were looking for a drummer. About this time a novelty punk band emerged, all aged about fourteen. Their drummer, Tiny, had become something of a young teen celebrity, a television appearance to his credit. After an introduction at a party, Tiny fancied joining our outfit as he eyed our disreputable company. So together we formed a working band and, with some rehearsal, we'd be back in action soon enough. We needed equipment, a PA system, bass guitar, amps, speaker, monitors. About a grand's worth of gear in all. A dealer friend of mine, Justin, suggested the boss of his straight job was interested in subsidising a band. Justin, like so many others, had transformed himself into a punk of sorts. Thanks to his drugs supply he moved into the scene. Most people though regarded him as a bit of a creep. He dropped a series of hints that he should be included in the band. I eventually by-passed him, securing an arrangement with his boss who happened to be impressed with my extensive knowledge of sixties and seventies rock. We agreed on money for equipment, a place to rehearse and a future clothing allowance. We managed to get the equipment, but even before rehearsals I'd had a blazing row with Justin. The unspoken condition of our subsidy was that Justin became our bassist. Taking such things as assured, he'd invested in a bass guitar. But the boat happened to be full, so I engineered a row with him over some trifle or other when Crispin, Stan and me went along to his house. Justin had been overdoing the business samples. Behaving like an idiot, he grabbed a girlfriend of ours, so I threw a bottle at him. Fisticuffs with little or no contact ensured, finally spilling out onto the street. We both squared up but I shouted.

"Justin! About the band! You're out!"

Justin lowered his hands, breaking down into a pitiful snivel.

"But you can't do that."

"Wanna bet, Justin?"

Minus Justin, the backer started getting cold feet.

"Couldn't you bring him back in any capacity?"

Sadly we couldn't. In rehearsal we'd begun to sound better, developing our own chunky punk sound.

Meanwhile, a new craze was springing up, Rastas. With the fashionable middle classes, it was considered the ultimate in hip to have some cool imaged Rastas hanging around. But these guys knew nothing about Haile Selassie, were only into cultivation of dreadlocks, puffing weed, pulling chicks. A group of of them hung about the squat, tagging onto a film maker who was trying to shoot the girl band on Super-8. I noticed these Rastas talked in London accents almost identical to my own amongst each other, but for the benefit of the middle class trendies they laid on the patois thick. They were cracking the Hampstead scene as I'd done way back. Malcolm, the fellow with Hunter watch and forced posh accent, had transformed into a high ranking dread in the Hampstead set. Here, I still hovered on the fringes, suspecting it to be a lot heavier all round what with the parents chafing on their liberal restrictions. Most of these Rastas didn't even have the saving graces I possessed, such as the bullshit. They were thick despite trying to appear meaningful.

Even though I looked like a punk I knew the majority of punks were also fairly dense, keeping them at arms length. In these early days punks were for the most part lads like myself, although many of the girls were middle class weekend thrill seekers. This represented no problem for me, given previous experience in such circles. One drawback to having a punk image was that shoplifting became progressively more difficult, being screwed out all the time. Even so, I always managed to swipe cans of strong lager from the off-licence without too much trouble.

We had to quit our squat sometime in the not too distant future due to numerous court orders. It didn't matter as long as I felt confident in securing our next intended residence, a nearby house converted from a small pub. Ideal. It had been empty for a couple of years, so me and Crispin decided to try it out. On our way there we met Davis, who gave out with enthusiasms when we told him our plan to crack it. Davis wanted to help, so once we arrived he jemmied the door, only succeeding in making a noise, leaving a mark. I spotted curtains twitching opposite, so we made ourselves scarce, taking a walk around the block cursing Davis for his dilettante stupidity. Davis split before a police car pulled up. Without the usual questions, they bundled us into their motor, driving to the damaged door. After searching us, finding our tool, a chisel, matching it to marks on the door, they whisked us to Upper Street police station, charging us with criminal damage. They slung us in separate cells, overnight stay. When you've been locked up, you've got all the time in the world to get on with thinking about being on the outside. I thought about Davis back home in comfortable surroundings, not having to worry about squatting, but then remembered all the things I ponced off that family and felt better. The police kept waking us up at night, making remarks about glue sniffers. Court next morning, formalities, probation reports. Still at least I had a while longer in the Square. I'd find another place, no sweat.

None of us were doing much smack, only now and again without after effects. The Hampstead lot though, were now getting into gear in a big way, some shooting up regular. Smack was virtually unknown on council estates. From my experience, it started of as a rich kids' thing. I couldn't help thinking back at how shocked they'd all been recently by the sight of me fixing up at the first squat. Sally, I heard, was going out with a guy who that shot up daily. The media failed to recognise this trend even though it spread rampant amongst their sons and daughters. They were too concerned with regulating the degeneracy of the lower orders. I became an early casualty of smack, contracting hepatitis from a shared needle. For no reason I started feeling tired, shuffling about like an old man. Someone pointed out that instead of the usual glazed red, my eyes were turning yellow. The GP sent me straight to hospital, where once diagnosed, I spent two weeks in the isolation ward, a room of my own, TV set, three meals a day. First time for ages I'd eaten regular or watched telly. A fortnight's rest, no great hardship. I only felt bad when they informed me that I couldn't drink alcohol for a year. Still there was always drugs for compensation.

After the door incident and subsequent court appearance, me and Crispin reported to a probation officer for sentence assessment. I could hardly take this seriously, fuss over a tiny bit of damage. Still having no choice in the matter, along we went. Just my luck to land a relative newcomer, keen and eager, a Scottish geezer in his early twenties, a practising Catholic who disapproved of my squatting and claiming dole. He laboured under the illusion, no doubt from reading garbled accounts in the press, that punks were fascists. He interviewed us separately with Crispin telling him straight away that he came from a respectable background. The officer arrived at a predictable conclusion: Crispin didn't need probation. Unlike myself. The probation officer took one glance at me smoking then started shouting about putting the fag out, to sit up straight. Stoned out of my crust, I couldn't help bursting out laughing. From this, he must have arrived at another media inspired conclusion: glue sniffer. Was I glad to leave that office.

After the summer of '77, success was in the offing for the girl band. Touring with a major punk outfit, they'd all moved out. Our proto band remained together, but lacking in the basic essentials. Crispin now drifted away, wasn't seen much in the squat, having made friends with middle class punks from that bastion of poverty and squalor, Hampstead Garden Suburb. I'd done that scene, wasn't interested. These were just rich kids pretending to be rough, wearing leather jackets. Crispin tried to exclude me but, being an old hand, I managed to sneak a few visits to these places of intense deprivation, wine cellars, swimming pools, helping myself to food and records. From the drawers, jewellery and money. These guys had plenty of drugs, in particular coke. Crispin enjoyed driving the parents' rollers while I thought we should be smashing them up or parking them in Highgate ponds. But Crispin seemed to be at home in such surroundings. Finally the bubble burst, Crispin doing the old vanishing act, moving into Hampstead Garden Suburb with a rich kid friend. Stan meanwhile moved into a warehouse squat by the river, inhabited by detestable types such as poncy artists and other wonderfully creative people. Days to go before eviction, alone, circumstances forced me back to the old man's flat at Archway.

CHAPTER SIX

So, aged eighteen, I arrived back home. Aladdin's cave had disappeared. I couldn't afford to ask questions, having nowhere else to stay and I wasn't exactly welcomed back with open arms. Rent had fallen months in arrears but I didn't have money for even a token contribution. The flat had gone to pieces, bags of festering stinking rubbish piled up in the kitchen and hallway, washing up untouched for months, stacked in the sink, a profusion of giant blowflies buzzing like hummingbirds. I felt physically ill at the sight of it all. I had a temporary base, but was forced into the position where my presence had to be timed to coincide with the old man's shift work and pub hours in order to avoid him.

Me and Crispin were finally sentenced. He received a conditional discharge, while my good self, having modest juvenile form, got awarded a year's probation. This entailed me seeing the Scottish probation officer once a fortnight. He seemed glad that I'd moved back with the old man as this represented stability. I studied him as he lectured me on right and wrong and why didn't I get myself a job. This bloke thought himself well smart while in reality being nothing but a repressed Catholic who wanted to succeed in his miserable profession. It took a while before he cottoned on that I wasn't a fascist, so to pass the time I opened up, talking about music and girls. I detected a glint of envy when I mentioned getting laid on a regular basis. As he attempted to moralise, I interrupted his flow telling him I suspected that he never managed to get laid, so he didn't know what he was talking about. The man spluttered, dismissing me early. Next interview he found the solution to my wayward lifestyle. Would I like to go on a scheme, working outdoors for a wage? At a loose end, thinking this might help me wriggle out of his clutches, I agreed.

Armed with a letter of introduction, I went to the interview. The scheme operated to help rehabilitate offenders: people on probation, released from jail or in trouble with the authorities. Even though I had a shock-horror punk image, the man in charge asked no questions so I landed the job, starting next Monday. Pay amounted to the grand sum of thirty quid a week before tax. But the job had some advantages, however, as it involved working in Highgate cemetery, a short stroll from the flat. The cemetery had become overgrown, our job to clear it. You didn't have to be in the genius category to figure out this would be a Mickey Mouse arrangement, entailing no work worthy of description. This would be a little holiday, a breather.

I reported to work at eight-thirty in the morning to a hut in the main cemetery. The foreman hadn't turned up, so old and young lags sat around. A joint circulated. That said more about the workforce than a handful of references. I knew I'd be alright here for a while. The foreman was a black guy called Winston. The crew warned me not to buy any dope off him as he had a reputation for being a rip-off merchant. Winston eventually arrived, so we all stumbled out of the hut stoned. A fellow named Coza attached himself to me, bending my ear from the word go about punk, what drugs did I take, music, did I believe in God? Coza was a schizo, veteran of many a prison and nuthouse. Our task for the morning had us hacking away at copious undergrowth with a blunt scythe. Most of the time we spent building fires, drinking, smoking, chattering. There was a fair mixture of offenders: a couple of Rastas who liked me because I was a punkyman, blokes with long hair and flares. Standing around the fire together, we looked like a bunch of unemployed Northern labourers. I'd never been thrown in with a crew like like this but, being of a gregarious disposition, I got on well enough, recognising all these characters were losers. It gave me a clue about how not to end up. Some of the geezers were worth talking to – I was no snob. Besides, after all, they must have tales or stories to relate. One of these was Pete, a huge stocky guy with a donkey jacket, in his mid-twenties, just out of nick. He'd seen Coza bending my ear, so on the way to the café for our hour long breakfast break, Pete drew alongside me, giving me the low-down on Coza.

"Had enough of him yet? … I think he's after your arse, old son."

I knew Pete was winding me up because I was the youngest, but it was still tongue in cheek. I found myself hanging around more with Pete than anyone else, even though, compared with the other lazy sods, he grafted, forcing me to break into a sweat on occasion. Pete knew all about the famous people buried in Highgate, talking about their lives, what they had written, composed or invented. He knew where Karl Marx's real grave happened to be, situated near the monument. For a few bob he'd show tourists. I considered Pete to be genuinely intelligent, unlike many Hampstead types I'd met, who were taken in by any old crap so long as it emanated from the right-sounding person.

Redd called over one evening at Archway. Just by coincidence I'd been to see my family GP about me having difficulty sleeping, so he'd prescribed weird jelly-looking pills called Normison. Bored, Redd fancied going up West, seeing a band in a pub. Arriving there we sat listening to absolute shit, so we decided to cure all this with a time-honoured solution – dropping half a dozen of the pills each. As we waited for the pills to come on, Redd told me about how he'd been into a nearby instrument shop, that it looked easy to gain access at night and would I fancy having a bash? The drugs started working after a couple of beers, so we started an ironic cheering of the crap band. I steamed over to the stage, trying my hand at singing into the microphone, grabbing a saxophone, blasting out a few notes. Closing time, with us both buzzing out of our heads, we strolled over to inspect the shop. The entrance lay just off Shaftesbury Avenue, with a quiet road backing on to the rear of the premises. Knowing what to do, I grabbed a couple of rubbish sacks, spilling the contents out onto the pavement. Redd pocketed the sacks, then I gave him the leg up, enabling him to slither in through a window. I waited, watching people leaving pubs and restaurants.

"Oi Dan!"

Down came a gleaming alto sax, the drugs making the instrument seem multi-coloured, blending into the neon. I placed it under a parked car. I must have looked a touch on the suspicious side, a giggling punk putting yet another saxophone, a tenor this time, under the car. A Scottish voice rang out.

"Hey you laddie!"

In my blurred state, I thought of the probation officer. Looking up, stunned, an off-duty policeman shoved his identification card in my face.

"And just what do you think you're doing to this car?"

"Nothing."

I backed into the road, the cop standing facing me, his back turned to the wall. He caught my roving eye as it wandered to those gleaming saxophones. In the meantime, he'd failed to notice Redd slinking silently over the wall, creeping away. I thought Redd was deserting me. The copper had meanwhile made the inevitable discovery.

"And just what the bloody hell are these, laddie?"

He glanced up at the window, noticing it ajar, radioed for assistance.

Redd returned, brandishing a huge lump of wood, putting on a comic voice.

"What's going on here? A mugging?"

Redd laid into the copper, cracking him over the head. I tried to take advantage, attempting a getaway. The cop leapt upon me, grabbing my neck, throwing me on the pavement, whipping out a truncheon, shoving it into my face while shouting at Redd.

"Back off! I'm a policeman! Try that again and I'll smash his skull in!"

Redd perceived the situation as hopeless, throwing the wood down, running off. Two police vans appeared, one pulling up, the other shooting off in pursuit with me bundled into the halted van, the copper punching me.

"Get in here, you bastard!"

It ended up just me, him and the saxophones in the back. The copper went berserk, hitting me, demanding to know about Redd.

"Who is he?"

The copper's jacket had been ripped. Now he screamed demented.

"See this? It's criminal damage."

The handcuffs were on already so I couldn't defend myself. The van finally halted at the police station, where they hauled me into the charge room, plonked me down, asking for a statement. I stalled to the best of my ability, telling them I'd met a black man in a pub, had a few drinks, that he'd persuaded me to come along with him. They didn't believe a word of it, telling me I'd go down for this one as they'd checked me out, found that I was on probation.

After a while, through the frosted windows, I saw a roughed up Redd being dragged in past the charge room. After taking my fingerprints, they charged me with burglary. The copper asked me another question.

"What do you want to play the trumpet for, anyway?"

"It's a saxophone actually."

This earned me a backhander.

"Don't be so cheeky!"

While washing the ink off my fingers, I looked into the mirror, saw them bringing Redd in. I gave the nod, Redd reciprocated with the wink. A torrent of questions followed.

"Do you know this person?"

"What's this fellow's name then?"

"Is this the chap who was with you?"

After I denied I'd ever seen Redd before, they locked me up in a tiny cell. Redd followed up soon after, slung into the cell next door. We stayed put all day and night with the slop they gave us as food consisting of congealed eggs, cold lumpy beans and tea, weak, virtually undrinkable. We didn't bother to touch it despite being hungry. We communicated with each other under the doors or through the flap. They questioned us separately but we said nothing incriminating. Time ticked by, us wondering how much longer they could keep us locked up, it seemed endless. Finally, after the second morning in custody they drove us to court in a police van, placing us in cells beneath the court. After a brief appearance in front of a magistrate, remanded on police bail to show at another date they released us, both charged with burglary.

As winter arrived, we'd spend most of the working day building fires. Apart from sometimes gathering undergrowth as fuel, this might be the only work done. Foreman Winston spent the afternoon in the bookies, leaving us free to wander. Come payday Winston would be there selling packets of moody weed. I didn't purchase any, which hardly endeared me to him but I had no intention of wasting my money on crap. As regards smoke, I could get Malawi, Thai, Durban Poison. At work, most of the conversations revolved around sixties music, drugs of the good old days, the goers they'd bedded. But the main topic, as to be expected, centred on crime – things they'd got away with, prisons frequently. Coza reckoned he'd been inside all the London nicks bar Holloway. Something I found it instructive during these chats was that most of the lads had been collared while under the influence of drugs, drink or both. Huddled around the fire one afternoon, a younger fellow talked about a geezer he'd met on remand who'd told him about a burglary done on Mandies. While on the premises he heard a police siren approaching. Escaping, he climbed on to a garden wall leading out on to the road. Being dark, he didn't realise the wall happened to be topped with broken glass set in cement. Once this tale had been related, an old lag dropped his pants, displaying an arse criss-crossed with scars.

"Yeah lads, me an'all ... Tueys."

The band continued to rehearse at the rear of the furniture store. By now Tiny, the young drummer, took smack. I felt worried, with his old man being a hard nut. Ex-villain turned milkman, friend of the bouncers, assorted heavies, Dad turned up at rehearsals, lecturing us on Tiny's talents.

"He's got more brains than the lot of you put together."

Much as we liked Tiny, it started causing apprehension. We didn't fancy any trouble and Dad could give plenty. At a party one evening, I turned our little friend on to a line of strong gear. Tiny went pale, spending the night puking. Lucky for us the band disbanded, otherwise Dad would have eventually cottoned on. Without gracing one stage, playing one gig or recording a single tune, the band finished before it started. Same old story.

Crispin's girlfriend, who I'd been screwing on the side for best part of a year, came over to the graveyard for a visit. Chilly weather notwithstanding, she dressed in punkoid uniform, leather jacket, mini skirt, high heels, dyed blonde hair, stockings, heavy make up, having the jaded workforce drooling. I did no work whatever, spending my time talking about a new band that so far only existed in my imagination. The lads all saw other tasty birds coming over, were aware that I'd never been banged up and lived a more interesting lifestyle. A new probation officer put in good words for me, helping postpone the burglary trial to later on next year. This new fellow happened to be yet another sixties hangover, corduroy jacket, long hair, knowledge of that decade's music. I got him interested in my ideas for a new band, guessing he must have dabbled some years ago. What with the girls I turned up with at the office, my line of patter, he half believed I'd make it, as I gave off the undiminished air of confidence.

Although I continued to live with the old man, I studiously avoided him. The social side remained good with parties, drugs – top of the world compared with the mugs at work who had nothing approaching this except telly, lies about sexual encounters, boozing. Coza must have been a bit of a sex offender on the side because he often tried chatting up a twelve year old girl in nearby Waterlow Park. One of the blokes sprung to his defence.

"Well, she looks nearly fifteen."

Coza felt indifferent to snide questions, possibly detecting a touch of envy.

"She's great boys, knows all about Elvis."

All made remarks but he laughed it off After all these months, Coza continued to plague me with moronic questions about star signs, religion and every other conceivable subject under the sun. About the only fragment of useful information I gleaned was that probation officers maintained a social fund and if you asked them, they'd bung a couple of quid in your direction. So with visits to my new officer, I never failed to extract the dough.

But one day the graveyard scene ended abruptly. Drifting in late as usual, I joined everyone warming themselves by the fire. Foreman Winston had a go about my time-keeping. Having a ready-made appreciative audience, I gave him plenty of lip, making him appear ridiculous. Winston wasn't to be denied, singling me out for not wearing regulation boots, absurd, considering no one including himself, sported a pair. After I'd countered with more cheek, Winston pulled rank, sacking me on the spot for refusing to recognise his authority. I argued seriously now, but none of the workforce did anything to back me up, standing like a collection of stuffed dummies. None of them, not even Pete or Coza, muttered a syllable in my defence, perhaps because Christmas lay a couple of weeks away and they needed the money. I wasn't unduly upset, knowing from experience they were all a bunch of losers so I didn't honestly expect much in the way of solidarity. All the same, having no money myself over Christmas would be a drag.

So I'd suffered a series of minor setbacks: moving back to the Archway, demise of the band and now loss of job. Although still buzzing, I felt strange, unable to put my finger on it. Christmas, as predicted, turned out to be the usual depressing fare, but even on the day in question I wangled myself into someone's home for the evening. Boxing Day I turned up unannounced at the Seaburgs. Having no money, the dole failing to materialise on time, didn't present as many problems as I'd originally envisaged. Working, I'd be skint Monday anyway. I still circulated in Hampstead, bumming drugs, seeking out the old Kingsway crowd. Redd popped over on occasion. Having succumbed to the temptation, we'd shoot up together, take last season's dried magic mushrooms, indulge ourselves with other goodies. With junk now all the rage in Hampstead, being a pioneer in that department, hanging around in this scene with monied kids, I found it easy to scrounge the odd hit or two. I also maintained my social contacts with the ex-Camden Girls. This, along with Crispin's faithful girlfriend ensured I had no difficulty getting laid, so my self esteem hadn't taken too much of a knock.

The lean winter passed then I landed a job due to a Hampstead contact, his dad being something big in the smutter trade. The work was in his old man's warehouse in the East End near Whitechapel. Both Lenny and Crispin had worked there during summer, claiming it to be okay. The formality of an interview passed during which I lied, spinning a yarn about starting as a college student in September, six months away. The man who conducted my interview, a Mr Burton, ran the show. Strict, an army type, he seemed past retirement age. I didn't like the look of him at all but having gone straight with presentable hair, I managed to get the job which paid forty a week starting Monday. By five past eight I found myself loading and unloading rolls of cloth to and from lorries. As I'd slicked my hair back, the workforce mistook me for a Ted. I began to get a new interest in life, cultivation of a quiff. The workforce divided on the usual lines, old boys, drivers and blacks, sitting at separate tables during breaks. Management juggled me about, putting me on most jobs including wrapping up lengths of cloth. Noticing the van job looked a cushy number, I got myself put on that one, assisting the driver. This meant just riding about all day, picking up tips. But Burton wanted me to sweat for my pittance, slinging me off the van, getting me back to stacking rolls of cloth. I found this physically exhausting, the only buzz, electric shocks from built up static. I spent more dosh than ever on booze, a direct result of the gruelling work. Because I knew the boss's son, the workforce regarded me with a tinge of suspicion. Most of them were of the deadhead variety, frightened to confront supervisors or foremen, so they took a lot of their inarticulate frustrations out on me. I didn't lose any sleep though. I'd noticed that although I rarely ate a square meal, doing this physical job enabled me to become somewhat muscular. At least I felt fit if nothing else.

Months just rushed by, little if anything accomplished. On the job the workforce were busy cracking jokes about my imagined drugs habit, making comments about smoking funny roll-ups. They didn't even know a fraction of of the truth. They'd also heard that the boss's son was into drugs without understanding anything about the matter, but they hated or feared the boss like most workers do. Some of these geezers were getting on a bit, scared of losing their jobs. I didn't care about them one way or another but felt annoyed about being needled because I knew the boss's son, as though they suspected I could be a spy of sorts. On the surface they behaved deferential toward authority figures, standing to the right-wing on just about every subject from hanging to immigration. It started to get under my skin so I went out of my way to prove to these deadheads I wasn't a boss's nark. I boldly insulted Burton, almost driving him crazy, dropping my pants in the canteen to the foreman.

There must have been a communication breakdown at the top as I retained my job in spite of growing insubordination. Possibly as I was a friend of the boss's son they let me be. Burton took a week off, so the workforce helped themselves to reams of cloth. One named Mick hesitated when he saw me looking at him in operation. Tired of the cloud that hung over me, I blurted out my frustrations.

"For fuck's sake don't worry about me! Take it! I'm not in love with the fucking boss. I think he's a cunt, same as you do."

Mick smiled, then proceeded to rob the firm. I eventually settled into the job, accepted by a minority in the workforce. In my dealings with Burton, I'd arrived at the conclusion he was nothing more than an old time fascist, follower of Mosley no less. All this without a shred of evidence. During the time I waged my private war I carried on with the nocturnal activities. I began to feel peculiar, elated without reason, unable to explain why.

One night I couldn't sleep. I kept hearing people talking outside the flat. Peeking through the window; I couldn't see anyone. As I lay in bed I suspected that I'd been followed from the pub. If I did manage a kip that night it must have been light indeed, for the next day I struggled into work, bleary-eyed. On the bus journey I read the headlines over the shoulder of a person in front. I appeared to be about a man named Vic, same name as the foreman at work. I had the uneasy sensation I'd been tailed by persons unknown as I walked into the warehouse. Arriving, Vic sent me to work with the Burton mob, a bunch of casual workers under direct control of the man in question. The mob were a tough-looking bunch, straight, short hair, a couple of them with Union Jack emblems sewn on to their clothing. Further evidence in my eyes of the Burton fascist connection. We set to work, loading up lorries but it wasn't long before I found myself engaged in a battle of words with the mob over a triviality. One took a photo of me, while I had a shoving match cum scuffle with another. They were fascists for sure, Burton their Führer. As I mulled over the implications one of the mob held up a sheet of paper, thrusting it into my face.

"We're on to you, son."

It looked like a police charge sheet, only one word plainly visible.

"Saxophones."

After an unpleasant time, they sent me to work on another floor where at least I'd be by myself. But I kept hearing strange noises, whispered voices in the background. Glancing over my shoulder, I couldn't see anyone. Maybe the Burton mob were sneaking up on me, trying to catch me unawares. I toiled away, feeling weird, thinking something terrible was about to happen. Then came wisps of smoke. Mick, the friendly worker, rushed up, bustling me out of the section as he extinguished a minor blaze at the back. Panic set in. They'd taken my photo, shown me the chargesheet and now set a fire to give me the blame, this all being part of some dreadful scheme presided over by Führer Burton. In my confusion I started adding up, two and two coming out as an odd number. Possibly some of the workforce were in on the plot. By the time dinner break arrived Vic the foreman sacked me, saying I'd gone crazy, that I should see a head doctor. The bullet didn't bother me, knowing I'd be coming into a fat tax rebate, so I departed without protest. Once outside the building I felt strange, like someone was shadowing me again. Boarding the bus at Moorgate, I met a geezer I knew from the Angel, accusing him of being a Burton man.

"You're one of them, aren't you?"

"One of what Dan?"

"You know what I'm talking about … Burton!"

He looked worried and got off. Next stop, another man stepped on the bus. I was wise to the situation, they couldn't fool me, this was the replacement. At the Angel I jumped off, only to be trailed by what I took to be yet another Burton man with an alsation. More blinding panic. Then I saw a familiar building, the church where we once rehearsed. Sanctuary. I ran, Father Mac would help me. Reaching his door, I pounded. Father Mac opened up. I dashed past, slamming the door.

"Please … don't let them in."

I appeared so terrified, Father Mac seemed half-convinced himself. Looking out, he saw nothing.

"There isn't anybody out there Danny."

"They're going to get me, you've got to believe it."

Father Mac gently escorted me into a room.

"Why don't you come in and sit down here for awhile?"

He left me alone in the room apart from a collection of cassocks, where I sat impassive, staring at the red and golden outfits. An eternity later, Father Mac came back, informing me that he'd called an ambulance. Once inside the vehicle I resigned myself to the unhappy fact that these ambulance men were part of the embracing Burton organisation. Arriving at hospital, I was jabbed with Valium, taken to the psychiatric wing. The paranoid sensation drifted away, as did everything else. Deep sleep on a bed.

I'd been placed in a single room, clothes spirited away, sectioned in Whittington Hospital, a stone's throw away from the Archway flat. My money had gone, placed in the hospital bank. Awaking, a Pakistani doctor and burly orderlies stood around the bed. I'd been sweating heavily throughout the Valiumed night but they were convinced I'd wet the bed, ignoring my denials. Escorting me to the shrink, they seemed friendly enough. In the background I heard screams, pretending to ignore them as they drifted in from the room next to mine where a large black woman lay chained to a bed. The shrink's office was small, regulation potted plants and a Van Gogh print. The shrink himself happened to be aged about fifty, looked harassed, overworked. Soon as I parked myself down he asked me what the trouble was. I spun a convoluted story, fascists following me everywhere, on my case. He asked if I took drugs and didn't exactly deny familiarity. Did I take LSD? Before I'd uttered a word in the affirmative, he'd made his mind up.

"We're going to keep you here to see what's wrong, see if we can help you out."

I told him I must be suffering from paranoia.

"I really think that's too extreme a word to describe your condition."

After this brief interview, the orderlies escorted me back to 'P3'. Here, they left me to wander the ward, dressed like the other inmates in pyjamas and gown. In this part of the building there must have been two dozen people, some were women, plus a fifteen year old skinhead with vacant eyes, dead to the world. Totally gone. Others played cards, watched the telly. I had a strange feeling, not too pleasant, somewhat comforting, that everyone here knew what was going on in my head. With usual gregariousness, I chatted to a forty year old geezer called John, who offered me a roll up. John was quite an imposing figure, six foot four with long hair and a beard. He shook continuously like a vibrator.

"They told me this is a hospital Dan. I'm not well … this ain't no hospital, it's the funny farm!"

I puffed on the roll up. John's pockets were crammed with discarded fag butts, the source of his roll up material. John had been a metalworker, made redundant, cracked up. I took my leave, walking into the TV room where a woman accosted me, asking if I had any spare cash, me telling her I'd invested it all in the hospital bank. Looking up at the screen, a soap opera played to the indifferent audience. Two of the actors discussed someone of my age coming into money.

"He's behaving a bit strange, but he's got a couple of hundred."

Oh no, I thought. Even the telly's on to me with my tax rebate coming up. John appeared, dragging me out of the room.

"Don't watch it Dan … Stay away from it Dan …"

Later, everyone queued up for the medicine as their names were called. Some had to drink liquid Largactil, this being reserved for those discovered dummying pills. Most were on Stelazine or Librium, the other treatment, Largactil pills, they handed me, so I swallowed them. I felt a touch drowsy but little else. In my state of mind, I reckoned myself to be safer here than on the outside where people were out there to nail me. Everyone went to bed when night nurses came on duty, me having the little room to myself. Doors remained unlocked. Owing to this wing being reserved for the worst cases, they wheeled them in practically all night. Some considered too loony were transferred immediately to Friern Barnet. As I lay down for the night, hearing noises such as disembodied laughter, voices muttering in the far distance and the odd scream from next door. The whole experience was like living in a dream with fear still lurking as I awoke in the morning. I met the shrink in a corridor, telling me he wanted to introduce me to someone named Wayne Macnamara.

Wayne was another patient here, long hair, beard like John, just admitted. The shrink made a remark about Wayne.

"He's saying the same thing as you. Fascists are after him."

As the shrink walked off, I talked to Wayne.

"So they're after you 'n' all?"

"Yeah, they're everywhere."

Wayne pointed out the window In a street below, two men loitered suspiciously.

"Look, there's some."

It made a kind of sense in my state of mind. Same with our observations of the visitors as they arrived in drips and drabs.

"He's one."

"See? There's another."

No disagreement. Here was someone who knew what happened to be going down. As we nattered away in the corridor, Wayne's old man turned up. They started rowing in German of all things, right in front of me. The dad spun around to face me.

"There's nothing wrong with him. He's only seen that *Cuckoo's Nest* film and he's trying to be like that guy, getting himself put in here."

At least my humour resurfaced so I made as to shake hands with dad.

"Put it there daddio."

I beamed, so he stretched out his arm to mine, whereupon I abruptly brought my thumb up to my nose, wiggling the fingers, making an idiot noise.

"Wooooowooooo."

Dad stormed off. Wayne creased up laughing.

Dinnertime, we took a stroll to the canteen. In the queue, Wayne ended up talking to the dinner lady in her native lingo, Italian. She piled our plates high. Wayne, I soon discovered, liked reggae with black dudes coming up to visit him. Apart from German and Italian, he could also speak fluent Spanish and French. Personally, I thought Wayne to be a bright fellow. Indeed, compared to the ordinary everyday morons I'd met from all walks of life I didn't think he had much wrong in the mental department either.

Meanwhile, I created a routine for myself, taking advantage of the therapeutic art section. On an energy surge, I knocked out two paintings a day. They also ran a woodwork room but the sight of John shaking all over the place, trying to hammer a nail put me off. Being young, good looking and a bright spark, I got on well with the young nurses, one of them asking me to sneak out to a party at her place in King's Cross. Leaving her shift, I told her I'd certainly be going later and that I'd also invited Wayne. She seemed distressed at this news. I was okay, but Wayne could be much worse than it appeared at first sight. I didn't believe there to be much to worry about, so later that evening, slipping past lax security, we both sneaked out wearing pyjamas and dressing gowns. We bunked the nearby tube, changing trains deliberately, at each stop, weaving through carriages, poncing fags. The two strange figures garbed in hospital attire didn't cause any comment, even though it should have been obvious we'd done a runner from the bin. Maybe they thought us to be in fancy dress, after all the destination was a party and we were in boisterous spirits. We arrived in a party mood. At the small flat, we munched through the stacks of food. A cool mixture of white and black people were here, the nurse had donned a punkish outfit. Weekend punks were coming into their own, punk now semi fashionable. Wayne steamed into the booze, sinking spirits like water. Prancing around the flat, he spluttered food particles all over the guests, trying to converse. Wayne took command of the sound system, kept changing records midstream. I busied myself chatting up the nurse, glancing sideways to observe Wayne in action. Folk were leaving thanks to his antics. He rooted out an electric guitar, plugged it into an amp, stood on a chair strumming, unable to play a single note, blurting out punky lyrics of his own invention. The nurse rounded on me.

"See? I told you he's in a bad state, didn't I?"

I promised to get him back to the hospital, by which time he'd cleared the entire party out. I guided Wayne back to the hospital. At least my paranoia had worn off, so our journey didn't bother me. Back on the tube, some people I knew entered our carriage, one of them asking about my circumstances. I replied, telling all me and Wayne were in a nuthouse, going home after a party. Everyone froze, realising that the clothing and Wayne's drunken ravings were for real. He belted out songs in different languages, much to the annoyance of passengers.

Up in the morning, I went straight down to the canteen regular as clockwork. Food was excellent, with breakfast, dinner, lunch for the first time in years. I'd always eat bran for breakfast, owing to the drugs making me constipated. Many others were in an identical situation. Queuing for dinner one day I glanced through a glass partition. I saw some kids playing on a patch of wasteland. I thought it to be a deliberate set-up, staged by the powers that be for my personal benefit. One of the kids, trailing behind the others, stumbled, unable to keep up with the rest. This represented me. A trick of light made everything on the inside appear to be in grainy black and white. Outside, everything glowed in brilliant colour. Not better yet, I figured. A black girl who'd suffered a nervous breakdown told me something interesting.

"It's funny how the same people keep coming back here into the bin."

Maybe they cured you but once outside, a crack up might be on the cards. Something to keep in mind for the future. A few visitors popped in, first being the old man. Noticing he wore a pair of my shoes, I threw a fit, ending with me dragged away then shot up the arse. Redd came over, finding me in the artroom producing another masterwork.

"What's all this then?"

The Barney Rubble voice. I found it difficult to unwind the chain of circumstances that led me to the Picasso room, most of the story going over his head. Redd thought it was all down to me trying to wriggle out of the court case, pretending to be mentally unfit to plead. I put him at ease on that one. Redd cheered me up by mentioning that the coppers said I'd grassed him up. I assured him the whole story was a pack of lies, nothing less. Redd left, wondering what it was all about. Crispin and Justin dropped in out of curiosity. I gave them a conducted tour, playing the genial host, introducing the residents, taking in the canteen along the way. For their part, they bunged me some much needed draw.

In the canteen one afternoon, I noticed Coza from the graveyard lining up for a meal. He came over, must have guessed I'd suffered a breakdown. Coza had some friends on the residential top floor, him coming in and out for meals. Largactil took effect, slowing me down. I'd have to think for a second before saying anything. In such an environment, it didn't register quickly, the whole place seeming so unreal. I didn't bother with TV as Wayne supplied the entertainment, still on the fascist trip, pointing out suspects. By now I felt secure, paranoia wearing thin. I chatted to a maintenance man. Nothing unusual here except that a few weeks previously I'd have suspected him to be on the Burton payroll, sent to check me out. Just an ordinary guy. A student nurse came around. Humorous again, I spoke to her for a while, all lightness and reason. Suddenly I asked here what she kept in her bag, that I wanted to search it, ensure she wasn't spying, recording the conversation.

She allowed me to peek inside, no doubt making mental notes. Next day I went along on a rare visit to see the National Health shrink, who sat in a room surrounded by students and doctors perched behind desks. He didn't beat about the bush.

"You asked the nurse if she had some recording equipment in her bag."

Not wishing him to think I wasn't making progress, I retold the conversation I'd had with the maintenance man, that I'd realised he wasn't sent to snoop on me, just doing his job. The shrink thought me to be on the level when I assured him I'd only been kidding the nurse up. He surprised me by saying that maybe he'd let me go in another week or so.

If you got out of order in this place orderlies jumped in. After the incident with my old man I found myself messing about with John demonstrating karate to each other, showing off all the preliminary moves. Without warning they swooped, dragging us away, John screaming, me trying in vain to argue. For our pains, they shot us up with something that knocked us out for twelve hours.

My pay plus tax rebate deposited in the hospital bank, dole coming in meant I wasn't going short, expenses here being minimal. Some of the people were in the bin for a scam, such as a few of those residing on the top floor awaiting council accommodation, hostel place or if lucky, a flat. They moved me into a four-bed ward along with the young skinhead with his uncommunicating gaze. Me and Wayne smoked dope supplied by his Rastas or my visitors. One puffing session, Wayne asked me how many crack ups I'd had. Upon telling him this happened to be my maiden voyage, he laughed, claiming his one represented his fifth. Before my departure to the outside world, a nurse approached me.

"Before you go home, you'll have to take a shot of this."

"What is it?"

"Modecate, stops you freaking out."

Without questioning further, I dropped my pants. She shot me up with a massive whack. This Modecate, it seems, worked as a long lasting sedative. I also had to attend as an outpatient and see a new shrink. Having nowhere else to go, I bade farewell to Wayne and the others, heading back to the old man's flat. My room, with the little it now contained, hadn't been touched, the only recent acquisition a thin dust layer.

I settled in again, landing a job as a French Polisher that consisted mainly offloading and unloading vans. I didn't mention anything about the bin but I'd have to be crazy to work there anyway, the pay being pitiful. The job helped get me out the flat, establish a routine in the land of the living. Work itself ended up with me going out with the driver on deliveries. Ernie, the old geezer behind the wheel, was a racist of low mentality, always going on about Pakis, Yids, Niggers between drooling over anything in a short skirt. Even though hardly an hour passed without remarks about 'Our coloured brethren' I realised he wasn't a paid up member of the fascist big league, just a moron. This simple awareness of plain facts was a sure fire sign of paranoia recovery.

I'd developed a desire to eat sweet and savoury things, pies, crisps, confectionery, biscuits. If I lacked cash I'd lift from corner shops, putting down this increased appetite to a combination of boredom and nervous energy. Something else started to occur, dozing off to sleep in the van. Ernie had to nudge me awake on arrival at destinations. I tried smoking dope, drinking booze, again crashing out. On top of this, I gained weight, evidence for this provided by increasing trouser sizes. Things weren't right but I couldn't put my finger on it.

CHAPTER SEVEN

Out of the bin I picked up the shreds of merriment again. Wanting to get back into the old ways, I circulated. Crispin now lived with a geezer called Mark, an oddball who attended art school who introduced me to some fellow students, rich vacuous airheads all. One night soon after discharge Crispin and Mark took me up to a party full of these types in Highgate. By this time, everybody who wanted to be somebody sported a touch of punk. Lucky for me, outrageous behaviour still happened to be the order of the day, if only for posing purposes. The parents were away for this party so I headed straight up to the bathroom treats in the cabinet. A veritable goldmine. I swallowed a mouthful of Valium and Moggies. Feeling well good, I wandered through the rooms. I noticed Mark from an upstairs window, uprooting saplings. Shades of a younger me. Things were swinging again. I opened another door, finding the girl who threw the party with yet another would-be artist, sitting naked together in a peculiar position. I hollered for everyone to come have a peek, which they did, laughing. As they were otherwise occupied by that sight, I rummaged through the drawers. Final incident I remembered that night was climbing on to a shelf, standing balanced precariously, reaching for the top of a wardrobe cabinet. The whole lot collapsing, me underneath. Morning time, I awoke in a bed, somewhere in the same house. Having sustained no injuries, I regarded myself as fully back on the road.

I got back into drugs, even the odd fix of gear as I hung about more in Hampstead. The only missing part of the jigsaw, the desire to form a band, didn't bother me as I still retained my popularity with the girls. I'd started dating a girl called Betty. She worked at a Bond Street boutique, taking me to a fancy restaurant, presenting me with a pair of leather trousers. Cost: Over a ton. Taking Betty back to the flat, I couldn't get it on. She left somewhat disappointed in the morning with me suspecting the medication jabs might have something to do with it.

I went to the new young shrink with a few questions about my putting on weight, eating binges, dozing off and not being able to rise to the occasion. Scratching his chin, he gave me the low-down.

"Unfortunately, the side effects of Modecate can include obesity, nervousness and a tendency to fall asleep."

"And how long will this last?"

"Oh, about a year."

I'd already had three jabs, so I demanded there and then, that they cease pumping such crap inside me.

"I wouldn't advise going off it yet."

I told him I'd had enough, so he ended only fixing me another appointment.

Another doctor proved more accommodating. I'd rooted out an old address from the punk days, a bent practitioner based in Harley Street. Phoning this Doctor Dingle, an appointment was arranged. Doctor Dingle dressed in the traditional white coat, pens sticking from his top pocket, stethoscope around the neck, tanned, grey hair. I coughed up twenty quid for this consultation, telling him I couldn't sleep, that Sally, a patient of his had been providing me with the odd Mandrax to help me sleep. Dingle didn't seem amused.

"Look, Sally isn't a doctor."

A responsible tone followed.

"I think you're a bit young for Mandrax. I'm going to give you some sleeping pills."

I hadn't forked out a score for nothing. I said I'd just suffered a nervous breakdown, that I'd also been taking coke, the first thing that came into my head.

"That's not very good for you, is it? You shouldn't take coke."

"I've got to have some Mandrax."

After much pontification, Dingle wrote me a month's script, sixty of the best. Enough for a mad week.

Redd visited me up at Archway one weekend so we hit a late night movie in Hampstead. Cutting back home across the Heath we skidded along the frozen ground, joking to ourselves. Redd thought he'd glimpsed people skiing on Parliament Hill, gliding down the slope. There were people alright but they weren't brushing up on winter sports. It turned out to be a gang of lads numbering about a dozen, rushing toward us. We didn't hang around to exchange pleasantries, running off. Just wasn't my night as I slipped on the ice. The pack leapt on me as I tried to scramble up. A couple pinned me to the ground while others took running kicks, steel toe-capped boots to my head. A screaming blinding flash with stars appeared with each crunch. Blood flowed in profusion from open head wounds. They grabbed me by the limbs, swinging my body as I uttered gurgling sounds, blood trickling from my mouth. I heard a gruff voice above the vicious yapping.

"Shall we bollock 'im?"

I thought the end had come. What a way to go, murder victim on a cold night. Our Father, who art in heaven … Another voice.

"Naah, leave 'im … he's had enough."

They deposited me without ceremony, forcing me to run, warm blood gushing from my head wounds. Redd hadn't fucked off, he waited further along in the dark, shivering. They'd managed to swipe the jacket from his back. Redd now tried to halt passing cars but the drivers didn't want to know. He resolved the situation by leaping in front of one, almost causing an accident in the process. Redd forced the driver to take us to the hospital. It proved to be a busy night, with me the seventh casualty in the last couple of hours. They injected my head, painful. After a shaving job, stitched up to the tune of an impressive twenty seven. After an overnight stay, I made it back to my bijou residence vowing to avoid Parliament Hill, an unlucky spot for me, it seems.

I'd been working at the French Polishers for six weeks, the job becoming progressively unbearable, dozing off in the van. During any waking period I'd stuff myself silly. Knowing it was all down to the jabs couldn't help me control the situation. The climax came during a delivery to the stock exchange to move some picture frames. Ernie went off to get his chit signed and angle for a tip. By the time he arrived back I'd made myself at home, sprawled out on a leather sofa, dead to the world, laying comatose. I heard a posh voice complaining to Ernie.

"What's he doing here?"

Later that day I got my pay and cards. Ernie had been bending ears. The owner palmed me off.

"You knew you'd be getting the sack sooner or later, didn't you?"

Nothing to say, I signed on next Monday. In my state I wasn't flustered about losing the job. I fell into deep apathy, becoming a sloth with impaired speech, faint treadmill shuffles thanks to the jabs. As I gorged, my weight rose steadily from a trim nine stone to thirteen. The leather trousers filled, legs working like overstuffed black puddings. My face puffed in proportion to my girth. Staring into a mirror, *Bonanza* Hoss grimaced back.

Evolving into a virtual hermit, I sported hair growth, took to wearing baggy overalls, social life on the road to extinction. Main exercise had me lumbering over to the library to read, where I'd fall asleep to be awakened by tongue-clicking assistants. Same story watching telly, waking up with test card blaring. Eating and sleeping became my main activities, exercise provided by walking to the dole office. My personal issue would be immediately blown on food at the nearest supermarket. You name it, I'd buy it. Pre-cooked chickens that could be steamed into straight away. Tubs of ice creams, trifles, pints of custard, ham, ready-made stuff. I had to buy stomach medicine, liver salts to help relieve indigestion. But dole money doesn't last forever. A couple of food splurges, and I'd go lifting again. Hunger attacked any time, quite often when watching food ads on the telly. Donning my baggy overalls and raincoat, I'd steel myself for supermarket raids within a mile radius, lifting bacon, peanuts, rolls. The bulky clothes concealed a multitude of goodies, enough to see me through any crave. For money I'd sometimes raid my old man's sty, going through the reeking clothes piled high bachelor fashion. Once, to my delight, I unearthed a crumpled-up tenner. On occasion I'd sneak into his room as he lay in a boozy stupor, gaze upon the snoring drunken heap, edging his trousers toward the door with my foot, dribbling the pants around festering mounds of rotting clothes. Outside the door, I'd dip the pockets then fling the strides back into the sty. No pangs of guilt bothered my conscience, regarding this as back-dated pocket money.

Ironically, for the first time in years I'd gone straight. One toke on a joint and I'd be out cold for hours. All time and effort went into food-gathering. But light winked at the tunnel's end, as slowly the jab effects diminished. All the same I knew I had no choice but to sit tight, ride it out, so no more work for the duration. As is usual with the NHS they foisted another shrink on to my case. I asked him for Valium to help me sleep, the reality of it being this had become the only cheap thrill I could manage, not getting out to hustle other goodies. He refused so I didn't return. The only interruption to this far-from idyllic lifestyle came from the court appearance for the saxophones, me and Redd dealt with separately. He got off while I pleaded guilty. The mitigating factors of my nervous breakdown and subsequent psychiatric treatment meant things went easy for me. Two years probation.

The only place I visited on a regular basis was two stops down the line, Kentish Town. Here, Redd and Stan squatted with an older geezer, Johnny Loader. I'd waddle my corpulent bulk down from the Archway, usually ending up crashed out in front of their telly. Apart from attempting to keep grip on a semblance of normality as I understood it, another incentive drew me down there. Loader's girlfriend worked in a deli on the High Street. Me and Loader mounted raiding parties whenever the boss was absent, to stock up on such delights as gefilte fish, smoked salmon, peanut butter, pickles, expensive cans of soup, ice cream, salt beef, the works. This fed the squat.

Loader struck me as a lively eccentric who'd do anything for a laugh. Unlike most squatters, he seemed together – colour telly, car, a phone in the hallway. Redd by now had generated his own little scene, having finally broken into the Camden Girls sorority. Trouble is, they were mostly fifteen year olds. The Barney Rubble accent mellowed to include more phrases, making him appear deep to some of those beguiled schoolgirls. Stan was going for one-night stands, tooting up the odd line of smack. So much for Mr Clean. He still played the guitar but now he'd failed to evolve, remaining a permanent seventeen year old, stuck in time painting, keeping photographic books, his infantile scrawlings adorning the walls. Stan packed a 35mm camera, went to foreign films, even visited galleries. All I did as a pastime was visit the deli with Loader, armed with carrier bags, even taking a suitcase once. The three of them had their own thing going, getting laid, going to movies, the odd gig. I couldn't handle this, nodding off all the time, unable to keep up with them in my condition.

The family GP refused Valium, while I couldn't afford the bent doctor. Instead of Valium, the GP put me on a drug called Trancopal. I dropped ten, giving Stan twenty. Apart from feeling slightly wobbly they didn't seem to have much of a kick. Bravado asserted, so I dropped another twenty, then went back to the Archway. Arriving home, I just crashed out, waking a few minutes before midday. I remembered little of the previous day except that Loader's girlfriend who worked in the deli, gave me some stamped prescription pads. Having use of a pushbike borrowed from Loader, I pedalled down to sign on. Trouble was, I now shook violently, barely able to maintain balance. Getting to the dole office became a dice with death, falling off twice, nearly ending under a bus. I met a friend who took one look at the state of me trembling and asked me what I'd been taking. The dole handed the form over to sign as I shook, desperately stabbing at the paper with a pen eventually affixing my signature. Outside, I came tumbling off the bike again. The chain came off, my friend fixed it.

"I think you'd better go home mate."

Managing to mount the bike, I rode off down the High Street and home. I crashed into the side of a vehicle as co-ordination went haywire. Just my luck it happened to be a police car. So I raced off to the left into a side street, then came flying off. The heavens opened, rain lashed down. Painfully scrambling up, I tried to remove myself and bike. A car skidded to a halt, a copper lowered his window.

"Excuse me sir, have you been drinking?"

"Oh no, not at all."

"Well then, have you got anything on you that you shouldn't have?"

He meant drugs. Lucky I was clean. I shook as he stepped out into the ram.

"Oh no, nothing like that at all."

"Would you mind emptying out your pockets please?"

Things being as they were, I handed over the bent prescriptions, thinking them to be mere scrap paper.

"And what are these, then?"

Between shakes, I remembered. Mind confused, reacting instantly, I ran across the road then slipped in the wet, landing face-down. The copper and his driver threw me into their pranged motor. Off to the police station, placed in a cell, charged with dangerous driving under the influence of unknown substances. They questioned me about the prescriptions. That black geezer in the pub got another mention. I wanted to go home, felt ravenous, still trembling at ten at night. Finally, they escorted me back to Archway, knocking on the door, rousing the old man, who threw a fit. Demonstrating solidarity, he locked himself away as they searched my room, unable to unearth anything apart from some old works. The policewoman brandished the hypo.

"What's this then?"

"Why, it's a hypodermic, what else do you think it is?"

Still cheeky, if nothing else.

"And what are you doing with it?"

"Someone must have left it here …"

She slapped me full in the face. Next day I appeared in court, case adjourned. Catching up with Stan later, he told me a tale or two. He'd gone off his head on the Trancopal, nicked a car, drove all night, crashed into parked cars, legged it home. The after-effects lingered five days, only wearing off slowly. I still had the Modecate to contend with.

The woman who processed my dole claims sent me for a job, knowing the whole procedure to be a farce.

"You might like this one though, it's for people who've been signing on for six months."

No interview required. Instead of the fifteen pounds a week dole, I'd be back on the grand sum of thirty. It involved removing graffiti and turning waste ground into parks. I started the following Monday on a patch of rubble near Archway, just me and another bloke who'd suffered a breakdown, this time after serving in the Territorial Army. The guy in charge, a thirty five year old longhair with shades, mumbled vague instructions before vanishing for the day. Like all the people on this particular project who had authority, he followed the teachings of a portly Guru whose greasy face filled up a large sized badge. The waste ground, a mass of building rubble, had to be cleared, so me and ex-army got stuck in. Out in the fresh air, even if only for a couple of hours a day due to us making off early, did me the power of good. An energy surge took possession, I felt reborn, ready to do anything, I'd broken the listless spell.

Ater a couple of weeks on the Archway site, they transferred us further down Holloway Road. Early morning we arrived at the new site where a hut had been erected. A dozen fresh recruits stood sucking thumbs. I patted my generous tum which thankfully now showed signs of decreasing its expansion, checking out the geezers who'd turned up. They didn't know the score as the man in charge had failed to materialise, probably meditating his navel. Game for a laugh, I took over, assuming responsibilities.

"This your first day lads?"

I guided them around the site, giving an outline of work involved.

"There's fuck all in it. Dig a hole, fill it up again, move rubble, put it elsewhere."

A Guru foreman finally appeared, glad someone had assumed responsibilities, shown the ropes. After self-enforced exile, I felt happy to be socialising in the wide world, even in this simplistic environment. Dope and booze no longer crashed me out, appetite decreased, speed helped reduce weight.

The workers on this scheme were old hippies, ex-schoolteachers, other dropouts and the odd black guy in trouble. I befriended someone called Kim, a professional bass player fallen on hard times. A typical day had me getting one of the foremen into a rock and roll rap, smoking blow, avoiding any semblance of work. Sometimes I'd slip the Guru into the conversation. Confessions of a uniform nature resulted.

"If it wasn't for the Guru I'd be dead on drugs."

We even had a *Mice and Men* Lenny type named Norman. As I'd done some book-reading, especially on the movies, during my confinement, I'd be rapping away on that subject all the time. Norman thought I was in charge owing to me hardly ever touching a tool, doing so much talking. I'd noticed a tendency here among the Guru types to proselytise the vulnerable school-leavers about the teachings of their leader. After a week, I had it all sewn up, like at Highgate cemetery. Pretend job. Soon, me and Kim enjoyed three-hour lunch breaks in the pub. It wasn't long before the rest profited by our idle example, jumping on the bandwagon. Two pints of strong lager got me merry. Four, dead drunk. I laid the odd couple of quid in the bookies, my luck being in. When skint, the entertainment cost a couple of pints, subsidised by willing workmates. On a warm afternoon some of us might slip away to the swimming baths.

We had a twenty five year old South African military deserter with a beard, named Curtis. He enjoyed my line in jive, sharing his dope. One of his mates turned up on site with a large plastic bag. He'd just done a chemists. I got a bottle of Dexedrine, jar of Valium, couple of Diconal and some Palfium. All on tick. After we'd been through the bag of tricks, most of the shirkforce were off their heads for days. The majority smoked blow, apart from some of the youngsters, however they soon got into it. We only had a couple of creeps, one a bloke I named Humpty, an idiot who voted Conservative, rode a moped. The other, a flash Harry, two years younger than myself. Flash Harry did my head serious damage, having done and seen it all. One afternoon, sitting on the hut steps, stoned, Flash Harry annoyed me droning on about the fights he'd won, tasty birds he'd fucked. I'd had enough, after all, I was the real star here. Smashing a bottle, I gripped the neck, shoving the jagged edges against his face. Everyone present freaked. I simply tossed the broken bottle aside, taking a bow next to petrified Harry.

"And that's acting, folks!"

A live wire again, main lead in the show with a manic tinge picked up since the crack-up. Whenever I didn't turn in, our site resembled the cuckoo's nest without Nicholson.

I met an old flame while getting through the Dexedrine, drinking in a pub at Highbury. Justin lived next door, still dealing. I chatted up this girl, Amanda, the old confidence sparkling. I landed her phone number in spite of looking a right old state, overweight, baggy overalls, high on Dexys. Within a couple of weeks, I dated Amanda regular, screwing again. Amanda's father was a famous artist, so I ended up hovering around the middle classes for the umpteenth time. She'd take me to those big houses, back to the lap of luxury. Alright for a geezer on thirty quid a week. I'd developed into a more articulate bullshitter from reading during my hermit period, so they all thought me to be some breed of intelligent Cockney. Patronising, but I took every advantage. People like this always delude themselves, believing they are more clever than anyone else including yourself. Desiring to shed weight, I didn't bother raiding fridges. Instead I'd browse through cabinets for drugs, drawers for odd bits of change. A pound still bought a couple of pints. Amanda introduced me to her friends, mostly people into fine arts attending the SLADE. She dabbled in post punk, surprised by my curt dismissal of the whole scene. Punk had become boring, played out. Amanda moved into London after living in the parental country residence. She'd done the black thing after having been to the West Indies on a paid trip, sent out for a smack cure. Able to buy almost anything over the counter there, she'd come back plentifully armed with Valium and bombers. Amanda hadn't been in London too long, but hit the scene with a vengeance. Drugs, black boyfriends, getting to know people in bands of the post-punk era, even though the whole thing had long ago become a stale joke. Now I'd recovered sufficiently with lard melting away, I started fooling around, screwing other girls.

In the meantime, I got Redd and Justin fixed up with a job at the site. They were pleased to see the old me back in action. Joking one lazy afternoon, I talked the workforce into a God trip, convincing them I'd seen the error of my ways, even the Guru freaks taken in. Down the road from the site stood a house where I'd scored smack, an old Kingsway connection. I became a regular customer after I'd conducted the whip-round for the smackheads, making the journey a couple of days a week, shooting up later in the hut as others pretended to toil. I amused myself, picking on the hapless Humpty, mimicry in full flow, talking about how good the Tories were for the country.

Owing to jab after-effects, I retained the mad eyes but most days here I'd been speeding, having been introduced to a new buzz by Kim. In the chemists they sold Benzadrex inhalers that contained a Benzedrin ingredient. Cost, a mere forty pence. I'd get Humpty to purchase them, not wishing to be regarded as an abuser by local chemists. Me and Kim would smash the casing, remove the thick strips of tissue paper that stank of peppermint, swallow half, washed down with a carton of milk. Then came an eight hour buzz, the rush resulting in prickly hair. So good was the feeling we'd even get stuck in sporadically, do some work.

During rainy days we sat in the hut smoking grass as I entertained the others. I'd been on inhaler juice but weed did the trick, everyone zonked. The manic urge seized me, so I decided to have a cheap laugh, annoy Humpty who sat reading *Exchange and Mart.*

"Hey Humpty, don't you ever want to get someone, hit 'em, really do 'em in, just do it for the sake of it, man? Walk and stomp all over 'em."

The act, once again, looked so convincing, they all got into it, nodding in agreement. I got carried away, tearing up Humpty's magazine, offering myself as a punchbag.

"Go on Humpty! Hit me! Just one on the chin!"

Humpty looked uncomfortable. I ran over to the wall, pounding it with fist and boot. To round it off I took a swing at the window. The whole show was calculated, me thinking the pane contained nothing more than perspex. Wrong. I smashed my fist through glass. Withdrawing my hand, the wrist sliced on jagged glass, striking red oil, blood gushing out, my audience getting sprayed. I'd nipped a main cable. People sat as if rooted, in a trance, in particular a trembling Humpty. Stemming the flow by applying pressure on the severed connection, I shouted instructions.

"Get an ambulance, quick!"

One of the black guys happened to be studying as a cab driver, so he drove me in his car. So concerned was this guy about leaking blood staining the interior, he took the wrong turning, driving off in the opposite direction. I ended up at Whittington again. Arriving, I rushed into a ward, grabbing a doctor. They examined the wound, stitched it after a jab. The troops all marched in from the site with my pay packet, laughing their heads off. Grabbing the money, I asked the doctor if it was alright to drink booze. He said sure, so off I went, two weeks' recuperation with pay which I spent with Amanda, lounging in big houses, raiding cocktail and bathroom cabinets. By this time I looked more like my old self. I'd lost three stone from the lard mountain.

With me, Redd and Justin working together, the hut soon turned into a shooting gallery. We didn't care, jacking up in front of workmates who failed to bat an eyelid. A few of the old geezers shot up also, including a bloke named Jeff, who turned us on to Codeine Linctus, fifty pence a bottle from any chemists. Justin tried it in the pub as he felt strung out, his face turning red after half an hour. He praised it, unable to finish his pint. It appeared to do the trick so I took note should ever I hit poverty row.

I met Loader as I avoided toil on the site. They'd all been evicted from Kentish Town, Redd going back home. Stan moved into a squat in Albany Street near Regents Park, full of pretentious arty types, along with Lenny from the Square. Redd, the obvious pleb, had been refused space, while Loader squatted a

Hampstead flat. It didn't take long before me and Loader started going out together on my extended liquid lunches. Upstairs, above Loader's squat, lived a dealer. Soon I called over there on a regular basis.

I'd heard some company were shooting a film inside my old stomping ground, The Rainbow. Loader and Mark from art school were unable to procure tickets as extras so I put my knowledge of the building to use, bunking in. Inside we chatted to the producers, picking up our twenty quid fee, then walked around backstage nicking headphones, clothes and other goodies, stuffing them into a plastic bag. Valium were doled out to my companions but after dropping them we lost Mark. Me and Loader slipped into the after-filming party at a trendy night-club uptown, finding Betty behind the bar. This resulted in free drinks for Loader and me. Soon the two of us were falling all over the gaff, time to return home, Hampstead squat bound. Leaving, I tried on the coats hanging up near the exit while bunging my hand into a couple of pockets, fishing out a couple of bob. I did the hunchback routine, departing with two coats on my back plus the carrier bag full of gear and some loose change. Once outside, Loader produced his keyring so we drove home in a stolen Morris Minor. We'd enjoyed ourselves to the extent of launching a three-day bender, nicking more Morris motors, drinking, dropping Valium. No mistake, I'd recovered from the crack-up.

I'd more or less ensconced myself in Amanda's flat in Highbury, looking after the place while she stayed in Paris. Amanda was desperately trying to be independent, residing in Paris with a friend of hers named Rob, a dyke from Australia who was on the game. I took it for granted Amanda would be plying trade as she was still going through the phase of doing everything. This, of course, being nothing more than a pose, so that some time in the respectable future she could boast at dinner parties that she'd 'done it all'. Amanda rang. She had loads of dosh, why didn't I come over? Why not indeed. I collected my wages, visitor's passport, picked up a load of Mandrax from Justin, set off to Victoria, caught a night-train out. On board, meeting a girl I knew named Kate who also happened to be going to Paris. The train was packed with racehorse fans heading for Longchamp and the Prix de L'Arc de Triomphe. Dropping Mandies, I chatted up Kate while swapping anecdotes with the punters, talk being only of horses, trainers, geldings, done me bollocks, turn of foot. Kate guessed I was taking the piss but not in a rude or aggressive manner, telling them I'd backed one in the National, that it fell in the paddock.

At Dover, I helped Kate with her bags then together we hit the bar. After sinking a couple, we stepped out for a stroll on deck. As it chucked down rain, we went back inside, walking about until I located an unused crew cabin. In we went. Mandies make you randy but it was all over in a matter of seconds. Premature ejaculation. As I apologised to Kate, the cabin door swung open. Four crew members looking like

U-boat captains steamed in, pushing me aside, grabbing Kate, feeling her tits and bum. I dived on them. Mandies gave you courage also. Without much effort they turfed me out, so I kicked and pounded on the door, shouting my head off. Kate somehow managed to extract herself from the lustful scrum, came flying out. We rushed to the bar, stayed put. It might have turned out heavy but instead we had another drink, laughed it off. At the train station in Paris we said goodbye, parting company as the punters poured off, away to the fleshpots.

I caught the Metro to an area that resembled St John's Wood, full of luxury apartments. The feeling hit me, good time coming up. I found Amanda's address, ringing the bell. A model type answered the door, screwing me out. I got the picture straight away, mentioned Amanda's name, was straight in. All the girls here were on the game. Amanda had caught a dose from one of her clients, so sex was out. Inside, the phone rang constantly, so I knew there were customers aplenty, dosh coming in. Rob, her dyke friend, handed me a bottle of Fragonal, French speed. Soon these were rattling down my gullet. Off again. The girls were loaded after a few hour's work and they wanted to spend it. The oldest one took a liking to my boyish good looks, taking me to flashy clubs where one shot set you back a fiver. I hit the dance floor, guzzled champagne, saw *Clockwork Orange* at the movies, which helped set the tone.

I rang up the French geezers who'd introduced me to smack. One was in the army doing National Service but home on leave. The other, Eric, lived in a luxury apartment, present from his rich parents. I went over with a couple of the girls and Amanda. The French geezers salivated when they saw all the money hanging out of their handbags and flash clothing. I looked fine, with hair dyed jet black, sporting an enormous quiff. We ordered smack and within fifteen minutes gear had been purchased. The conscript was an ace at fixing people up, doing Amanda first, me eagerly awaiting my shot when I heard a crash followed by a thud. Amanda had overdosed, flopping out of the bathroom, falling on the floor. By now, due to extensive drug experience, I'd become well used to dealing with such situations. So I grabbed Amanda, hauling her limp body to its feet. She looked ghostly white with blue lips, eyes at the back of her head like a stiff. Slapping Amanda around the face, I walked her around the room, helped by the army guy. I tried mouth to mouth resuscitation as a nightmare unfurled before me, visions of newspaper headlines 'Famous artist's daughter dies of drug overdose'; 'Police search for youth from Archway'. Photo of me and quiff. The army guy brought her back with a shot of adrenaline and she started coming to. By now I cried out for a fix. Eric administered to my needs as Amanda sat up. But he only doled out a tiny amount on the spoon. I protested.

"That wouldn't even give a mouse a hangover."

"Huh, she said something like that too."

I grabbed the packet, pouring myself a small mountain. It didn't take long before I'd banged the whole lot into my arm. I took enough to murder someone but as I'd taken lots of Fragonal just before, it kept my metabolism regular, allowing me full benefit of the gear. The most comfortable feeling imaginable descended as I sank into bliss on a sofa, my eyes taking in the scene. Of the two French geezers, I disliked the obvious rich kid Eric. Spoilt rotten by his family, the apartment contained eight electric guitars and he couldn't play a note. I didn't like the creep, nor did the girls. I later caught the vibe of Eric going into the bathroom to toot up coke on the sly without offering any to us. Evening, we sat on the sofas, eating cream gateaux, drinking coffee. I hit up Eric.

"How about some of that coke, eh? You've got some, haven't you?"

Upon denial, I lost my rag, plunging a whole cream cake into his face. Me and the girls decamped. I never saw the French geezers again.

After a week of the high life Amanda left to go back home and get a cure for her social disease. Rob and her mates looked after me. Oysters, drink, drugs in abundance. I'd only booked a week's holiday but wasn't going to quit when the going was so good. I stayed. Rob took me out on jobs, while I waited in bars and cafés. It turned out I wasn't the only one with a touch of the prematures as she once came back with a thousand francs for ten minute's work. Another week of being flavour of the month, I decided to return home.

Back at work Monday, I had a row with the foreman, him pissed off that I'd taken a fortnight off. Nevertheless, he had to pay me as I produced a doctor's note. In the meantime, Redd had been moved off to another site and Justin developed his first habit as I slid towards my second. I didn't exactly help wean Justin off with my stories I'd heard about Turkeys. Him being a coward into the bargain, he'd now got too frightened to come off as I told him of hot and cold flushes, praying to God on bended knees. Justin had to stay up, never to come down. I turned him on to Diconal, a little pink pill, crushed, fixed like smack, the quickest, strongest rush in town, tricky to handle. If you failed to hit the vein, you could lose an arm, or even your life. A real killer. Even so, it graduated to the status of morning treat.

Back on the site; I felt inexplicably weak, unable to lift up a shovel. In a couple of hours I couldn't even raise a cup of tea to my lips. Upon reflection, although my weight had hit normal, it seemed to be plummeting recently. My shit turned bleach white, piss dark. Thanks to fixing up, I'd caught hepatitis again. Skin and eyes changed yellow overnight. By the time I'd collected my pay, I could barely stand, so I limped over to the hospital in a state of near collapse, asking to see a doctor, telling them I'd contracted hep. Being a contagious disease, they dealt with me instantly. I told the nurse that I'd used a needle to take drugs. From her hostile glance I could tell she lacked sympathy for drug abusers. Smack had started to get well into circulation, she'd seen plenty in my state, ordering me to drop my pants, bend over. I peeked over my shoulder, saw her fitting on a crackling rubber glove, eyes cold, magnified through pebble glasses. But like a horror movie, she didn't entertain any ceremony, sticking her finger right up my arsehole, me letting out a yell of pain, needing something to bite on. The smear taken away for examination, another nurse took a blood sample. In half an hour, the result. Hep. Straight to the isolation hospital, them ringing a cab. Just my luck that at the bottom of the hill leading up to the hospital, the cab blew a tyre in the pissing rain, forcing me to walk uphill. The driving rain lashed down, my side ached like hell, me clutching at it. As the rain bucketed, my quiff hung limp down to my chin. Reduced to pulling myself along, gripping railings, groaning in agony, the scene resembled something out of a gangster's last moments, Hollywood style. Finally, I somehow staggered into the hospital, collapsing in a sodden heap at reception.

Woke up in a bed, my own private room looking out to trees on a lawn, door leading to my bathroom. I noticed a portable TV and wage packet resting beside my bed on a table. On this first day, a geezer I knew from way back popped in to see me. Leaving from treatment himself, he gave me a lump of dope and a beaver mag. Diet here consisted of white meats, plenty of fish. Streams of visitors poured in every day, including people from work. I was in for a comfortable convalescence, told by a doctor I couldn't drink booze for a year and, after that, no spirits. Some good news though, with him saying I could take speed, even inject it if I used a clean needle. They jabbed me up with vitamins, skin pops every morning. Wage packets were brought over personally by the foreman who used this as an excuse to skive off. He must have been pissed off to see all the nice girls coming in to see me as I watched the telly smoking joints. In a moment of triumph I hit him up.

"Bet your fat Guru's never got you anything like this!"

He hated handing over the money, knowing I'd got away with so much. Others brought in weed and coke. I sometimes lay in the warm bath reflecting upon my misspent life, feeling tranquil. I'd lived the life of a star, girls flocking all around, drugs aplenty, yet without having to live onstage or have any noticeable achievement whatever. I wasn't even a one-hit wonder. I felt my brain speeding up again, getting on well with the nurses, reading more books.

Popular music had long since died a death so I didn't bother with the radio. I gained half a stone in three weeks, then out again back to work.

Once out of hospital I moved a few more of my possessions into Amanda's flat, settling in, returning to work. Here, like Highgate, we only built fires now we'd hit winter with no real work to do. The workforce, starved of entertainment, were glad to see me back. I speeded all the time now, unable to touch booze. History repeated itself with us all redundant a week before Christmas. They paid us off a hundred quid each. In my case, the whole lot went in a couple of days. Smack and coke. Woes came, Amanda booting me out. Things hadn't gone too well. She'd got pregnant, with all the accompanying mood swings, then had an abortion. A bit like living in a kitchen sink drama. Amanda now hung out with a bunch of pretentious theatrical people, the irony being that I'd introduced her to them. I'd had to mix with a bunch of actors who I detested, making it plain and clear to all concerned. All these bozos could do was to lisp about themselves, boring me rigid. We attended third-rate plays, watching these second-rate actors mumble through their performance. Simply fucking wonderful darling. They really thought they were it, number one. I kept having a go, telling them I preferred movies. Just before Christmas I went back to Archway and the old man just to dump some gear in my old room, intending to stay with a woman dealer friend of mine, Thelma, for a couple of weeks. All my stuff had gone, the room stank of socks, pictures of simians with hurling sticks along with the Kennedys and the Pope decorated my wall. My old man had installed a Paddy and his common-law wife. So I was out for good.

Thelma was a dealer in her mid-thirties I knew from the drugs scene who lived in a loft home with a real fireplace, nice and snug, cosy flat with open-plan and beams. The phone rang constantly, she'd have different people over all hours. I performed Thelma's odd jobs, the pay quite good. Opium, Mandrax, dope and coke. No smack, but then again, you can't have everything. If I felt tired it was just a case of crashing out on the sofa. Her ex-boyfriend thought I'd become her lover. She'd given him marching orders after five years, he resented seeing me there, even though nothing of a carnal nature passed between us. Thelma often left me in the flat alone to deal. This turned out okay money and drugwise but I knew this to be a halfway house. Sooner or later I'd have to leave, find somewhere else. I got out and about, even buying a saxophone from a junkie. I'd been previously banned from his flat owing to my shooting up. Now they were all on it, these Hampstead kids. Shooting up too. I started dating another girl. In all, I was having a right old giggle despite no wage packet or nowhere to live proper. When you're young, you don't care.

I felt fine, exuded confidence, looked good but I'd also got a baby chimpanzee on my back.

One of Thelma's friends, a hard case, ripped off a hospital, nicking an ounce of morphine. She delegated me to flog it. As I'd never been much of a business man, I ended up getting through most myself, the rest dispatched for next to nothing. The morph helped fuel my gear appetite. I ended up flogging the saxophone for smack. I moved again rather than overstay my welcome, ending up in a squat near Camden Town, living with a Cockney dope dealer, Ozwald Finney. The place seemed squalid and bare after Thelma's. When I moved in, Ozwald's girlfriend lay in bed sweating out a Turkey. Ozwald, though, struck me as alright. At least he didn't hail from the ubiquitous middle classes. A guy named Simon was in the process of moving out, coming into Ozwald's room as I laid plans to move in. Simon cursed, telling Ozwald he'd caught scabies, scratching violently then peeling off all his clothes, rubbing a foul smelling lotion on his body. Simon borrowed some clothes off Ozwald, went out into the garden and burnt his infested clothing. For obvious reasons, I decided not to move into his recently vacated room, so I settled in a room at the top with empty floors below. This was a padlocks on all doors vibe, my only furniture, a mattress. The whole street seemed squatted with junkies of every nationality flocking to this Mecca. Nearby, the Hampstead junkies had also moved in, usually managing to obtain slightly more respectable co-op housing. Ozwald shared his Methadone with me but moved in some other junkies.

CHAPTER EIGHT

Justin wangled himself a room in a large squatted house in Ridinghouse Street, down the West End near Goodge Street. I fancied a change of location and circumstance so, thanks to him, I moved in. This place had electricity but no running water. The residents kept large containers of water in their rooms, the supply fed from a hosepipe running from a derelict building next door. Most toilet functions were performed from windows into the stinking backyard below. Apart from Justin, there were a group of Australians led by a couple of shady characters named Smith and Jones. And a young punk from up North where the fashion had now spread, thus heralding its ultimate demise. I started off with a room at the top, my only furniture the mattress and a chair.

Some of the Aussies worked in a nearby hospital. I still claimed dole but the money wasn't enough to meet my needs for a day. Luckily I could earn some cash by scoring for people in the house who were all into gear and I also scored blow for nurses in a nurses' home just around the corner, which I'd visited for creature comforts. For a quid, I ate well at their canteen, using the shower units and swimming pool. Once again, I'd changed my appearance, weight starting to sneak back due to munchies induced by drug abuse. Loader departed to Thailand for a long stay. Before leaving he'd cropped my barnet. I'd taken to leisurely strolls around the area, sometimes using pub or restaurant toilets when caught short. I soon noticed how coats belonging to customers would be hanging upstairs, while those of the staff were left below downstairs. The first time I tried my luck was coming up from a basement bog, seeing the coats in a blind spot. Here was a chance. I looked around, people were otherwise distracted, talking office business over lunch. I rifled through the pockets, striking gold, a wallet. Leaving, nodding thanks to the staff, I hurried home. In my room, I emptied the contents on to my mattress, creating a little pile. Everyone gathered around. Cash amounted to thirty pounds, enough to buy gear for all assembled. I didn't know what to do with the credit cards, giving them to Smith who dashed off to Tottenham Court Road, returning later with a guitar, camera and he'd brought me some clothes. These were needed because by this time I approached raggedness, down to flares and a sweater. As I wore sandals, Smith also re-shod me. This episode encouraged me to repeat performances.

The Aussie guys, Smith and Jones, were about the best of the bunch. Jones had come out of the nick after a smash and grab went wrong. Everyone here was on some fiddle or other, most putting in the odd degree of work, even Justin, who did a boardman's job in the bookies next door. Smith worked as a motorcycle messenger. I'd taken to wearing tinted glasses, concealing tell-tale signs of drug abuse. My habit now required plenty of money, ten to twenty quid a day. The chimp had graduated into an orang-utan.

I visited restaurants, student doctors' bars, the nurses' home, also plundering the hospital, plenty of drugs around just crying out to be nicked from mobile cabinets left unattended. Also, boxes of works were filched, so we'd always have supplies laid in. Morphine-based heavy stuff was too well guarded. Smith busied himself swiping kegs and crates from the student bar so, in the rare event of no gear, we'd raise a booze party. With shoplifting we'd sustain everybody, even Justin getting in the odd bottle of wine or box of pasta. Me and Smithy made a good working team, me taking a sports bag, him a rucksack, passing ourselves off as tourists. Hitting small supermarkets, we'd do our routine, one piling stuff into a wire basket like a genuine shopper, the other ambling through the store. We'd meet in a blind spot such as an empty alcove, security mirrors proving an asset, making it possible to glance up to see if anybody was screwing us out. Smithy knelt down, rucksack open while I'd empty goodies into it, after which we placed a coat on top then he'd walk out. I'd continue filling the basket, dumping it on the floor. If questions were asked, I'd pretend to have left my wallet in the car. All booty here was shared, my only financial obligations lay in purchasing gear.

Social life revolved around the squat. I didn't see much of Redd, Stan or Crispin, my old friends considering the squat and its inhabitants squalid. Despite these reservations, I knew sooner or later they'd turn up whenever there happened to be an abundance of smack on the premises.

I got stopped in the street by a girl named Clarissa who I'd met during my short involvement in the art scene when coming out of the bin. Clarissa chatted me up, extending an invitation to come see where she studied, an exclusive school populated by upper crusts and cream of the middle classes.

Having nothing better to do, always sniffing out a prospect, I accepted. Clarissa certainly wasn't my type, a bearded lady with ginger hair. But she had lots of tasty friends whose folks were rolling in money. A doddering old gent made me sign the entry book and I was in. This place looked like a spacious old house, a veritable mansion. Clarissa herself, being in the final year of her diploma, seemed extra confident, taking me up into the student's common room. I got the vibe Clarissa was showing me off, look what I've found, so I played up the salt-of-the-earth routine. She enjoyed this up-front behaviour, me play-acting opening doors for women. Clarissa lived at home and I knew I had her snug in my pocket. Her parents owned a house in town plus among other properties, a factory. She knew where all the groovy parties were held, me soon finding myself a regular attender at these soirées. I liked to party myself recognising opportunity when I saw it. I'd started to feel bored with the Ridinghouse scene, beginning to think ambitiously, like roping in a gullible rich girl. As most were idiots, despite my handicap in the breeding stakes, I felt confident enough to pull it off. That and some luck. Parties were held in fashionable Chelsea and Knightsbridge, my adventures in Hampstead ensuring I wasn't browbeaten or impressed by these types. The more money they had, the more likely they were to be totally stupid. Clarissa certainly carried a torch for me but I couldn't reciprocate, adroitly body-swerving my way out of any compromising situations. My reputation preceded me to a degree, but I turned it to advantage. Better to be known than a nobody, even if my fame rested on notoriety. After all, many of these girls were thrill-seekers.

By this year of 1980, smack usage permeated into the upper echelons including politicians' brats, even parts of the neo-aristocracy. Smack also spread up to the murky North, appearing on council estates. It didn't take long before I figured out Clarissa and the art school crowd were into gear, wanted it but found it difficult to obtain. They wanted smack as a status-enhancing symbol, something they could boast about at dinner parties in the year 2000. They didn't have a clue where to score as dealers wouldn't touch them. If these rich kids got nicked, they'd always squeal to the law, who'd get their address books into the bargain. Slinging them into a cell for an hour guaranteed to spill their guts. I decided to take a calculated chance, fill a market gap. So I finalised the business, collecting their dough, shooting off to the dealers, skim for personal use, overcharge, get fares for taxis, pocket the money, bunk fares on the tube. This represented a regular source of income. Although they guzzled champagne as a main tipple, smack soon took a hold. Clarissa participated, keeping it to a weekend basis. But for many of them these weekends became longer, Thursday to Monday, some at the stage where they wanted gear Wednesday after sweating it out all Tuesday. They'd beg me to score, waving cab fares and banknotes under my nose.

The art school provided another source of income for my enterprising spirit. They all needed materials like sable brushes, me writing down thickness to order. Also watercolours, cobalt grey flavour of the term. Art shops proliferate in the West End, with display cabinets usually unlocked. I even lifted an easel complete with stand, a helpful customer opening the door for me. I flogged the stuff to the would-be Rembrandts and Van Goghs. High-grade morons, they didn't know this to be all stolen, me spinning an implausible yarn about my father owning shares at Winsor and Newton. Believable, as most of their parents owned companies and sat on mountains of cash. These were by far the most idiotic bunch I'd come across, only their monied background cushioning them, protecting against the real world. If they weren't studying here, the boys would have been clicking heels at Sandhurst, girls doing photography or running non-economic dress shops. These people's parents owned mines in Southern Africa, a famous chocolate brand dating back to imperial days, were film directors, even the odd political connection surfaced. In other words, the stinking rich. I wanted some of this but it was all a narcotic-induced dream.

Truth was I lived in a den of thieves, nest of junkies, myself a leading protagonist. I'd moved downstairs near the front door to deal with the endless stream of enquiries, the art school crowd now appearing midweek. No rest for the wicked. I could tell they were withdrawing owing to large black pupils. I'd been through all this myself with a mild Turkey but this lot didn't know what was going down. Addiction or dependence never entered their in-bred minds. So here they were, coming to the hole in the wall. Having endless streams of money, they'd pay double the odds if required, but I wasn't too greedy, already charging extra, doing alright. Usually I dealt with the girls, who were more together when it came to finances, although I had to keep things sweet, reluctantly dealing with their deadhead boyfriends, the Julians and Aubreys of this world. Smithy went out on the prowl, dipping a purse in a local cinema, netting a cheque book and card. I told him of a bird who'd kite it, Crispin's girlfriend Jo. I hadn't seen much of Crispin as of late, he hung out in another scene with Jo in her flat. I still regarded him as a creep but when it came to freebies, Crispin was no slouch. Jo agreed, so the two of us set out on Saturday down King's Road. We fitted up with shoes, jumpers, champagne, food from supermarkets, stashing the loot back of her mini van. Hours of shopping later, we retired back to Jo's flat. Crispin sat waiting, seeing the goodies he became ecstatic. We gulped the champagne, Crispin getting drunk, happy with his new clothes. Me and him adjourned to the kitchen where he was all over me, extra friendly, wanting to tell me something, asking if I could keep a secret he'd never told anybody about before. I'd gone off Crispin long ago so with satisfaction I agreed.

"You know me Crisp ..."

Then came the tale of woe about how when he was young, his father screwed him on a regular basis, forcing him to give blow jobs. I played Mr Understanding.

"Don't worry about it Crispin, it's happened to lots of people, you can't blame yourself."

He felt reassured, glad to get it off his chest, retiring early to bed, drink having taken its toll. Before I left, I had sex with Jo as Crispin lay in his stupor. I also told her about his naughty dad, departing smiling to myself. It's a rotten, cruel world.

Clarissa won a cash prize and medal for her First at art. Having sold many of her paintings at the promotional show, she had tons of money to spend, asking me if I fancied going to Amsterdam. An accomplished freeloader, I leapt at the chance. Justin was green with envy as he'd laid Clarissa a couple of times and felt entitled to go. I hadn't slept with her at all, having no intention, not being partial to bearded ladies. Smithy however appreciated the situation.

"Amsterdam on a grand. Sounds great."

Off we went, Clarissa packing tons of baggage. I knew she was panting under that shaggy face to get me into the sack but, as an expert in the escapologist department, I'd been able to wriggle my way out of that fate so far. Arriving in Amsterdam I was dying for a fix, us going straight to a bar meeting an acquaintance of hers, a lecturer named Scott who'd put us up. Scott showed us around, ending up in the red light district. I noticed street dealers, suggesting to Clarissa she bung me some guilders so I could go score. Both her and Scott seemed to be into the idea. After scoring we snorted up the gear in a bar. Heading back to Scott's place, he turned anaemic, puking into canals all the way home. Scott went to bed, remaining there for the duration. Now Clarissa's brother turned up with girlfriend in tow. I saw this developing into a snooze scene, that I'd require plenty of gear. Despite the brother living up to expectations, in other words a creep, I'd gone out, scored for him within the hour. When we awoke in the morning, some of the creep's money had gone astray, me singled out as the obvious culprit. An afternoon of the creep moaning about his missing cash, walking with him, the girlfriend and Clarissa, meeting their boring friends, visiting galleries and the Van Gogh museum reduced me to numbing despair. Out of the blue, I met a mate named Bob who was living here in Amsterdam squatting. Bob asked if I had any holiday money so I tapped Clarissa, who grizzled at being left, me telling her I'd return with gear. I scored, shooting up at Bob's place, staying all day. Upon returning Clarissa informed me her brother had found the missing money. Nothing resembling an apology was forthcoming from that quarter. Fed up with the bedridden lecturer and the tiresome trio, I went back to Bob's. He wasn't in but someone there had clear Methadone, double strength. I downed the bottle in one, causing my benefactor to gasp in disbelief. For an hour, everything felt okay, then it hit, multiple puking as I staggered back. In the meantime, Clarissa booked a hotel so the two of us could be together. I was relieved no end to see this happened to be a single bed establishment, collapsing into a deep twenty four hour comatose sleep. Clarissa's amorous advances were successfully repulsed as I fought her off in my stupor. She'd had enough of the procrastination. Unable to get her nookie, Clarissa suggested I go back home. The ride played out to its logical conclusion. I arrived back at Ridinghouse clutching a brace of duty-frees. Suffering after effects of the Methadone, I sunk into another day-long slumber.

All good gold mines get played out. I'd started to get ostracised on the party circuit, sometimes refused admission while others turned nasty making accusations which I denied. Keeping in with Clarissa, I still gained access on occasion. Owing to these restrictions, I spent more time in gloomy Ridinghouse, down to a couple of quid a day. Bad enough, but ten times worse with a habit. I did Codeine, bought from the chemists. It had a mild smack effect, okay if you were undergoing a poverty streak. Swallowing the whole contents of a bottle, the smack hit lasted an hour, setting you up for the day while hustling money for a bag. Some of us hung around in the bookies, gambling quids. Whoever won treated the rest, more often than not someone striking lucky. Trade continued with art school wonders calling over to score. Useful for party information or who wanted to confront me over a missing wallet. None of them ever summoned up the courage to do so. I made sure that whenever I arrived at a party they were all so sloshed no one noticed or cared about my presence. I did the dips double quick, leaving directly after.

Redd popped over for the odd fix. He wasn't working but drove a van around town nicking fireplaces from derelict buildings. Redd took me on his expeditions where he'd find a derelict or empty building, sneak in through a back window or even boot the door in. Once inside we'd produce the matloc, a fireman's tool shaped like a pickaxe, one end having teeth, the other a flat crowbar. Redd smashed the sides of the fireplace with a sledgehammer, demolishing brickwork. The fireplace itself would be eased out with the matloc He often returned to collect furniture, doors, anything that could be moved and sold. We even did a couple of Nash houses down Regents Park. Many of these places were used at night by junkies or winos, bloody needles, bottles and shit all over the show:

The art school parties were held in what can only be described as mansions, centrally located. There might be bodyguards and bouncers, ex-soldier types on hand to repel riff-raff. Any cloakroom proved a boon, gaining access once I removed ten wallets. Open season. American Express cards were the thing to get, at that time you had to be super rich to own one. I worked out a smooth routine pretending to be asleep on the bed where people threw coats down in a heap. I'd appear to be dead to the world, a couple of empty champagne bottles artfully placed next to me. I'd moan, tossing and turning in my phoney drunkenness, extracting cards and money. The smack habit had to be paid for, the chimp had become a gorilla. Clarissa, my hairy escort, knew what I was doing, stealing from her friends. I explained that only the bank lost out with the cards. As for the dough, it was nothing worse than losing pocket money, these people having money coming out of their ears. It wasn't like nicking someone's dole money. Clarissa agreed, still hoping to get me in the sack. If Clarissa had been an Eskimo I could have sold her fridges.

These parties were easy enough to get lost in. Many huge rooms dimly lit, champagne, food spreads. I'd talk to the bouncers, being thick they were easy to con, laying improbable yarns on them, claiming to be an art student but not like the ponces that they minded, a salt-of-the-earth guy. The girls were willing but the habit had started getting to me, I wasn't all that interested in sex. Owing to the accent, they couldn't figure me out as I was able to converse rationally about subjects like music, cinema and art. This just about covered their limitations. I could have helped myself to portable valuables in these bastions of privilege, but needed money and credit cards. Galleries also fell into the itinerary, along with exhibitions, diploma shows and openings. Good for catching party info, going mad on the drinks if I'd been off gear.

I'd been almost a year at Ridinghouse, hustling money a full time employment along with scoring and nicking. What with my by now notorious reputation, the art school connection had shrunk to Clarissa. Even she found herself uninvited to parties in case I tagged along.

Me, Justin and a couple of blokes I knew from the Hampstead scene started boozing together. One of their girlfriends died of an overdose. And this after being off the habit for three years. We'd all been off smack ourselves for a few days, compensating with a booze binge, but this worked out no cheaper than gear. Afternoon, we sat getting plastered, waiting for a diploma show and the always-available free drinks. I presented no glowing picture of health, didn't care about the way I looked, having shaved my head close to the bone. Smack had diminished the sex drive so my interest in girls boiled down to whether I could squeeze a few bob out of them. Most women were a sight more practical than men, always carried cash for an emergency. I had to work hard for this money, hitting them up with witticisms, making them laugh and feel relaxed, wanted. One dip show ended with me perched on the stairs with a bottle of wine after viewing primitive daubs that rejoiced in the name of paintings, meeting stuffy parents. As I supped, a girl nicknamed Boo planted herself next to me. I knew her from Hampstead parties and her old boyfriend, Sam, just happened to be one of my drinking cronies. She'd ran a couple of punk shops after punk became commercial. Expensive stuff, fifty quid for a sweater. Boo lit me a cigarette when I became friendly.

"How's things with you, Boo? Found yourself a new man yet? Like my new hairstyle?"

Boo laughed, knocking back the champagne as I went into the old routine prior to hitting up for a couple of quid. This also meant showing interest, Boo saying she'd been writing songs, would I care to look at a few? I said okay, thumbing through them. One was about me. This certainly provided a surprise, wondering what was going on here? Boo could have any geezer she wanted being good-looking, loaded and no more idiotic than the rest here. She paid rapt attention as I read the lyrics out loud, finally reaching my ditty. I sang it.

"Danny don't die. Danny, oh why?"

Belting it out dramatically, Boo thumped me on the shoulder laughing.

"Not like that!"

I lied, telling her it was good. I asked if she fancied going into the hall to get drinks. I met Sam, wanting to know what it was all about, the song, her gushing over me. Sam just said I was more than in with a chance. I found myself whisked off to her flat back in old familiar territory. The building sat off the Heath, view like countryside, trees, ponds, rolling lawns. This flat had eight enormous luxury rooms. Only Boo and her mother seemed to live there and mum was away. We dived straight into the bedroom, spending all night rumping, sniffing coke, drinking. When I awoke Boo sat staring at me like a person in love. I'd hit on to something here. And knew how to play it.

Boo was all over me that weekend. Pleasant enough, but I couldn't understand the attraction. We dined in Hampstead, her footing the bills. A couple of days later, back from a fruitless afternoon at the bookies, Smithy collared me. A flash bird in a fancy car called over. Who was she? Oh, I said cool as possible, that's only Boo, she's got the hots for me. Smithy had been impressed by her looks and obvious wealth.

"Landed yourself a good one there Dan."

I shrugged then heard a hooting outside. Boo in a black Jag.

"Excuse me, lads."

I left the others who'd gathered, winked to Smithy, went outside jumping into the car, speeding off to Hampstead.

After a further week of wining and dining at her expense I had enough, going back to Ridinghouse to see my mates, itching for some gear. Boo laid twenty notes on me. Returning, the lads were free with the advice, Justin saying I should marry her while Smithy congratulated me on landing it. After my fix, I sank into the mattress ruminating. Why had Boo selected me? She could have any guy she wanted, rich guys from Hampstead. I was only a thieving junkie living in a squat with no sanitation. Short sleep, then a knock on the door. Boo. She needed somewhere to live, explaining how she'd tired of living with her mum who'd come back. I told Boo the place was full up, her asking if she could move into my room for a couple of days until she'd sorted out alternative accommodation. Playing hard to get, I finally agreed. Boo sped off, returning with a carload of personal items. Colour telly, sound system, perfumes, sun lamp, creams, a small chest of drawers. I threw my rubbish out, transformed the room into a lounge. Boo often nipped back to Hampstead, availing herself of facilities often to eat and sleep. Boo stuck by my side at all times while Smithy looked after the room using the colour telly and sun lamp. I preferred Hampstead to Ridinghouse any day of the week. In Hampstead I'd be walking Boo's Yorkshire Terrier, Horace, on the Heath or working out on her exercise bike. I helped Boo clear out one of her old shops, advising her to keep the stuff as maybe I could sell it on a stall. In all, Boo simply refused to see my bad side, knew I took junk but it didn't bother her. Bewildering!

When my dole cheque arrived I put a suggestion to Boo. Why don't we go visit Paris? She agreed. I had the makings of a beard on the go, looked far removed from an advertisement for healthy living. The two of us made a striking contrast with Boo wearing the latest Bond Street gear. Stan now lived in Paris so he put us up in his cramped flat for the weekend. I went off on a wild bender, Boo providing subsidy, Stan doing the scoring. Boo tried this gear but her constitution couldn't handle it, her out cold for the day. Upon recovery, another round of flash restaurants, presents such as a suede jacket, fancy flick knife. Boo wasn't working but still had plenty of money from the time of running her shops. I didn't see much of Stan that weekend. This once clean-living lad had acquired the inevitable habit, fixed up and lived in Paris, attracted by stronger French smack.

Back home, on a rare day away from Boo, I visited Loader's girlfriend. Leaving, I noticed another door in the block ajar. Inside, just peeking out, a doctor's bag. My eyes lit up. Doctor's bag equals drugs. I grabbed it, heading back to Ridinghouse, wondering what delights were contained within. Prising it open, no drugs or prescription pads. Maybe this didn't belong to a doctor, just a trendy with a hip looking bag. Disappointment however was soon mitigated by thirty five pounds cash, cheque books and cards. I got together with Smith that night, cashing a cheque in a bureau-de-change. We had a meal, bought some clothes. I split from Smithy, making my way over to Crispin's place. Come morning, I topped myself up with Valium, Crispin's bird Jo driving me to a bank. I went in armed with all the identification documents, inside writing out a cheque, requesting cash please. They asked me to take a seat sir just while they checked something out. Valiumed out of my box, I failed to notice time ticking by, only brought to my senses by a tap on the shoulder. Mumbling, I looked up from the floor. Surrounded by uniforms, arrested, taken to the police station, strip searched. They checked my arms for tell tale marks, nodding to each other. Another junkie.

Charged with burglary and fraud, the latter charge dropped for some unknown reason, the lawyer trundled out the usual circumstances which must have worked the oracle that day, given previous convictions. He stressed my mental breakdown, that I lived with my dad, trying to secure a place in a rehabilitation clinic. I ended up with fifty hours community service, allocated to a nun who presided over us wrongdoers every Sunday, building chicken coops for urban farms. This felt like working the graveyard but without pay. I eked out the sentence usually slipping away for a sly drink. The people here weren't very interesting, young geezers who talked about joining the army, Paddys who thought there were too many black faces in the country. I'd outgrown this tiresome nursery scene long ago.

Time ran out for us at Ridinghouse, a court order for pending eviction arrived. Justin moved out to Essex Road, Islington, took up dope dealing again. Luck was on my side. I'd managed to obtain keys of a flat in the heart of the West End, Shaftesbury Avenue. I lost no time getting over to inspect the premises. Above, a shop, side door opening on to a spiral staircase. The flat itself contained a high rise built-in bed, hot water, bathroom, toilet in working order. Ideal. So me and Boo moved in without hesitation along with Horace, her little Yorkie. I'd been assuming some form of respectability, a job in my old trade, working afternoons at a bookies as boardman in Camden Town.

CHAPTER NINE

As these events whirled past I still couldn't help wondering why Boo picked me above any others. A year before, I might have understood. Then I looked presentable, fine quiff, streamlined torso, Clarissa telling me I had classic features, how good I appeared to the discerning eye. I'd heard that before from other quarters, taking it for granted after a while. I didn't even rate my looks all that much. In the past year, opiates led me to sugar addiction, breakfast a Mars bar, living for the most part on a diet of confectionery, the all-time favourite a whole Marks & Spencer trifle. This, and the growing anthropoid on my back did nothing to affect the glowing confidence. I figured out the attraction must have been the this perceived warmth, as I seemed to radiate emotional honesty. For example, I pretended to be myself, not ashamed to admit I was a coward to a room full of people. A bona fide coward would never admit to such a thing. There were always girls around who'd believe this to be some kind of meaningful sensitivity. I could turn on tears to order if need be, claiming to subscribe to a higher entity, God no less. Most were fooled or wanted to be by this drivel. All this despite me robbing them right, left and centre. Advantage Dan. Clarissa became dead jealous of Boo, having observed me leave the dip show with her and especially us now living together. Clarissa behaved amicably enough to us but I knew it was just an act. I still had the bearded lady in my pocket, her dreaming of the impossible. And I wasn't going to shatter her delusion, never knowing when I might require her services. Clarissa also bunged me money for gear now and again. In this incestuous circle, Boo had also previously gone out with Clarissa's brother and blown him out, breaking his heart. Silly sod.

I'd applied myself to some research, starting with Boo's family tree. Her grandfather, patriarch of the whole family, Alfred, was a Polish Jewish immigrant who came over during the onset of the depression. About this time, Marks and Spencer were setting up business in corner arcades. Alfred worked his way up to become one of their main suppliers of cheap material based on expensive designs. By the time Boo's dad Anton was born, Marks & Spencer were well on their way to making a fortune. So was Alfred, who still turned up everyday at the office to oversee his burgeoning empire, Anton being groomed to fill his shiny shoes. Although Anton had officially assumed reins, Alfred was omnipresent, keeping a rheumy eye on things. Boo went to her local grammar school in Hampstead, her only true ambition to be a dancer. Her mum wasn't Jewish though. In spite of her attendance at the grammar school, Boo didn't know anything about the world and its workings, past or present. She'd be hard pressed to name the leader of the opposition in Parliament.

What Boo had been groomed for was the rag trade, leaving school at an early age to do pattern-cutting at art school. After that the family sent her up north to work in one of the factories they owned, but obviously let her nowhere near the rigours of the production line. Easy ride notwithstanding, Boo almost suffered a nervous breakdown. As a consequence, she returned to London, recovered composure, dad providing readies for her to open the expensive punk clothes shops. Business was brisk. Boo went out with a guy who became an alkie. The relationship went sour with his condition bringing on arguments. Five years of this, then everything collapsed, along with the business. This is where I made my entrance.

Boo transformed the Shaftesbury Avenue squat into a Wendy house, putting up nice curtains, laying out carpets. We had a duvet, food in the larder. Boo only liked dope, so coming up pinned and zonked, I'd light up a joint immediately with her, pretending the blow was responsible for my state. Able to deliver goods in the sexual department a couple of days a week helped keep her happy. Boo was blindly in love, unable to see a single negative characteristic, her mentality being roses in the garden. By now I'd accumulated a wardrobe of swanky clothes, Boo paying. She wasn't working regular, but that didn't mean she was skint, having her mother, a healthy bank account plus family handouts. I hung in loose there. Had Boo dropped me, it wouldn't be the end of the world. I didn't see her as the ultimate meal ticket but it was handy all the same. Nor did I have to do much shoplifting or hustling for gear, Boo had provided a breather from the manic pace. I'd met the dad, Anton, briefly when he came over to the flat intending to check it out and the new person in her life. Anton ignored me as though I didn't exist, thinking this must be a rented apartment. Anton was in his late forties, bald, a permanent fat cigar in his mouth. He also reeked of money. As he talked to Boo, I retreated to another part of the flat. Leaving, he asked her is she was okay, catching a glance at him thumbing through a large wad of fifty pound notes. Anton peeled off a few, giving them to Boo, asking her to come up and see him on Thursday. Boo had been trying to realise her life-long ambition of becoming a dancer. She knew a few top dancers of the day but didn't have an agent. Attending various auditions, Boo never came up trumps.

In the meantime she'd just landed a part-time job working on a perfume counter in a famous department store. This depressed her, working for others, but when Boo came home, I'd be there to crack her up, making with the jokes and she'd have been thinking all day about Danny boy.

Thursday, Boo went to see dad. Curious, wanting to see the office, I tagged along. The place was nearby, just off Oxford Street. Inside, walking through a carpeted corridor past smiling commissionaires who all knew her by sight, Boo pleaded with me not to say anything. The office itself I took to be a boardroom, long table with empty chairs. Anton paced, puffing his cigar. He didn't waste time, making it clear the whole affair was nothing to do with me, so I gazed out the window, pretending to be invisible as drama unfolded at the other end of this office.

"Boo, what are you doing with yourself? Are you working?"

"Yes, I'm working at Debenhams."

"They pay you well? Are you happy?"

Boo had already been thrown on to the defensive.

"I'm only filling in time, waiting to be taken on as a dancer."

Dad exploded.

"A DANCER?"

Then with his voice raised in despair, Anton pleaded to me at the other end.

"What do you think?"

Audience participation.

"She's just waiting for the right job to come up."

I meant dancing but Anton had his own interpretation.

"She doesn't have to look for a job, she's got one here."

Anton gesticulated, me having it now figured for an act. But he hit the mark, playing on family loyalty. More melodramatics followed.

"When I was your age, I wanted to play football for England …" I chipped in.

"Way they're playing nowadays, I reckon you're still in with a chance."

He laughed for once.

"And what do you do?"

I said I played drums for a hobby, that I worked in a turf accountants. He nodded, turning to Boo.

"Think about it, there'll always be a job here for you."

We left after this, me playing Mr Understanding, encouraging her to continue with the auditions, knowing this could only go on for a few more weeks before she'd exhausted all the possibilities.

In our domestic situation a row blew up about next to nothing. Smack is a drug where if you fail to score the required amount, you're on a short fuse, creating a bad temper, an edgy feeling. Horace crapped on the floor and I threw a tantrum. In the middle of my rantings, I blurted out to Boo that I didn't need her. Welling up in the back of my mind, aided by an unsatisfactory hit, were rumours circulating that I only went out with her because of the money. I told Boo to leave, go back to her mum, take the incontinent dog with her. Boo went off in tears.

"And you can get all this stuff out of here, colour telly and all!"

Word got abroad that I'd blown it by giving Boo the elbow. People were confounded. but when I came to my senses I knew she'd be back simply because I'd got away with so much in the past. By now I was thinking Boo believed me to be a regular guy despite my glaring faults, that she wanted to mould me into a different man, maybe save me from myself. Two days passed. Working at the bookies, a contrast to the usual clientele walked in causing scrofulous heads to turn. Boo came in holding Horace. Soon massed drunks patted him. She let it run around, the dog eventually jumping up on to my platform yapping. I didn't have to utter a word of apology, just diving into the motor after the final race. Boo asked if I wanted to return to Shaftesbury Avenue or Hampstead. Having a taste for comfort, I said Hampstead. Off we sped in the Jag past departing dossers.

Most good things come to an end. We got a court order forcing us to vacate the premises. I didn't panic, knowing we could always go back to the mum's flat in Hampstead, camp there for a while. Boo wanted the illusion of independence but circumstances dictated, we had no choice except move there for a stay while looking for somewhere else to live. There was room aplenty in this spacious luxury flat, enough to bivouac a platoon. Boo had two brothers, Algernon and Alex, both younger than me. Alex had a junk problem, parents packing him off to New Zealand in order to dry out, work in a job with a lucrative salary obtained via connections. The younger brother Algernon was at boarding school. I knew this temporary halt wouldn't last forever but I thought I'd take maximum advantage. The mother, the only other resident, knew Boo and I lived together, so that presented no problems. Being on a housing list for West Hampstead co-op, I naively assumed it would only be a matter of time before we were re-housed. The flat itself had a large divided kitchen like the *Galloping Gourmet's* set on the telly. This felt as if I was staying in a different country. I made myself at home, settling down realising it might be about two months before things started turning sour with the mother. By now I'd given up working in the gentlemen's club in Camden while Boo meanwhile bowed to the inevitable after a string of failed auditions, painlessly slotting into a job in dad's office as a commercial designer. This job consisted of buying up top fashion magazines from every leading country. Boo looked at the latest expensive fashions from Paris, New York, Milan, then copied the designs, toning them down. The finished product was then cobbled out of cheap material for a mass market. Boo also got sent to fashion shows in Paris and Milan to do the copycat game. I didn't know how much she earned but, apart from her salary, Boo could have anything she wanted. They gave her a brand new Mini Metro for starters. I'd long deduced she'd never be broke. The mother was wary of me, probably the accent playing a role in her judgement. The mother herself looked quite well preserved for her age, and had an ageing Italian toyboy, steward on an airline. Her personality was nondescript, narrow petty mentality, interested in nothing beyond her own limited world, the only reading material a *Daily Mail*, punctually delivered every morning.

The mother had another family job that commanded an unbelievable salary. This involved buying fabric, taking her to exotic spots such as Hong Kong and Bangkok. I had to undergo a charade, rising when it was time for Boo and the mother to leave for work. They'd leave home just after nine-thirty, so I crawled out of bed at the last possible moment, slip on clothes, splash my face, climb into Boo's car while the mother followed in her motor. This would be me pretending to search for work. I wasn't entrusted with a key but I'd already persuaded Boo to cut me a copy. I'd get dropped off by a tube station, they'd drive off, me waving to Boo and the mum. That done, I'd drop into the bookies, lay bets, return home immediately for a touch of the good life. I'd take a shower, make a hearty breakfast. After breakfast, I'd be searching every pocket and drawer in the place. At least I had no worry about procuring food and drink, they got it by the carbootload from Marks & Spencer at a discount. Next, I'd be on the blower calling up people like Clarissa who might be interested in scoring. I'd always have a hit together before they returned back from work. The local dealer had already been sniffed out, Justin and Redd would come over some afternoons bringing gear or to score themselves. I loved fixing up in the plush surroundings, preparing gear on hot plates in the comfy kitchen then retire into the front room, sinking deep into a sofa. Relaxing, I'd phone up horse racing results, watch telly with the sound down while nattering on the blower. With Justin, I'd follow horse racing if they had a meeting on the box. In his case, there was a tinge of jealousy about how I'd ended up here while he had to be content knobbing the bearded lady. My only task of the day was to take Horace out. If it rained or there happened to be racing on the telly, he'd get no further than the forecourt. Other times, he'd get a short stroll on the Heath.

With the flat so large, them having so many new gadgets and things of interest, a good deal of spare time went into exploration. Whole wardrobes crammed full of new clothes including the brothers' gear. I took to wearing their Lacoste sweaters and Armani suits, Brown of Bond Street shirts. Boo's mother, removed from reality, thought these clothes were mine. I trawled over their photos, read letters, building myself up a family portrait. Conclusion, dullard mentality. This place was full of adult toys, seventh heaven for me, amazed that everything remained virtually unused. Fishing rods, skis, golf clubs, remote control aircraft, a whole Dodgers outfit from the States, baseball gloves and bats, a bike, always handy for quick scoring. I couldn't gain access to the mother's room as she kept it locked solid, but I had the run of everywhere else. The only missing constituent from this was drugs in the cabinet, mother being on a health kick. My favourite part of the flat became what I called the playroom, eight windows and a table tennis set in the centre. This huge room they'd filled with numerous goodies, boxes of expensive gizmos, clothes they didn't need anymore, lots of Boo's shop stuff, including fixtures, such as dummies, lights, lamps. Best junk shop I'd ever seen, everything nearly new, only a year or so out of date. I started mulling over the idea of setting up a stall.

Usually, I'd have a fix before they arrived home. If I'd have been busy, it would only be because I'd been out searching for gear. When the key turned in the lock, I'd spring up from my sofa encampment, offering to make Boo a meal. After which, if we hadn't eaten out, she'd take me for a drive, maybe see a film or even whizz over to a dealer or party, the Clarissa scene. I was still on the dip, concentrating on purses, skimming off the odd note or two, building up a wad, getting cards. Cash however, always came first. I kept to the old crashed out routine in the bedroom. Boo knew about the stealing but didn't pass any judgement. I gave out identical excuses as I'd given Clarissa. Whether Boo was capable of understanding these half-baked rationalisations I don't know, but she turned a blind eye to my dirty deeds.

A free Saturday market was held in Swiss Cottage, middle-class kids selling their old LPs, clothes and gear nicked from parents, many flogging off stuff to buy smack. I suggested to Boo that I sell some of the clothes from the flat, old toys and other clutter, giving me something useful to do. She agreed, at least for home consumption this would give off an illusion of work. Boo drove me to the market where I'd unload the goods, set up shop putting clothes on a mobile rack, underneath nearly new stuff, bits of pine furniture, the brothers' albums. The high class junk dried up after a while until I concentrated on dresses alone, Boo bringing back samples from work. No difficulty shifting those. I picked up trading jargon over the weeks, inventing my own, dealing with people at all levels. Thanks to the patter and quality merchandise, for the first time ever, I had a regular wedge, handy for scoring, easy enough considering the junkie hordes frequenting the market, making it possible to buy pills, anything. Redd and Justin came along with people like Ozwald Finney from Camden, Ozwald maybe selling a bit of the green stuff, Methadone, if gear was late in coming. Once the market closed, Boo picked me up, driving back to Hampstead.

The fat wad started burning a hole in my pocket, so I hinted to Boo that we take a proper holiday. I fancied the sound of Italy. The mother's ageing toyboy lived in Rome, so we'd be able to stay at his flat. Boo got the tickets together, being summer, she took a couple of weeks off, allowing us to travel by train. The flat turned out to be nice and comfortable, situated near the Colosseum. As the sun beat down I got into drinking. Not having gear didn't cause worry at that point, I made out well enough, eating and drinking the best, plenty of sun. I was initially interested in the city but after a couple of days found it boring, solving this problem by more drinking. The ageing toyboy did his best to entertain us between airline shifts. I had him well sussed out, glancing at his tiny book collection, they were all Ron Hubbard and Dianetics. Boo hadn't told me this fellow was a Scientologist. I found this rather puzzling, Boo had been here previously, but then again she only read fashion magazines. I later discovered she'd never heard of Scientology. I charmed toyboy, arriving at the conclusion he was a plonker. He liked me though, as I made him laugh. I excelled myself, rattling out jokes, witty remarks, imitations. Toyboy took us on an excursion to Elba where he had a friend who owned a big wooden boat with an engine. We chugged around the island, put up in a little house. The friend was on painkillers, he'd broken his leg which was encased in plaster. I searched, finding them. With the aid of plentiful booze, we went down to the harbour in their company. We sat drinking beer until I'd found someone with a guitar, borrowed it, started playing and singing. Soon the locals gathered for the show, joints appearing. I could see Boo was proud of me being centre of entertainment and attention. But I'd begun to feel a Turkey coming on. I thought this great, speeding up mentally, more of a laugh coming out with blinding remarks, doing perfect imitations of film stars, weaving dreams about auditioning as an actor. I believed it easy, riding out this Turkey. In fact, I was merely blocking it out. Senses became exaggerated. If I did an imitation, I'd conjure up the tears as optional extras. Returning to Rome, I felt trippy, getting into heated arguments with bar staff over imagined short changing. I'd begun to struggle with this Turkey. I felt edgy, dying to get home, tired of Italy, thinking of the gear back home, dealers. Boo didn't seem to notice the grumbling volcano, no idea of what was going on, about my heavy habit. She certainly didn't have a clue about what a Turkey was like.

I started to feel manic, didn't know what to do, writing postcards home, telling folks I was off gear. I picked fights with Toyboy. He didn't know about the habit either. Boo never thought gear to be a problem with me. Not knowing what was going down, her happy and cheerful, laying in the sun on the patio, covered in layers of cream. I couldn't face this, sitting in a chair, listening to Toyboy's crap records, irritable with everything. Boo's outfits, Toyboy, her busy pointing out landmarks such as fountains, statues, piazzas, window shopping having run out of cash. Boo simply telexed more in when departure date neared. Shopping one day in the relentless heat. I lugged beer and wine, her the food. Boo was in a playful mood, winding me up, taunting. After I'd exhausted all pleas to be left alone, I erupted, telling her to shut up, ending with me screaming.

"For God's sake! Leave me alone"

We stood near a doorway in a deserted street. She still failed to notice flashing danger signs, persisting. I went bananas, punching her on the face then kicked her. I knew I'd been totally out of order, fell into silence, biting my lips. Back at the flat, I sat on a sofa drinking with Boo next door. Half an hour elapsed, then she came into my room wearing a leotard. Knowing what was expected, I rallied, not bothering to apologise, giving her one on the sofa. The incident was closed, not mentioned, but she hadn't learnt anything from it.

Finally, we came back to Hampstead. My need for a hit was imperative.

After a phone call or two, I got wind of an afternoon party next day. Unable to sneak out and score I had to play happy couples in front of the mother, entertaining her with tales about how wonderful it all was. When you've been off gear, you hit the bottle with a vengeance, so I sampled the cabinet spinning holiday yarns, mother lapping it up. I didn't sleep much that night, thinking of one thing only, knowing half the people at that party had marmosets on their backs, so I'd a chance to score. Boo always took an age to get ready, this time was no exception, a whole hour. When we eventually arrived everything seemed to be in full swing. Bearded lady, Loader back from Thailand juggling in the garden and Redd. Straight over, not wasting time, I collared him.

"Look Redd, you can't get any gear for me, can you?"

I was desperate, prepared to pay over the odds.

"What do you need gear for? I got your card, thought you'd given it up."

I'd seen him collecting dough when we arrived, scoring for the rich kids, so I shoved the money into his hand, disappeared, off to mingle and wait. Boo started moaning, wanting something to eat having got wind of a new restaurant at the party. I told her I couldn't leave at the moment, had a stomach ache. Redd turned up later, pinned out of his nut.

I grabbed him.

"Where's mine?"

Redd handed it over, my cue to shoot off with Boo. I knew of a twenty four hour chemist so she drove me as I complained about fake stomach cramps, giving her an earful on the topic of peptic ulcers. Once inside the chemist, I bought a bottle of Kolanticon and two 5ml hypos with needles, driving back home, Boo oblivious to the extra purchase. I rushed into the mother's bathroom pretending the medicine had loosened me up. I put on a hot bath, plenty of steam to pump into my veins. Getting the tackle together, sitting on a bidet, I did the job, driving scag up the arm, wrapping up evidence in a tissue, throwing it out of a window into the bins below. Bullseye on both counts. A powerful hit indeed. Usually a hit gave me energy, this one knocked me out. I puked. Boo knocked on the door so I told her I was alright, just the medicine taking effect, that I was about to have a refreshing bath. Once inside the tub, I started nodding off. Another knock. Jerked out of my impending slumber, water covered my face. I managed to gurgle.

"It's alright, just having a bath."

Then pulled the plug, allowing water to drain, just laying there looking at my naked torso and pinned baby blues in an adjacent steamed up mirror. I rose eventually, put on the towel robe, unlocked the door knowing Boo would be back soon, over to the sink mirror to brush my teeth. The knock again.

"Come in Boo, the door's open."

In she walked, looking at my reflection in the mirror, me giving her a peck on the cheek, telling her I felt tired due to my stomach, wanted to go to bed. They permitted me to lay in next day so I crashed out all morning. In fact, I just about managed to scramble out of bed before they arrived back late afternoon.

While waiting for Redd to score at the party Loader gave me some useful information. Redd, who like me was on the West Hampstead housing co-op, had landed a large flat, moving in a junkie couple and Loader himself. Seems I'd been forgotten or maybe Redd moved in those junkies rather than his old mate. As I'd been more concerned about scoring, I let the matter pass, but within days I paid him a visit at the new address. Here I noticed for the first time that Redd had reeled in a middle-class girlfriend, raising her on a pedestal. He'd do anything for his Fiona, utterly infatuated. I told him about wanting to move, the flat here in Gospel Oak was large enough, room for me and Boo. Redd procrastinated but aware that Boo was well-wedged and the trickle down effect could help feed his monkey. He agreed, sub-letting us the smallest room. I didn't mind, so we both moved in, setting up our designer grotto. Loader meanwhile took off to sunnier climes again so Redd moved in Justin. Another gear connection. Redd had a small racket going, getting gear for ex-Camden girls who called around all hours. Apart from Boo and Fiona, everybody in this gaff was a junkie.

We settled into our new love-nest with Boo off to work every morning. I was on a fiver a day pocket money which purchased a bottle of Codeine, dog food, with change to try my luck in the bookies, maybe win money for a hit. Justin nearly always accompanied me on these jaunts. Redd's girlfriend Fiona went to Central School of Art, doing theatrical design. It was as if Redd had placed himself under voluntary hypnosis. Apart from his habit, everything revolved around fabulous Fiona, mentioning her name constantly to the point of parrot repetition. From close observation, I figured out she lived with Redd to annoy an ex-boyfriend, part of a grand strategy. Once Redd's habit was paid for, everything else went towards her needs, him buying anything Fiona required, mainly art materials. Redd also became rent collector, always demanding money pay-day. I knew this would all go up his arm. Redd must have collected forty quid a week on average, me holding him at bay, aware that the real rent for this flat was a token tenner for the whole place. These co-ops were nothing more than hidden subsidies for Hampstead rich kids, hence the difficulty joining one. Justin had a fair-sized bedroom littered with newspapers, empty Codeine bottles, burnt spoons, the black and white telly permanently flickering. People called to see him, pretending to be worried about his health. In reality he also, like Redd, ran a small business scoring gear for them.

Me and Boo checked out bedsits in the area. Without exception all were depressing and expensive. Boo hinted about moving back to the mum's flat, my ears ever sensitive to reminders of comfort but I said nothing, guessing it would only be a matter of time. We'd tired of Redd's incessant demands for money and besides, we already spent enough time up at the mother's during weekends. On these visits I'd become more familiar with the mother, who'd grown accustomed to my accent, having now started to make both her and Boo laugh together, rustling up the repertoire of imitations, telling stories. The gear habit now smoothed out to an off-and-on basis, held at bay by drink and Codeine. I still attended the odd party, my hands busy in other people's pockets, wallets or purses, respectable Boo offering perfect cover for the redistributory activities. With Redd and Justin showing up at the occasional event, blame began to shift in their direction when cards and money went missing. Proof in any direction was never forthcoming however. I didn't give a toss, having started to burn bridges along the way.

Redd continued his sideline of stripping empty houses, but his luck finally ran out and he got his collar felt by the law. He'd already chalked up an outstanding case which he hadn't bothered to answer, failing to appear in court. Now fabulous Fiona knocked on our doors, telling us Redd had been remanded in custody, news greeted by all with inward rejoicing. No rent or bill demands. No Fiona. Things would be cool for a while in a more relaxed atmosphere. A couple of days later, Redd's giro arrived, ending up on the kitchen floor with our household sitting perched on chairs, staring at the envelope. Debate ensued, the question being, who'd cash it? I scooped the giro, grabbed Redd's driving licence, headed off to the Post Office. With the takings I bought Horace dog food, Boo flowers, the rest of us a hit. Failing to get anywhere suitable in the way of rented accommodation, Boo finally caved in, loading up the designer grotto love-nest, driving back to mother's.

Moving back to the lap of luxury in Hampstead represented no hardship for me. In a way, it was a load off my crowded back as I preferred to adopt my own routine without Redd or Justin hovering. I knew Boo would eventually find a nice comfortable flat just for the two of us. I'd done my part, putting our names down for another flat on the West Hampstead co-op list. There were two more residents in the flat now, Algernon the younger brother, back from boarding school for summer break, and the prodigal son Alex, returned from New Zealand. Alex seemed to be in a bad way, on the verge of cracking up. Alex had some heavy homosexual experience down under and was now convinced he'd aged prematurely. He could hardly read or write, but the family fixed him up with a little job in the firm, driving vans, collecting cloth. Alex also dabbled in gear. So much for the cure. Neither of them noticed that some of their sportsgear had vanished, sold at the market. Not that it mattered as they were regularly presented with best brand new, up-to-date stuff. Alex felt a bit surprised and at first annoyed at me prancing about wearing his designer clothes, but as he'd always liked me even from the early Hampstead days, things soon sorted themselves out. Alex was on medication, the family also forking out for him to see a shrink. It seemed obvious to me that he was heading towards a breakdown but the family donned blinkers, refusing to recognise it. Alex didn't want to work for the family, having dreams about being an actor. They'd previously sent him to an expensive acting school but he lacked the concentration to persevere. The younger brother, Algernon, aged about fifteen was straight, like something out of military academy. He was into sports like running, rugby, fishing, supplied with all the latest equipment, of course. And also learning to drive. The mother was glad to see me back as I helped out with minor problems in the brood. Or so she thought, deluding herself that a man's hand, even mine, could sort out any difficulties.

This indeed was a thousand times better than at Redd's. I exercised my culinary skills, constantly engaged on the two telephones, freshening myself in the shower. We were in a smaller room than before, but Boo transformed it into a luxurious pad for two. Colour TV, cupboards, comfy bed. I spent a lot of time retreating into this room, reading, watching telly. Come daytime, when they all departed for work, I was at last in the position to drop the pretence of searching for employment. At an art show I'd met a photographer who wanted me to do some fashion modelling for him. I roped in Alex and a couple of lads. The job, which only lasted an afternoon, consisted of standing in the streets, dressed casually, looking cool, background for the star model. Alex demonstrated his lack of concentration by wandering off mid session, not returning. As luck would have it, the pictures appeared almost immediately in a glossy magazine, the illusion had been planted that I might be heading for stardom in the future.

Afternoons, Algernon did little overpaid jobs for the company or else indulged in some boring sporty youth activity. Alex popped in and out all day. One thing about Alex though, along with all these rich kids, despite being hopelessly dense, he always managed to get money together. Money, as they say, always goes to money. Some afternoons, I'd meet up with Justin lunchtime, do Codeine, hit the bookies. He chalked up a big win, over five hundred, all very hush-hush, only I knew. So I made the effort to climb on the bike, pedal over to see him for the odd fix, gently milking him until it all went. Small price to pay for my company. Another reason I went over to Justin's was to fix up, not fancying doing it at home where the two brothers stood a chance of catching me red handed. The 'workers' arrived home at six, so I usually lay out a meal for Boo, the mother passing through the kitchen, getting a whiff, thinking what a wonderful chap I was.

One typical Sunday summer's day, I lay on the comfy bed wearing a pair of shorts, barefoot except for socks. I never wore shoes in this gaff, no need with wall to wall fitted carpets. Happy Hampstead. No outside noise apart from twittering birds in trees. I dozed, meditating about how life had become pleasant for me, going at such an easy pace. I then found myself disturbed by a sharp tapping on the window. A Barney Rubble voice followed.

"Get your arse out here Danny."

Redd. Sounded pissed off, so I went to the front door where he stood clutching a stick. Redd wanted his dole money but I gave him some bluff.

"It's real good to see you out Redd."

He wasn't having any of it.

"Don't give me that shit. Where's my money?"

"What's wrong Redd?"

"You know! My fucking giro! Get me that money and now!"

Lacking cash, I called Boo over to my aid. She didn't have any spare but Redd reluctantly agreed to accept a cheque which Boo dutifully wrote out. Redd remembered the exact amount down to the last penny. Afterwards, he stormed off.

Boo came rushing in one morning disturbing my narcotic slumber. News of prospective employment, phone had rung, some agency having seen me in a magazine. They wanted me over to their West End studio for a screen test. That very afternoon Boo drove me, brimming with enthusiasm, me dressed casual, the natural look. Inside the studio I filled out appropriate forms and they took polaroid snaps of my various poses. No big deal for me but Boo was certainly confident I'd land the job in a jeans ad as an extra. All this fitted neatly into Boo's plan for my rehabilitation and well-being. They phoned me back, I'd been shortlisted.

I grabbed my slim portfolio and we headed on down West. For some inexplicable reason I felt nervous, uncomfortable. So on the way I dropped off into a chemist for a bottle of Captain Cod. Downing the Codeine in one, on came the relentless headrush followed by a settling down which arrived as I walked into the agency offices to be ushered into a room. Now I saw the competition. A huge blond muscleman, a couple of actor types plus two simpering model girls. I spoke, trying to break ice. A waste of energy. These people had nothing in their heads, making me wonder how others could admire or wish to emulate such deadheads. By the time they called me into the interview room, my Codeine came on with a vengeance. Here, the panel confronted me, asking me what I did for a living. I spun yet another yarn, this time about how I was a musician who busked regular.

"Where?"

"Covent Garden."

A catamitic voice screeched.

"I haven't seen you there."

By now, I'd moved into the stuttering phase, eyes shining bright, pinned. They must have dealt with drug abusers previously, maybe used to it in this business or possibly their darling offspring dabbled with gear in art college. The whole thing terminated abruptly, me walking out knowing I'd flunked it. Pity, because this would have been worth a couple of grand. I told Boo outright that I thought I hadn't landed this one, perhaps I was the wrong sort for this particular assignment, failing to mention anything about Codeine. Boo stuck to the belief that soon enough I'd be on the road to a career, but the phone call confirming my assumption soon shattered her illusions for the time being. I was surprised that people were impressed by me getting as far as the interview, even being offered drinks on the strength of it. I was happy, at least Boo and mother could see I'd had a try. It ended up with me more accepted in their dream world existence.

As months passed life with Boo became more of a hassle. She started getting into the job, meaning I endured at least an hour's worth of shoptalk a day. They were rushing out copies of Lady Di's clothing which became all the rage among the brain-dead. As autumn advanced we continued with our house hunting expeditions. A succession of dreary bedsits, the sort of place a serial killer might live in. I could see by the expression on Boo's face she didn't take to any of them. I'd mention the dog to help hurry her decision.

"I don't think Horace would like it here."

At least this gave me time out of the mother's place early evening. The strain of this house-hunting must have shown, because her dad raised a suggestion. Why not opt for a mortgage? If anything was wrong with Boo it could be bad for business, consequently bad for him. So now the saga moved on to another level. We were no longer searching out bedsits but looking for a one bedroom flat, maybe with a patio, hallway, lounge and other conveniences. Again, we looked but even these places weren't much better than the Nilsen flats. In desperation we went to an agency. Lucky for us, one of the girls working there took a liking to my oily charm, ringing me one morning, would I fancy going to look at a flat just come on to the market in the desirable Gloucester Crescent, Camden Town. I zoomed over, collected keys, went to have a look. The location seemed like a patch of Hampstead jutting into a more vulgar area. I went up to the middle flat in a large terraced house, swinging a door open. Perfect. Storage space, small but compact kitchen, enormous fireplace with enamelled marble in excellent condition. Two of them, no less. And a couple of large rooms. Being a nice day I sat down, placing my feet up on the marble, perched on a chair, birds twittering away in the distance. I closed my eyes. Best by far, I thought. Cost, thirty thousand. Later, I played a little joke on Boo, telling her I'd seen the worst dump yet, persuading her to go and look at it anyway. Boo soon realised that I'd been pulling her Kenzo-stockinged leg. Now I took advantage, hitting Boo up with the dreamtime. Should I paint this wall a different colour? Maybe this bit of furniture could go here, would Horace like this space here? As there happened to be a tiny market around the corner in Inverness Street, wouldn't it be a good idea if she gave me a few reject dresses to sell? Boo thought samples might represent a better proposition. I'd managed to slip that one in skillfully. She wanted the flat, so all that remained was for Daddy big bucks to get steaming in with a deposit.

During my final months at Hampstead, I could see clearly that Alex was heading towards a mental breakdown. The parent blamed drug abuse. In reality, among a myriad of interconnecting causes, his sexual identity played tricks on him. Alex suffered bouts of depression after going through the delusion of wishing to be an actor. And he had the rag trade hanging over his head. Alex didn't have an ounce of concentration, but paradoxically learnt to drive at an early age. Judging from photographs, he'd been good-looking in the past. Now, Alex appeared twenty two going on forty. I didn't believe his troubles were entirely down to drugs, regarding him as a mere dabbler. I'd previously indicated to the mother that, having once suffered problems in my upstairs department, I went to the hospital for help. This had to be broached diplomatically, not directly mentioning Alex, only relating my own personal experiences, hoping she'd achieve the impossible, make two plus two add up to four. Alex contracted mood swings, happy one moment, despair about perceived ageing or sexual orientation the next. I had to earn my keep giving him confidence-boosting chats as part of the unspoken duties. All of course to no avail. One moment he'd be rattling on enthusiastically, then he'd sink into the sloughs of despair or self pity. As Alex had his own contacts and money, I didn't score gear for him. Occasionally he offered me a surprise hit, so under the guise of dishing out soothing advice, we'd lock his bedroom door, whack it up. I knew this was playing with fire. If discovered, blame would automatically fall in my direction, I'd be out on my ear. Another reason for wanting to live alone with Boo. I'd usually feed her some caring drivel about going to have a quite private word with Alex to cheer him up, so please don't disturb. After shooting up, we'd lay on comfy beds in his locked room in a mind-numbing stupor. In his company I needed extra dosage.

I also played the role of peace-broker whenever hostilities broke out between brothers, physically separating warring factions. Stiff fatherly admonishings followed, the mother, if present, nodding in agreement. In a way, I'd become a temporary young dad to these grown up pampered boys. I found myself cleaning up behind an increasingly incontinent dog, becoming its keeper, taking the smelly brute for walks and to the vet. Other duties included kicking a ball around the Heath with Algernon. For this ritual, he'd don full kit, one of many. I'd get him involved in other people's football games while afterwards sneaking off for a sly puff on a jay, faking interest from the sidelines. Alone together, I put in a good performance, leaping, saving his shots, but after ten minutes I'd be in need of illegal inhalation. We played frisbee, easy for me as it requires virtually no exertion. This slotted in between Algernon's scuba diving or caddying for dad. I made sure I never uttered a word of criticism concerning dad, as they all stood in awe of the great man. I handled the mother by appearing to be mature, responsible, arranging for Her Dimness to see me in the kitchen, giving the illusion that I was engaged in useful work. I'd time my hoovering off the same square foot of carpet to coincide with her arrival from work. I could have had a workbench, been sawing away at the same plank of wood everyday, so little did she notice. I even left copies of magazines laying about with job advertisements circled. The mother even believed that visits up to the nun for the remnants of my community work sentence were connected with volunteer charity work. Late at night I might sit up with Boo and the mother, resisting waves of boredom, discussing Alex's problems over coffee, me hinting that he may require further 'professional help'. During pillow talk sessions with Boo, I'd try to describe what Alex's problems were like, using my own experiences as an illustration. It felt like trying to describe colours to the blind. These people put all unpleasant things out of their tiny minds. War, famine, injustice, poverty on the telly, they just didn't want to know, even on a conversational level, reinforcing their already abysmal ignorance. Me and Boo had to get out before the inevitable Alex implosion. Eventually though, something must have percolated down to the uncomprehending minds because they sent him to an exclusive psycho unit, where they jabbed him up, after which he went horse riding as therapy. This hardly represented hell on earth for the boy, more like a garden of Eden with medication.

Christmas in Hampstead was well over the top. Healthy Santas charity collecting, one staked out every hundred yards. Carol singers with old fashioned lamps. I'd already experienced the summer equivalent, happy jingling Morris Men. The first flake of snow meant Swiss sweaters, green wellies, chrome toboggans on the Heath along with the odd snowman dressed better than the majority of the unemployed. With shops and pedestrian precincts virtual Dickens postcard all year, this time it became Noddyland with snow. Boo did most of the Christmas shopping, all paid for with plastic, me always on hand to pitch in with prezzie suggestions. The only present I forked out money for, apart from a cheap ring for Boo which I proclaimed to be a rare antique, was a toy for Horace. Boo made up my other shortfalls.

Christmas houseguests were the mother's two sisters, one of whom had married a Portuguese geezer, bringing her young teenage daughters along. They spent all their time talking about that evergreen subject, men, failing to detect my stifled yawns. I became an octopus, with a being-useful juggling act. Laying tables, filling glasses, pouring wine into decanters, polishing silverware, arranging flowers. I cracked tasteful jokes, behaving like a civilised gentleman, flicking lighters for the aunties' cigarettes, entertaining the blushing daughters, asking them about boyfriends. I piled on superficial charm in seasonal helpings making comments about how well they all looked, what nice clothes. Presents consisted of such things as ludicrously expensive glad rags, perfumes. Again, I fulfilled the role of absent dad, me being the closest approximation to a man on the premises, Alex and Algernon hardly measuring up. I performed all the ceremonials bar saying grace. As to be expected, food was magnificent, drink mostly vintage wine or spirits. Even the Christmas crackers had to be handled with care as they contained small china or porcelain *objets d'art*. I fielded a perfect all rounder, catching them as they tumbled out. On the great day itself I had a hit. It was also, of course, a time of domestic flare-up, me pouring oil on troubled waters, acting the man. All in all, no expense was spared.

Seasonal duties included enduring shows up West for which they obtained block bookings. The crap I sat through always had me gasping for a fix or trip to the bar, but I felt obligated to endure the dreary fare with Boo's family. But I carefully planned, nipping off to the bogs just before the interval. They were well kept ones with bright lights, handy for locating veins. Before setting out, I'd have armed myself with a small tool kit. Once in the cubicle, I'd unwrap the silver spoon, lighter, gear, works, placing them on a cushion of bog paper on the low cistern top. Sweating with anticipation, off came the belt, toilet flushed for water, then I'd do the business. As the hypo hit home, I'd hear the applause then dispose of evidence, concealing it in the leather wrap that had transported the goodies, placing it neatly into my inside jacket pocket. As the audience filed into the bogs, I'd be sitting on the throne, slumped.

"Splendid so far, don't you think?"

"Wonderful performance!"

This acted as my cue. I'd dive out, heading for the bar, buying drinks all round, cokes for the girls. Boo would slip me the money, after which, back to the second half smacked out. I guessed this might be something I'd have to put up with the following year, thinking that far ahead. I'd certainly done well for myself, a welcome change to previous Christmases. Better than a shared cold Kentucky Fried Chicken.

CHAPTER TEN

Before we finally moved into the Crescent officially, I implanted the suggestion that I go live alone on the premises for a while, do a touch of painting, carpet fitting, rearrange plumbing for dish washer and washing machine. Selflessly volunteering to stay over, I'd kip on a mattress, work through the day, exercise the mutt. Truth is, after the loony brother and airhead mother, I needed a break. The chores themselves would have taken a genuine workman a day and a half maximum but I certainly took my time. Boo gave me dosh for painting equipment and the paint itself. I entered the decorator's shop willing to pay, couldn't find anybody who would deal with my needs. Impatient, I looked at the apathetic staff, then strolled out the door removing a couple of large tins at a time, repeating this performance as if fulfilling an order. The only things paid for turned out to be rollers and tray. Money saved went on gear. On the very first day of caretaker residence, a couple of local junkies called over. So from day one, the place became a shooting gallery. I had them score nearby, then we'd sit on the mattress, fixing. Whatever your circumstances, once you've fixed up, all worries or concerns simply vanish as you float on air.

Half an hour before Boo came over, I'd start painting, the other tasks had been delegated to workmen. Boo failed to grasp how slow the job progressed, except that whenever she saw me working, I'd be applying myself with extreme meticulousness, glancing over, happy to see her, walk over to the windows pointing to the Crescent below. Fruit trees, old fashioned wrought iron lamp-posts, architectural features, weaving dreams. I reinforced illusions, wearing working clothes with designer splatters, a costume job, fit for the stage. All evidence of hanky panky scrupulously removed ensured I didn't blow the scene. In a set-up like this, you might only get one chance. Horace would be strategically placed so that upon Boo's entry he'd be gazing at me perched on the ladder, stroking paint on woodwork. Evenings, she'd swish me off to a meal where I'd pre-empt her with shop talk of my own, yellow paint put people in a good mood, white made rooms look larger, red creates discord and violence. Stalling for almost three weeks, everything was now ready, time to move in.

Boo only moved in her bed, along with the little drawers for her creams, a sofa, telly and kitchen utensils. In front of Boo I seemed cool, relaxed, in control of my destiny but well aware the inevitable question of me gaining useful employment would be next on the agenda. So far, this problem had been neatly side-stepped, the only blot on the horizon, my pocket money didn't cover the cost of gear. I found the previously hinted at solution to the problem just around the corner, Inverness Street Market. This part of town was completely different from our semi Hampstead outpost. Just off the tiny market, on the crossroads to the left, stood a probation hostel with a bingo hall opposite, drunks and alkies sheltering or socialising around the exits. Further up the road from here, dominating the back streets, Arlington, the huge doss-house that supplied the area with a generous percentage of the select clientele who helped make up the low life.

By now, I'd reached the stage where gear dosage increased. I needed more on a daily basis to feed the hungry primate. The market offered a solution to both work and money problems. Cash for little or token effort. The seeds had already been planted. Me running a stall selling samples while I tried to get a place in acting school. As for the neighbours in the Crescent, they were the usual collection of boring artists, actors, telly performers, lecturers and assorted high-brow scribblers. I couldn't give a toss about them, wasn't in a hurry to make acquaintances having seen it all before in Hampstead proper. I didn't come here to integrate, I wanted money for a regular supply of the strong stuff.

Sure enough, Boo presented me with a brand new collapsible rail with wheels along with sixty dresses which I reckoned to knock out a fiver a shout. One morning I hooked them up, walking the rail down towards the market. Naturally, I'd jabbed before stepping out. This was a quiet day, midweek, just right for testing the water. I pitched up next to a second-hand section not able to secure myself a space in the market proper. Vibes from established traders were heavy but my image threw them. Clear pinned eyes, jet black dyed hair and blooming quiff, the visuals did most of the talking. All the same, I got a bombardment from the market gentry.

"Oi mate, you can't go there."

"This spot's taken, sunshine."

Having had a hit, I didn't feel perturbed by this idiocy. I pushed my rail over to the second-hand geezer.

"Alright if I pitch up here?"

"Do what you want, chum."

The reply, although sullen, was welcome as I wheeled the rail over to a traffic barrier. Within five minutes, women flocked, dresses flying out, me giving it all the old patter.

I whipped out a tape measure, doing inside leg measurements, much to the amusement of the traders. Half an hour later, I leaned over the barrier flicking through a wad. Over a ton. I bought flowers in the market, arranged them tastefully around the flat. That always pleased Boo and after I'd handed over her cut, she'd get more dresses. Old habits die hard though, I still signed on. It became 'look to the future' time, everything possible, me telling Boo I'd apply to drama school. By now, curtains were fitted, new cooker installed. I busied myself building real coal fires in the grates, Boo coming home to a roaring blaze, Horace stretched out, warming himself by the flames. I'd be pinned out, her none the wiser. Sometimes, I suspected she might be examining my eyes for signs of a sneak hit. I maintained the old charade, a half-smoked joint nestling in the ashtray, me pretending to be stoned or gaze back like a schoolboy in love. Work now commanded more of her attention. New lines, job changes, travelling to fashion shows abroad. She'd gone up a few steps in this closed shop, extra money, more expensive gratuities.

I needed a hit everyday now, increased dosage, had started to buy gear for a pick-me-up in the morning. Boo thought I might be up to something naughty if she saw people like Justin hanging about. She'd wait until they took the hint, departed and pop the question in the form of a half-hearted suggestion that maybe I'd been indulging. Depending on the situation, the most admitted to would be a wee dabble, then everything was hunky-dory. I'd fool Boo by wearing glasses, slipping them on, people changed their perceptions of your image. You look more intelligent, so I'd be wearing a pair, watching news on the telly or reading a highbrow paper when Boo came in from work. It became more necessary to lie as Boo got persistent in questioning about gear. Works were stashed in secret places such as under the sink. On occasion, it was touch and go fixing, although I always managed everything in the nick of time, Horace sounding the alarm with grunts as Boo ascended the stairs to our happy home. If caught short by her arrival, I'd step into the bog, finish the job, straining sounds, adding to authenticity. I spent twenty, thirty a day on the crave.

No longer could I operate without gear, staying indoors until a result came in on the phone. My Codeine stop-gap had lost its effectiveness. All the same, I still held together the illusions at home for Boo. In the market, stallholders thought me a straight regular guy, enjoying me in action, thinking I was a natural born trader, a clean-living lad who only supped the odd half. They figured out Boo had money but thought the dresses a product of my own individual enterprise. These stallholders knew we were buying a flat in the Crescent. And I had the same accent as themselves. No snob this fellow, doing well for himself into the bargain. One thing mystified them, my succession of weird rail visitors, people like Justin, guys with leather jackets and spiky hair, hippy types. Most, of course, dealing illicit substances. The image received a substantial boost by my easy banter with office girls who flocked in and the girls from the Camden, Kingsway and Hampstead days.

Apart from the rail, home became my focal point. Parties and other such frivolities took a back seat as I didn't need to do wallets, now having a regular virtually unearned income. I'd make sure though, to get out and take in a couple of movies a week. Justin was my frequent visitor, he'd been going through the process of getting edged out of his new squat. So now Justin was worried. I told him to sign on for a room at Arlington doss house, the dole would pay, no trouble. He agreed reluctantly, no choice really, so I queued up with him, offering moral support. Justin signed in, that night kipping on Boo's sofa. She wasn't exactly overjoyed, reminding her of Ridinghouse and Redd days. I told his rich friends about the predicament over the phone. They lived as a couple just around the corner, had plenty of space and exhibited class solidarity, taking him in. So Justin escaped the dosshouse by the skin of his yellow-brown teeth.

Seeing plenty of people from the Hampstead and Kingsway days, I noticed some weren't doing too well. The perfect Rasta, Malcolm, who'd crashed the Hampstead scene and helped freak me out during my bad trip, turned up in the market. He'd suffered a breakdown, was now bloated up on medication, a total wreck, his eyes hadn't a glimmer of half-life in them. The end of a high ranking dread, gone off his head. As had Antonio, the smoothie who'd pulled all the birds at Kingsway with his combination of charm and perfectly patched jeans. He'd become zomboid, probably the result of acid, evolved into nothing more than a gibbering idiot. To think I'd once admired him in a naive manner, for his pulling prowess. Redd slid out of the woodwork, me peeling off a fiver for him to get a drink. Darling Fiona had gone, but Redd dug up another half-wit with requisite middle-class credentials.

Lady Di styles were snatched off the rail like the proverbial hot cakes, money worries now banished. We had virtually no interference from the in-laws, just me and Boo together. As for living day to day, a pampered junkie, I didn't seem to have as much natural energy as a couple of months ago. Boo's suspicions faded, unaware that all my energy now came from smack. Once skagged up I could do anything, rapping, joking, loverboy stuff, selling, being generally sociable. I knew the habit was running riot even though on the surface, all appeared to be well with the world, Boo taken in by my enthusiasm for the flat. All a happy dream for her. She even threw a housewarming party, mostly people from work. Justin came over before the event, us slipping into the bedroom for a fix. I'd built up real fires, laid the table out with glasses, drinks, flowers. I donned my glasses, Boo tucking me into a little Japanese suit, a highwaisted jacket that fastened up on the outside with strings lined with silk, dark blue material with flecks in a loose check pattern. The trousers, made out of the same stuff, short, rising well above the ankles. Reinforced by my fix, I busied myself with Boo's empty-headed guests, playing the role of perfect host, answering the door, pouring drinks. If I hadn't been on gear, I'd have got roaring drunk, disgraced myself. It looked to these people that I made a model companion for Boo, only sipping from a single glass of wine. Boo effortlessly dealt with guests at the party, some of whom enjoyed a coke toot in the corners. Boo, partial to a line, joined in the fun. I heard them talking about me.

"What a fellow!"

"Aren't you the lucky one Boo."

Boo's housewarming proved to be a success and I'd done my bit in putting on the show.

Gear controlled me. I knew I could just about struggle through a couple of days off the stuff maximum. This however was only on the level of theory. Methadone, the green goddess, helped supplement my habit on a daily basis. Alex returned to Hampstead, seemingly cured by a spell in the expensive bin. Trouble was though, he now fixed gear every day. Boo worried more about Alex and his habit than anything I might be doing, her method of blotting out the terrible truth of my goings-on. I took far more gear than Alex and, despite the handy sidetrack he provided, Boo once again began to suspect all wasn't right with me. In Alex's case, money came to the rescue once again. The family shoved him into an expensive rehabilitation centre, with dad forking out five hundred quid a week. This place, a mansion located in the home counties, contained rich drug and alcohol abusers. The whole system was geared to making them responsible bourgeois citizens who'd function in the outside world giving orders, passing and enforcing laws, moralising to the lower classes while raking in the cash.

Boo started springing the odd surprise inspection now and again. She'd jokingly look at my arms whenever the subject of Alex came up, sometimes unearthing evidence, leaving me to invent ludicrous excuses. Horace bit me there, a coat hanger produced that bruise. Deep down Boo knew something was amiss, however I pre-empted her inspections by fixing in the foot or hand. By now I took a gram or more a day plus Methadone. If Boo didn't face up to the facts, sooner or later, I'd be forced to. Question being was I ready or willing to?

Certainly not right away, as months passed in a drug-induced blur. Coming up to yet another Christmas I felt grand. Things were booming. I'd even splashed out on an electric guitar, had two rails on the go, kiddies and adult gear, all top notch stuff. After fighting customers off for a couple of hours, I'd jack it in, dole out some charitable contributions to the alkies. Having all this easy money, I didn't mind spreading it around a bit. A typical day after a brief sale would see me down 100mls of Methadone followed up later by my evening fix. Repeating this ritual for the umpteenth time, I'd spread out on a huge couch Boo bought, laying there like a vegetable, eyes lazily drifting toward Horace nestled in his little basket. He'd look back at me until we'd both established eyeball contact. Horace reminded me of someone. Myself. Totally dependent on Boo and me, while I was equally dependent on Boo. Lingering over Horace's sad almost weeping eyes, I realised the gear habit had to cease before I ended up in a basket. Just to rub it in that very night we watched a documentary on the telly about opium addicts in India undergoing withdrawal and the drying out process in a hospital. No doubting what I'd have to go through should I ever quit the habit. The programme I felt to be an omen, finding myself wondering when I'd take the plunge, go for it, break the deadly cycle. Then again, with Christmas knocking at the door, I had to get on the blower, pay a few visits, get the seasonal stash together.

On the rail Christmas Eve, I took a packet, patted the wad, shot off to collect the doings. Coke for me and Boo, the hardy perennial dope, a couple of 100ml measures of Methadone plus a special treat, two g's of pharmaceutical heroin half-inched from a hospital dangerous drugs cabinet. This year most of the shopping had been done by Boo, after all, I was a busy man myself. She'd also taken care of all tedious arrangements. Christmas morning meant a drive off to an uncle's. His daughter happened to be drying out in rehab. I didn't care as I sipped the finest champagne. Then off to the mother's in the afternoon. Throughout these ordeals, beaming smiles were the order of my day. And why not, being pinned out of my bonce? Prodigal Alex had in the meantime returned from his stint in the revolving door system, finding a new crutch to lean on, 'Narcotics Anonymous'! He thrust some literature at me which I tucked into my pocket to forget.

Later, back in the comfort of our Crescent, me and Boo snorted coke, smoked blow. Boxing Day, I took a short stroll over to Justin's to watch racing. The couple who were putting him up had gone away for the duration, so he had the place to himself. We didn't waste any time, whacking up the pure stuff. I kept missing the vein, leaving abortions hanging off my arm. Finally, I hit home. We sunk into the racing, hurdles and chases blending into one another. We chalked up a couple of winners but didn't care. I started thinking again. Why not give it up? Go to Boo. Give her the low-down. We had a junkie rap, the one most junkies subject themselves to at least once a week when they convince each other they'll pack it in but never do. Now was the time to call a halt to the process before a team of neanderthal hunter gatherers evolved from the primates on my straining back.

Boo awaited my return with Horace and the warm fire. I got down to the nitty-gritty straight away, telling her I had something serious to talk about. She'd have to bear with me on this one as I explained the whole situation. Boo looked perturbed, her face dropping, thinking I was about to confess to an affair. The only affair I'd been conducting was the one with the devil. Boo sat as I paced.

"I've been doing lots and lots and lots of smack. And Methadone. And I've decided to knock it on the head altogether. That means I'm going to get very sick and I'm going to need your help, Boo."

Boo knew she'd have to come to terms with the awful truth, but at least it was now out in the open between us. I told her she'd have to ride it out with me, withdrawal would have to be stone cold, no pills or booze of any description. She wouldn't be able to be with me all the time, but I'd have to, for the time being, abandon the rail, going out, even entertaining at home. Having a limited concentration span or memory for anything beyond fashion, sun creams and office gossip, she'd already forgotten the entire content of the opium addict programme, so eventually I acted out the scenarios she'd have to face. Drawing on my final spark of energy from the afternoon hit I described using word and body, the entire gamut of withdrawal.

"All night and day fidgeting, sweating. It'll be like that for a few days, it's a bit like a bad dose of the 'flu. Then my stomach will open up, I'll stink the bog out."

Finally, I got the message over. Boo started to blame herself for complicity in my habit. I told her it was too late for that. Could she face it? Yes, she claimed. I slept fairly well that night, effects of the day's jab had been enough to make slumber smooth and easy.

Next day, I felt okay, just a bit tired after missing my early morning pick-me-up. I wondered what the lead to new year would bring. Things weren't too bad for a couple of days. When Boo asked me how I felt, I reminded her that I had to remain clean no matter how long it took. So no booze, drugs or medication. I knew the Turkey wouldn't come on immediately, preferring to lurk in dark corners before sneaking up on me, clouting me over the head. I puffed my way through packets of fags, swigging endless cups of coffee. Certainly no dope, aware it might freak me out, bring on the abdabs. By day three, the reprieve had wavered; the Turkey came on with a vengeance. I'd already severed contact with the outside world, pulling the phone from the plug. My sense of smell now increased. I heard shouting, voices in the far distance particularly at chucking-out time. Taste buds returned. Watching sad things on the telly had tears welling up. I retreated to the bed, fire going, colour telly for company. At night, I'd camp on the sofa in the other room. No sleep, no rest, listening to late night radio, stoking the fire continuously, Boo periodically checking on me, enquiring into my well being. My head ached. Boo wanted me to swallow a couple of aspirin. I refused all medication of any description. If the Turkey stayed at this level, extreme discomfort but little else, I could handle it, no question. Just sit it out for a few more days and I'd rapidly improve. Snow fell outside but the warm fire embraced as I took comfort from the plush surroundings. Even with my imagination working full stretch, I found it difficult to envisage me going through this in a squat.

In between hot and cold flushes that came on at regular intervals, I'd get dressed up, take Horace over to Regent's Park for a walk. I'd run about for a while, put colour in my cheeks, even once going for a dip at the Swiss Cottage Holiday Inn, using one of Boo's plastic cards. New Year was upon us. Having heard it took about five or six days to come off, sleeping relatively well, I thought the main barriers had been negotiated, that I'd past the worst phases. Trouble was, I hadn't taken the

Methadone into consideration. The Fairy Liquid stays longer in the system than smack. After the New Year's eve swim, I couldn't relax at all. Boo had to cancel a party visitation as the goose-pimples were up again, size of bumps, eyeballs turned all pupil, stomach cramped, hair bristled. Hot and cold simultaneously. Boo tended me as outside a new year came in. Three in the morning, second of January, I left home, my whole body screaming in agony from withdrawal, heading for Regent's Park. I ran blind into the freezing cold, trying in vain to tire my body. Ran until my chest burned, throat rattled red raw. I froze almost beyond sensibility in hell itself. Clutching park railings close to the road, my hands were sealed to the metal by a bolt of frozen electric current. I squeezed the railings, unable now to draw my blistered soldered palms away, just a couple of petrified fingers. In despair, I sunk to my knees uttering a lonely desperate cry that rent the night. The knees cracked through the upper crust of slush, me howling out again to the deserted streets, pleading with God to lift the pain, I'd never do anything bad again, please forgive me for all the wicked deeds I'd done. One more chance, have mercy. I wheezed and groaned then rose, gently peeling my blue hands from the railings, slush dripping down my legs. I didn't feel better, but somehow a strange calm descended upon my tortured brain. I ran back to the house, wind cutting into eyes, almost tearing them out. Hauling myself up the staircase I resolved to be more determined than ever to stay clean, knowing I'd get stronger, slowly, but not kidding myself. I'd have to ride this nightmare day by day and that I was still located slap bang in the middle of it.

For the next few days, purgatory continued, though somewhat diminished in scale. I wept more bitter tears over inane TV movies, shook with uncontrollable laughter at the abysmal sit-coms, keeping close to the fire, huddled up, swathed in blankets. When shivers and aches came, I did press-ups, took plenty of hot baths. I'd never been so well-scrubbed in my life. The tastebuds underwent another renaissance as I toiled now in the kitchen doing creative cooking. After that, a swim or jog round the park. This regime lasted over a fortnight, pleasing Boo who hoped it could be kept up. I joined the rest of the human race, shopping, even making arrangements with the toy stall man to go to another market on Monday and Tuesday once I felt better.

January and February is the kipper season in markets, everyone skint. I'd fixed up my arrangements with the toyman who collected me, collapsible rail, dresses, making our way in his van to Church Street, off the Edgeware Road. To my surprise, once pitched up, all the dresses flew out leaving time to go into the bookies laying out a quid or two. Temptation nagged as I walked past various chemists and off-licences that dotted the area. For the first time in years though, I remained straight. In spite of being lively and rejuvenated, boredom crept in until Boo mentioned to me that Daddy had a place out in Florida, maybe we could go. This inspired me to save dosh and we started laying plans. I had to get a full passport. I knew that if I obtained an Irish one I'd get a visa without too many questions being asked at the US Embassy. Calling back to the Archway, going through biscuit tins, searching for relevant documents such as the old man's birth certificate. After which I got some photos, all signed by my old family GP, then shot off to the Irish Embassy, filling in forms. Within the hour, an Irish passport. Next step, visa. I completed more forms at the American Embassy, simply answering NO to all dodgy questions. Then came the interview with an official who sported a John Wayne drawl.

"If I came along to your market in April would I still find you working there?"

In other words, you're not going to be naughty, try to stay over illegally in the land of the free are you?

"Of course, I'll be there."

More drawl.

"I'm gonna give you a visa for the rest of your life."

Stamping me an indefinite one. This was encouraging to say the least. Now we planned in earnest.

Late February, Boo's dad paid fares for both of us to Florida, about nine hundred smackers. We'd stay in his condominium apartment on a little island off the coast. First time I'd ever flown on an airplane, a boring nine hour experience, only take off and landing affording any sort of thrill. Upon going through American immigration I realised coming here would be a mistake, the place being squeaky clean, full of smiling Moonie look-alikes. Next, we departed to the island on a tiny aircraft. Once on the island, we caught a cab to the condo, our driver coming out with the ultimate corny line.

"Welcome to paradise."

Boo lapped all this up. Town itself only had one cinema, a church and a single supermarket. The rest consisted of luxury tower blocks facing the beach. Here was the combo. Residents were mostly old fat people making heavy weather of walking about, the rest drove. Once inside, I couldn't complain. Every convenience including cable TV, jacuzzi, downstairs a swimming pool and private strip of beach. I soon realised though, there was nothing else to do here except relax, go to the beach, watch American telly. It rained incessantly despite always being hot. We didn't socialise as everybody else had at least forty years start on us. As way of consolation I began to. get stuck into the amply stocked drink cabinet. Every drink imaginable and plenty of it. Everyday, I got well sloshed but it didn't produce a bad temper, just a taste for more booze. My libido still operated, I did my duty keeping Boo happy. Deep down inside, I wanted to get back to the markets, make money, meet people. I kept thinking, if only we'd gone to New York instead of this. I wasn't seeing anything of America, this was like being on a large well-manicured golf course. Anyway, we arrived back the contented couple, with me resolving to work out at the local gym, give up drinking as I'd now developed a taste for the hard stuff.

With all the hyped-up enthusiasm of the born-again, I enrolled in the local multi-gym for an hour in the evenings. Workout, toning up the stomach, lower and upper abdominals, sit-ups on a bench, expanding deltoids, push ups with weights, skipping. More press ups. Biceps started to bulge. Even lifting weights with my legs. All done in the hour, mechanical fashion. Loader re-emerged helping me out on the rail, coming over to the gym, where I got him on the same regime. Loader kept telling me of a neat little town in Holland where he'd been a few years previously, called Maastricht, on the Belgium German border. Another Noddy town but Loader made it sound good. We'd only need a couple of hundred quid each to stay for a fortnight. No sweat getting that together from the rail.

With spring advancing, the rail going well, I felt like a version of Mr Clean. Not a worry in the world, sun-tanned from Florida, fit from the gym with self-confidence and esteem back. And straight, only a couple of well-earned cold beers with Loader after the gym. It seemed that me and Boo were getting on together better than ever, despite the almost total lack of intellectual stimulation from her end. I amused myself playing guitar, telling Boo I might play in a band again. Just another excuse to avoid true employment, having the rail and wanting to keep it that way. I'd reached my quarter century and couldn't feel better.

Boo had been away to Paris working as she called it, bringing me a dark green suede coat that set her back a couple of hundred quid. Boo seemed pleased that I'd be going off with likeable Loader, who'd by now become a regular visitor to our home. Older than me, with distinguished grey hair, Boo believed him to be a restraining influence. She agreed I'd earned a break, having covered so much ground. After all, I'd been off gear for six months now. So me and Loader took a stash of Valium, dope and off we set. This felt more like a proper holiday, zonked for the entire journey, we took the long boat ride. No set plan, we eventually arrived in Maastricht early morning. Even after Florida, I'd never seen anywhere so neat and tidy. As we sipped coffee, Loader reassured me, saying this place was okay as I'd find out sure enough. We moved off to the main Square where folk congregated. Loader claimed to know plenty of people here and sure enough started bumping into them, chattering away. As Loader socialised, I nodded off in the forecourt of a bar for an hour. Waking up from the doze, I couldn't believe my eyes. Good-looking women all over the show, better even than movie stars. They came from nearby fashion colleges. And hardly any blokes around. Loader came over, pleased as punch.

"Bull is in the bar."

Loader led me inside, introducing me to the man about town, the biggest coke and dope dealer in the area. This Bull fellow didn't mess about.

"You take a sniff."

Coke. Went to the bog, snorted, coming out raring to go. I cracked Bull up with jokes, him promptly inviting us to stay at his place. Here, we snorted well into the evening. Ten at night, I was going strong, playing the guitar while Bull cooked. In town, the girls were all drinking in the bars. Still no geezers, I noticed. Everyone smoked dope openly, I'd forgotten it was all but legal here. Me and Loader wasted no time chatting them up, having no end of a giggle in the process. When the bars closed Bull drove us to Belgium where he knew of a place open until six in the morning, me jiving on the dance floor, nose tingling. I arranged to meet one of the girls, Marie, next day in Maastricht, thinking her well tasty, like a chic French actress, big eyes, long curly hair tied up, about my age. Night-time, Marie came over to Bull's, supplied with abundant coke. I played all her favourite tunes on the guitar. Later, upstairs for some how's yer father, just like the old days except now I'd become a geezer. Boo never intruded into my thoughts, it didn't matter, after all, I was only on holiday. Me and Loader easily established ourselves. Up at twelve, shopping for dope in coffee bars. Then downstairs to hubblies left on the premises, off to the Square blitzed, breakfast and sleep by the lake come afternoon. Bull took us out driving in his old American car. This was the life. Evenings spent drinking, guitars dropping on to my lap, everywhere coke, raving until four in the morning then bed with Marie. I'd commute between Marie's and Bull's houses. We told Bull to come over to London, me presenting him with the coat Boo bought me in Paris. Being an expensive cut, it fitted perfectly even though he stood six foot two. We suggested to Bull he could pay for his London holiday if he brought some coke over. After our two weeks, we left knowing everybody worth knowing in town, planning a return visit. We'd established a good connection.

Arriving back, Boo was annoyed I'd given the coat away. More galling to her were the developed photos, me and Loader in a Noddyland full of attractive girls. Boo started firing questions.

"Who's that?"

Somehow, she'd singled out Marie. I distracted her with a romantic kiss and cuddle, explaining the girls were all Loader's friends. I told her how Bull was sure. With Boo off to work, I'd be on the phone to Bull and Marie. Old habits set in. After doing the rail, me and Loader neglected the gym in favour of going down to the West End where we'd bump into the likes of Clarissa and her ilk, handy contacts for Bull.

Bull finally made it over, me taking him straight to see Boo at the Crescent. Being an impressive looking hunk and pulling out a huge stash of instant happiness, Boo was delighted. More so when Bull drew up a long chunky line. Next came the round of West End watering holes and parties, us trying to sell his wares, but it happened they were overpriced in an already over-saturated market. Eventually, we managed to shift it, mostly up our noses.

I hung about with Loader quite a lot now, real buddy-buddy stuff, with him working with me on the rail, drinking together. Boo started to get wary of Loader's supposed influence over me but more probably because of all the girls he knew, some of whom might lead me into temptation. Nevertheless, not too many objections were raised, her going along with everything as I'd come off gear. In the hyped up aftermath of coming off, I was fun to be with, a never-ending source of scattershot entertainment. Me and Loader usually met Boo down the West End after she'd finished work, for drinks. By now Boo was doing alright out of the family business, with her blinkered, distorted view of the world, wanted me to do well for myself. So she agreed when I told her that I was going off to Maastricht, visit Bull, try to make a few bob in the coke business. All I really fancied was a change of scenery and to see Marie again. I'd been off gear for nine solid months. Boo often travelled or went abroad on business, so she raised no objection to my absences. If she harboured suspicions, Boo kept them to herself.

So over to Marie's. She was delighted to see me, even though I'd run out of money having blown the lot on duty-frees and laying in plenty of coke. I wondered about getting back, so I wrote to a friend for a few quid to get me back. For a couple of days I went out with Marie, visiting her mates, wining and dining as she showed me off. This soon became one long yawn, me wishing to be back in the Crescent. For a while I enjoyed sex but then, very much to my surprise, a coke withdrawal started coming on. I managed somehow to control my temper, which underneath the pleasant surface bubbled up, making me feel agitated, needing to drink. Come evenings, I simply flaked out in front of the telly.

Waiting for money to come in, I found myself forced to endure Marie's uninteresting friends. As I shoplifted to supply myself with booze, my reputation took a nosedive. A wallet went missing, evidence pointed in my direction, irony being that I was innocent of the charge. By the time it turned up, my name had become dirt in some quarters, people ducking and diving in order to avoid contact. This town didn't have much to offer without Bull who'd disappeared over to the border with Germany in furtherance of some shady enterprise. I grew tired of listening to Marie and her friends whittering on about art and the cinema, something about which they knew next to nothing. Pointless to interrupt. I could no longer bear waiting for the friend's letter anymore so I borrowed the money off Marie, who'd provided yet another incentive to return home. She'd started acting like Boo, going to the extreme of trying to fix me up with a job in, of all places, a pickle factory. I bunked most of the journey back, spending the money on drink.

CHAPTER ELEVEN

Back in London, me and Loader decided to go over to Holland, help Bull out with a dope run into Germany. I went back to Boo, having no hesitation informing her about the business I'd hoped to become involved with. At least I'd tried to earn a crust, showed a touch of enterprise. Just as long as I didn't have anything to do with gear or other women, all was fine with Boo. I told her about my plans to journey abroad, do a job with Bull also knowing if I got into trouble she'd bail me out.

I met an old flame, Betty. She lived in a place near Swiss Cottage, a small flat. I told the ever gullible Boo that I wanted to spend some time at Loader's. She acquiesced, no trouble. Instead, I headed straight over to Betty's, interspersed with visits to service Boo, create an illusion of happiness and of course do the odd rail. Betty lived with a gay junkie from the punk days. He wasn't making any contribution toward her rent but, in return for living space, fixed her arm up or gave her Methadone. Instant dislike, the guy a slimeball, me on the high moral crusade having quit opiates. Sampling speed, downers and drinking booze with Betty helped fuel my manic moods but, as I quite liked her, it didn't take long for me to start wising her up to the machinations of the junkie. I asked Betty to come along to Maastricht with me, explaining that some business I had over there could be combined with an attempt to help dry her out. She agreed, sounded like a good idea.

Just before we departed for Holland, I knocked out a final rail, Friday afternoon taking about two hundred quid. I'd promised to hand over the bulk to Boo, helping her to pay the telephone bill. This time, however, I wrote her a short note explaining that I'd been forced to borrow the money and goodbye I'll be back in a couple of weeks, love, Dan. Outside, Loader sat in his pride and glory, a convertible Triumph Herald, roof down, sunning himself. As I taped the note to an inside door, it suddenly swung open. Boo. Back early from work. What a surprise. I shoved the note in her hand, kissed the cheek, then legged it downstairs. For once, Boo had no difficulty comprehending the written word, as she thundered down in hot pursuit. I dived into the motor shouting a one word instruction.

"Drive!"

From the corner of my eye, I saw the figure of Boo, flinging herself on the boot. As we turned away from the market, Boo managed to clamber into the back seat, Loader now slowed up as he drove into the traffic near Parkway. Boo gained the front seat where I sat, a ferocious struggle erupting, her pulling my hair, clawing my face with red fingernails. The vehicle shuddered to a halt, doors swinging open, the brawl spilling out on to the road. Hordes of zomboidlike creatures, dossers and drunks, staggered from their watering holes at the bingo hall exits as I pushed Boo away, her face distorted with rage, screaming

"Give me my money!"

I pulled the wedge from my pocket, threw it loose into her face.

"Here! Fucking have it! Stick it up your arse!"

Then, jumping back into the motor, I shouted at Loader, "Drive!"

As we sped away, I glanced once more into the rear view mirror at an insane scrabble. Dossers, drunks, traders, passers-by and Boo all fought in a heap for the money which billowed like leaves along the kerb. We drove to Betty's, adrenaline buzzing.

Back at Betty's I took stock of my accounts. No readies, they'd been given the confetti treatment. I decided to take some of the designer clothes and my electric guitar which I'd stashed at Betty's to act as collateral. With Betty's dole cheque we got a one way ticket to the Hook of Holland. Loader would drive over, join us in a few days, meet us in Maastricht after collecting his dole cheque. From the Hook, we had no money but caught a cab, heading straight to Marie's. Here, I knocked on the door, Marie opened it all winsome smiles, glad to see me but only for a few seconds. She'd spotted Betty in the cab. Immediately Marie's mood changed, demanding to know what was going on. I retrieved the unopened letter from my friend containing the money, told Marie I'd catch her later, driving off to a bank, changing the money, paying off our driver. Bull greeted us with open arms, Betty hitting it off with his girlfriend. That enabled me to sneak away with Bull to do some sampling, this time strong grass from India, a whole brick of the stuff. As usual, he'd got some Charlie together, so the binge started, me telling Bull to expect Loader over within a couple of days.

When Loader finally materialised, the two of us walked around town discussing the dope run. Things didn't look too good on that score. Someone had failed to deliver the goods. We bumped into Marie, who grabbed me.

"What's going on? Who's that girl you're with?"

I pushed Marie aside, hurried on, rapping about the deal. Loader dropped some acid and I split to a bar. Alone, over drinks, I started to think about returning back to London. Midnight, drunk, arrived back at base. Dramatic events had transpired. Bull's girlfriend came over, looking perturbed.

"I'm worried about Loader. I think he's had a bummer, he jumped into the canal, came back drenched, now he's disappeared."

I went out to search for him. Before I did the rounds of the bars, I noticed Loader's car under a flyover. He sat in the vehicle, a blank stare on his face, as though he'd been taken over by an alien entity. I knocked on the window, Loader winding it down without averting his gaze into the void. I climbed in, lighting a cigarette as Loader sobbed. I asked him to return, come back to the house but he insisted on remaining, so I went back shrugging my shoulders. For the next couple of days, Loader didn't budge an inch, me taking him food and drink which he never touched, miles away in a different dimension. Meanwhile, our money had long run out. Then one night, Loader and motor simply vanished into thin air. Bull changed his appearance for another run, himself alone this time, while Betty had a mild Turkey. I survived by shoplifting food and drink from supermarkets, all of us in a state of mild shock because of Loader and his subsequent disappearance. Betty rode out the Turkey in a matter of days, ending up looking a picture of health, the only plus point to the trip. I sold the guitar, bade farewell to Bull who laid some grass on me. At least I'd emerged from the drama in buoyant form, stealing duty-frees on the return journey.

Arriving back, we went straight to Betty's flat. I knew Boo would still be soft on me but felt I'd leave it for a while before any tentative attempt at communication. The task at hand would be removing the junkie. Watching him prance about, poncing himself up in the mirror, I sprung an argument on him about leaving his used works all over the show. I'd been fuelled up by a few drinks, so I confronted him, launching an attack, with remarks about not paying his way, dirty habits and I didn't want no junkie hanging about now Betty had come off gear. With the arrogance of a pinned man, he retorted that it was nothing to do with me, it's up to Betty. Riled, I told him that he happened to be mistaken, I lived here now and there wasn't room for him anymore, goodbye. To emphasise the point, I picked up his record player as a disc turned upon it, then heaved the lot out of the window. Now he knew. This was serious. It finally clicked. I told him I'd be going out for an hour, if, when I came back, he still regarded himself as resident, he'd follow an identical flight path to the record player. A few stiff drinks later, I returned steaming, only to find he'd packed up, fled back to suburbia and his parents. Me and Betty spent most of our time together hustling for money in order to provide her with a diet of downers, mine for booze. I didn't bother changing dole offices, so the cheques still went to Boo's. But I had the key. Nevertheless I phoned her up, telling Boo I'd be coming over to collect my cheques. She sat there waiting. Hardly a surprise. Soon we'd re-established talking terms, even joking about the flying money whirling around the street.

After making exhaustive enquiries about Loader, I finally found out about his whereabouts from an old girlfriend of his. She told me Loader was in the bin, that someone had previously seen him dossing in the streets at Charing Cross. She'd helped him get into the bin, me picking up the feeling she blamed me for the turn of events. Being curious, I fancied going to visit but she said he'd withdrawn entirely into himself, didn't want to see anybody, no exceptions. Loader, it turned out, suffered from manic depression, sometimes slipping into a semi-catatonic state. I decided to respect his wishes and kept away.

I told Boo about the unfortunate Loader and she sympathised. I hinted during our conversation about being skint, did she have any stock going spare? Love is blind, probably half-witted, such was her desire to hang on to me. I ended up doing a rail every weekend. One thing led to another, me soon staying over at Boo's during those weekends. It felt like old times once again, barring one major exception. I stayed the rest of the week with Betty, spinning Boo a yarn about getting my head together at Lenny's. Come Friday, I told Betty I'd be working with 'a friend' on a building site. As I always now carried plenty of money upon my return, Betty, like Boo, felt happy and content, never asking questions. By Tuesday, the money would be gone, spunked on booze, speed and downers. Rest of the week would be spent shoplifting, tapping people for money.

One of the few visitors who came over to Betty's was Justin, still on gear. Sometimes during the week, I'd nip over to his nearby flat in Kilburn Park, boasting about being off junk. Justin knew I stayed at Boo's weekends, so he thought he'd try his luck with Betty, who constantly rebuffed his sordid advances. I had a word in his unwashed shell-like after she complained, telling Justin to leave her alone. I could see Justin ached with jealousy about what he regarded as my success, giving up gear, manipulating two tasty birds. He hadn't been laid since the days of bearded lady. And he was skint, unable to support his habit, on codeine, a couple of quid a day. One weekend, doing the rail, I'd noticed him lurking. Getting back to Boo, she confronted me, saying Justin came over, claiming I'd shacked up with another girl weekdays. Boo knew it to be Betty so I brazened it out, unable to deny facts, telling her I loved Betty and yes I lived with her. That did the trick, Boo bursting into tears, then hysterics, shaking all over between strangled sobs. I comforted her with hugs, pleading with her to calm down. Boo pulled away blubbering, saying she needed me, couldn't exist without me, loved me, wanted me to stay with her. The girl had it bad and I had to make a decision. As Boo clung to me again, I felt the wad pressing up against my thigh. It didn't take long to tell Boo not to worry, I wouldn't desert her, I'd stand by her, go over to Betty's Monday to pick up my stuff.

After an idyllic weekend pampered by Boo, I finally went over to Betty's, getting a frosty reception. I told Betty sorry but I had to move back with Boo. Betty didn't wait for excuses.

"It's because Boo's got money."

I felt truthful for once.

"Yes, I guess that's right."

I pulled out the wad, peeling her off a few notes. Betty didn't refuse but made a comment about me only liking rich girls. Typical, after all, Betty came from a wealthy family herself, the mother being an author. I left a few things, telling her I'd be back at a later date. Betty didn't raise any objections so I guessed I could pop over anytime I fancied.

Having re-established in the happy home, I found myself forced to adopt certain precautions. After the flying money incident Boo went into work, emotional. Daddy noticed something wrong, wrung the story out of her, then went into predictable melodramatics.

"You go with rubbish! Why?"

Boo now felt embarrassed, guilty about taking the rubbish back indoors, arranging a phone code. I wouldn't answer the blower on the off chance Daddy rang. Anybody else had to ring, hang up immediately, ring again straight away. For the rest of the year I settled back into the accustomed comfort. Boo was overjoyed to have me back but even I couldn't figure out why. The only service I had to deliver came two or three times a week, the old bedroom duties. Back with the rail regular, the market folk were all glad to see me.

The Christmas period became a carbon copy of the others, this time however, the only Turkey served up came crisp and brown from the oven complete with trimmings. As for myself, I fired on all cylinders, felt as fit as a fiddle, able to satisfy Boo. I'd lost weight and my quiff became four inches of well-combed jet black Pekinese tail. Loader, in the meanwhile, resurfaced, out from the bin. I met him in a friend's house, us laughing, joking about the previous year's adventures and the unhappy aftermath. Loader claimed ECT helped him out. The zapping seemed to have performed the oracle, this being the Loader of old, surrounded by women friends. Loader also heard on the murky grapevine that Redd now resided in the nick. Wondered why I hadn't seen him about.

Boo started thinking that maybe the rail wasn't such a good idea. Before, the money went on gear, now I juiced it in the local bars. Boo didn't like this one iota. Nothing to do with economic considerations, more like it giving me the opportunity to converse with other women in a relaxed social atmosphere. This suspicion soon encompassed my chatting with female customers on the rail, her thinking I'd be asking them for phone numbers, addresses. She started hunting for clues, glancing at my collar for lipstick smudges, sniffing for the scent of perfume, scanning new numbers in my phone book. Boo had also taken alarm at my evolution into a lush, a consequence of which was gaining weight. She seriously suggested to me that I start taking elocution lessons, her footing the bill. I felt insulted by this. If anything, both my comprehension and vocabulary had increased considerably over the years. Even now, I avoided profanities in my everyday banter, thus adding to my charm.

I'd put two and two together. Boo was trying to measure me up for a nine to five, probably, once it had all been squared up with Daddy, in the family business. So I had to be presentable, speak in the correct mode. The whole idea being ludicrous plus those constant reminders led to me losing my cool. I snapped at Boo.

"Okay! What do the words procrastination, impalpable, subsistence mean?"

Unable to provide a single explanation, one solitary word, Boo conceded defeat on that point. In reality I'd outwitted her on all scores, knowing only too well the difference between vocabulary and her true target, my accent. Subversion shifted on to another level, with Boo starting to hold out on the dresses before she delivered her follow-up punch.

"The new Mackie D's are looking for staff, Dan."

The penny dropped. This unsubtle hint dropped in her idiot baby talk was that I should get a job in the new Macdonalds opening in the High Street. Countering this suggestion, I told Boo about Third World exploitation including deforestation upon which I blamed Macdonalds. Unable to understand this concept, I simplified the matter for her, picking up Horace, sarcastically aping the stupid coy voice.

"See Horace? Little tail, little head and paws? Well, do you know what goes into their burgers? The whole cow. Head, tail, hooves, the lot."

Boo seemed shocked by this revelation, her being an animal lover despite her pride and joy of a mink coat. I mimicked the mincing process, holding Horace upside down. Nothing further mentioned on the subject, I'd skillfully avoided the vexed question of employment. Boo had taken to laying in packets of coke, two of them representing a week's wages at Macdonalds, to counter my boozing. She meant to keep me at home, the sex life going and to sober me up. But after mention of that job I needed a drink pronto. I drew out a packet from her stashbox.

"See this stuff? About two kids died in Latin America to provide you with this. It's the same as Mackie D's. I'm going out for a drink. Have a toot yourself, I prefer good clean liquor."

Off I stormed, confident I'd captured the moral high ground, that I'd enjoy a good night's boozing. And as if Boo herself would have lasted more than a week at Macdonalds. As for living on the pay ...

It seemed almost everyone I knew who was unemployed, even friends of friends, turned up Saturday afternoon to the magic rail or the pub where I'd sup to keep out seasonal chills. Never able to hang on to money for any length of time, I'd stand drinks for all comers until three o'clock closing. People were feeding off me but I didn't care, given my attitude to money. I started getting to know Mark a lot better. He'd always been on the fringes of my scene since the dip show days. Mark himself was far from handsome, ginger hair soaped up into wings, looking like a dosser, about Loader's age bracket, middle-class but very much the lower end of the spectrum. We hit it off owing to our similar Cockney Irish cultural background. More educated than me in the formal sense, ex-art college, I'd become impressed by his ability to wax lyrical. Mark earned his drinks bending ears. Like me, he also had a reputation for being uncompromising and slightly individualistic in his behaviour.

Mark also appeared to be undergoing the beginnings of what I understood could result in a nervous breakdown, me enlightening him about my own experiences in the loony world. Mark's thought patterns somewhat drifted, him dabbling in contemporary religions ranging from Alice Bailey to Ron Hubbard. Ron's scribblings made the greatest impression. In Mark's confused state of mind, he believed this to be his final stint on earth, having knocked around in previous lives. Mark had once stumbled across a pictorial history of the Wild West, his attention drawn to the photograph of Billy the Kid. That clicked. His previous life. All that from a superficial resemblance. I advised Mark later that he'd best keep this revelation to himself, a lot of people might not understand associations made when flipping your wig. In spite of encroaching lunacy we formed a bond, me desperate for intellectual stimulation. Mark popped up at the rail, keeping me company during slack periods. I acted as his benefactor.

On a slow rainy Saturday Mark brought a crowd of people to the rail that he'd been putting up at his small flat in Holborn. Loader, Justin and some others. Downcast, miserable weatherwise, I hadn't taken much cash so I had to stay by the rail, whip up custom while Mark and the others drifted off to Camden Lock. I'd clocked a stranger amongst them, a swarthy individual who seemed friendly enough. Justin remembered him from the punk days, introducing me to Mario. Hours later as the drizzle wore off Mario turned up again, this time alone. Offering Mario a can from my charity pile, he declined, opening up his coat instead, lifting his shirt. Concealed underneath, a woman's handbag. Mario gave me an evil leer.

"Stick this in your pocket chum."

Mario handed over the purse which I automatically slipped next to my slim wedge. Meanwhile he'd delivered the handbag to oblivion, throwing it into the teeth of a dustcart crusher. Mario bowled over to the rail grinning.

"Your mate Justin got the horrors, ran off."

This guy was an old fashioned bag snatcher. I understood such matters. As Justin had annoyed me in the recent past, with Mario mumbling something about letting him have a cut, I chipped in.

"Fuck him mate. You took it, you keep it."

This pleased Mario. Here was someone who understood the business. I advised him not to linger in the area for too long. He asked me what poison I went in for so I told him I'd always been partial to a bit of speed.

"You got a bit of paper Dan?"

Fumbling, I located a losing betting slip. Mario wrote out the address of a bent doctor in Hornsey Road.

"Bent as a two bob watch this geezer. It'll cost you forty quid for sixty Durophet but you can flog 'em for two quid each and he'll bung you sixty Valium on top."

Mario shot off, me tucking the information into the back pocket, deciding to do the rail a while longer. Twenty minutes after this encounter, Justin arrived, looking like he'd seen a ghost. Justin told me the Mario character was a maniac, claiming that he'd been threatened for refusing to provide cover for the blatant nicking. As the others returned, I built up a picture of Mario. Off his head, into violence, spent most of his life in borstal and prison. Even his nickname, Mario the mugger. Mario seemed harmless enough compared to some of the charmers I'd met, so I didn't give it a second thought. Later at home, I tucked away the doctor's address for future reference.

I paid visits to Justin's flat, which owing to his filthy habits, stunk to high heaven, flies everywhere, even in winter, empty Kentucky Fried Chicken boxes, chip packets. This, mingled with a musty odour of semen. The only ornamentation provided came from mountains of empty Codeine bottles, some balanced upside down, waiting for dregs to filter down into the caps. A reminder of what I'd escaped from. I still lectured Justin on the rewards awaiting once the shadow of the devil had been cast out, the soul cleansed. With his present frustrated lifestyle, he wanted in particular to hear about the money and women that would become available once he'd kicked the habit. From my own experience, I guaranteed rebirth, so Justin made the decision to call a halt. It wouldn't be difficult like shaking off smack. Owing to pecuniary disadvantage he'd already weaned himself down to Codeine. Justin eventually overcome the obstacles, me conversing with him over the phone as he sweated it out. I'd helped him again, not able to figure out why I'd bothered. I must have been his unwitting guardian angel.

Boo now searched me out in pubs after I'd finished the rail, her paranoia concerning rivals from the opposite sex had grown. Screaming matches developed, her getting the odd slapping, bits of china smashed. About this time a wee surprise came through the post, something that coincided with my defensive posturings against Boo's onslaughts. I'd been feeding her the line that I wanted a degree of independence, to live my own life, travel, do my own thing, earn my own money – ironic, considering my dependence on the rail. While she chewed over these statements, I gained breathing space during her now more determined attempts to control and remould. Boo went along with these vague suggestions in order not to cause a ruction and continue to hold on to me. Goodness knows why. The letter said I'd been allocated a flat in a house, care of West Hampstead housing co-op. A ground floor one bedroom affair. I shot down to the co-op offices, picked up the keys, went off to look at my new abode. And what a shock I got. Upon entry, an alsation dog menaced me, a Scotsman restraining the creature. Inside the flat, the living room looked okay, plastered, bay windows, but the rest was nothing more than a glorified Ridinghouse Street. Bare bricks, floorboards missing. The rest of the house had a familiar whiff to it, a junkie den. One look at the geezer and his straggly missus who came downstairs convinced me of this. Despite the decrepit state of the place and tenants, I thought it might provide a good rendezvous for future amorous liaisons. Besides, I'd still be availing myself of the creature comforts back at Boo's. I could also camp here in times of friction. Loader came over to survey the dump. His opinion, the place was a virtual write-off, impossible to effect any lasting repair. Nevertheless, I did get a few things together, folding collapsible bed, mattress, a couple of chairs and a scrap of carpet. I went back to the co-op, said I'd take it, paying a couple of weeks in advance. As the rent only came to six pounds a week, it didn't exactly break the bank. In reality, I wasn't in any great hurry to give up my space in Boo's nest. Most of my property remained there but I gave her the pretence I'd really move in, that Loader would help me decorate.

Loader went up to the bent doctor in Hornsey Road. As he looked older, grey hair, respectable, it seemed better to play it safe. Loader came back to the rail beaming. He wasn't one for speed but knew I'd be pleased with the result. He held a legal script for sixty Durophet, black bombers, concentrated amphetamine in time-release capsules. Loader went to Boots, arriving back with two bottles. Dropping one bomber each, we had a strong but mellow high.

The following day, I took a trip down to Hornsey Road. The doctor's name, Nico, stood out on a copper plate, complete with the letters denoting his professional qualifications. The surgery was set in a modern low level concrete complex, inside on the walls more qualifications in Greek and English. I told the receptionist I wanted to see doctor Nico privately. She gave me a dirty look but made the arrangements. With only a couple of elderly patients waiting, I got seen quickly. Doctor Nico himself stood behind his desk, a small stout balding man with a white coat and regulation stethoscope hanging from his neck. Doctor Nico addressed me in a thick Greek accent.

"What is it you want?"

"Durophet."

"Durophet? … Let me see …"

He asked my age, I told him the truth, twenty six, adding embellishments, lying now about how I did the same job as the guy who'd come over the other day, Mr Loader, that we worked together in the theatre, our job involving driving, travelling, mostly at night. I pulled out a wedge, flicking the notes.

"I believe it's forty pounds."

This fellow didn't waste any time.

"Yes, forty pounds."

As I slid the cash across his polished desk, past medical promos, he wrote the prescriptions which he then handed over, asking me a question.

"Which chemist you go to?"

"One at King's Cross."

"Good. Don't go next door, never to the one next door."

With that precaution out of the way, I left telling him I'd be back in a month. I'd hit on to something good here.

I tried punting the amazing bombers about but had trouble convincing would-be customers. Never mind, more for me. Taking them made me glow. I looked polished, gleaming like I'd come out of the Betty Ford clinic. The Bombers did wonders for my sex life, keeping Boo happy for a while a least. One by-product of that increased libido enabled me to shop around for women, not worrying about any consequences. If you took a whole bomber, the time release capsules had the effect of bringing the buzz on in waves. They took an hour, then my head exploded, blood rushing through the system, sheer excitement pumping along the veins. Ultra confidence burst forth, I could do anything and more all at once. Chatting up, getting laid, solving people's problems, drink volumes while remaining in total control. As everybody else on the bandwagon lay around steaming drunk, I'd monopolise the bar, ordering drinks, opening cab doors for the ladies as the bombers came on in waves. For an hour or so I'd be witty, discursive, mellow out for another hour or so listening intently before yet another wave of pure energy came surging. People didn't know you were on weed owing to the deceptive phases of relaxation. The effect lasted a whole day.

Mark now became generally accepted as Billy the Kid by the population of drunks, druggies and various hangers on, giving him a sort of right to get away nth the most outrageous statements and behaviour. Mark gave me the impression that in spite of his eccentricities such as ignorance of soap and water, apart from that slapped on his ginger barnet, he was a true survivor. Armed with usual verbal skills and a dirty appearance, Mark was an enigma to the others. He certainly had the gift of the gab, meeting people on the streets at random like an Irish dustman who'd read Voltaire, this being good for a couple of drinks having a chinwag. Mark was on his own personal bender, the bombers adding to the merry-go-round.

So by now a typical day would see me dropping a bomber in the morning, after setting up the rail, Loader or Mark would turn up, drinks then flowed, so by three, I'd have swigged six pints of strong lager and an equal number of whisky chasers. Back to the rail, drop another bomber, collect money, sell the remainder of the dresses. If coming up on the bomber I'd sometimes throw a wobbler, jumping up and down on a dress during an altercation with a customer trying to bargain me down. Arriving home high, I'd walk Horace, clean the flat out and when Boo got back a dinner would be on the go.

Having my own place, with the possibility that I could always move there permanently if necessary, helped keep Boo in line. Though I'd moved some gear inside, I hardly ever visited the place, having become accustomed to the Crescent home comforts. Going over one day, just to check on things, I noticed the Alsation had raided my room, chewing up my clothes and a pair of shoes. The Scottish geezer came down, full of apologies, asking me up to his rooms. He seemed nervous, distracted by my clean glowing look, mistaking me for being young and straight. Upstairs, suspicions were confirmed. Codeine bottles, zombie girlfriend, couch and carpet peppered with cigarette burns, futile attempts at domesticity, mismatched furniture. I broke the ice, mentioning certain pharmaceuticals, dropping hints I'd been a junkie as I talked about rock music. This helped them establish my age, them thinking me to be a lad of eighteen who'd just left home. Now things changed, they both readily chatted about drugs, which, if there isn't any about for consumption, can be boring.

"Do you remember Chinese Rocks?"

He saw my interest drifting.

"Wait, I wanna show you something, wait till you see this man."

He pulled out a copy of the *Sunday Mail* from the chest of drawers. This contained a story about the variety of illegal drugs available in London and an introductory photograph with a caption 'THIS MAN SELLS HEROIN'.

The man pictured lived above, in the top flat. I read the article, a full four page spread. A reporter had been hanging around in the London drug scene, or part of it – being so extensive in Camden alone, it really could have filled several fat encyclopedia volumes. The article dealt with where you could obtain drugs in London. Glue sniffing at King's Cross, cocaine in Chelsea, ganja smoking in Brixton, heroin in darkest Kilburn. This part of the story contained information, including the photo of the guy upstairs and the names of the junkie couple I sat with. Thrown in for good measure, another photo that clearly showed our door number and my bay windows. The Scottish bloke protested.

"Look at this lad, they didn't even spell my name right."

So this was my new would-be home, probably police in plainclothes staking the place out in cars over the road. Leaving soon after, I realised this dump should be used by me for extreme emergencies only, such as the odd bit of horizontal recreation, nothing more.

Doing the rail one sunny Saturday afternoon, something hit me out of the blue. Before me stood the Dutch girl, Marie, all smiles, and female friend. Marie gushed, friendly, all pearly white teeth. I arranged to call for her next day, Loader had been putting them up, screwing her friend. I told Boo I was going to the flat, do some improvements, might stay the night. Hours later I threw a small exclusive party with the girls and Loader at the co-op flat, rustling together dope, lots of booze, bombers and a radio cassette. I acted fast and furious under the influence of this heady cocktail, having a great time. Marie still loved me, staying when the others left. She'd been shocked by my presumed living conditions, unaware I lived in the lap of luxury back at Boo's. Blowing out the candle, putting on her favourite cassette, I gave her what she wanted and come over for. Marie departed the gloomy flat in the morning while I crept back to Boo. I maintained the juggling act for a couple more days, making plans to visit Marie later in the year. I also had a couple of drunken one night stands with fat barmaids. This just about represented my only sojourns in this dump of a place.

When Marie departed for Holland, Boo also left, off to a fashion show in Milan, leaving me with half a rail of dresses and a half bottle of bombers. I expected her back in a few days with cartons of cigarettes, bottles of booze and clothes from the top designers in Europe. Within twelve hours of Boo's departure, I'd sold the rail contents, launching a booze and bombers binge with the takings. I hit town sporting a gift from a previous trip, a black woollen blazer. Sitting dominating the bar, surrounded by drinks, I heard that old Barney Rubble voice.

"Danny boy!"

I spun around, throwing the arms up in mock greeting. "Redd!"

He seemed to have gone a bit on the downward slide, seven o'clock shadow, droopy mac, long but now receding hair swept back, baggy eyes. Redd smiled, pointing to my blazer.

"Daniel Hechter."

I offered him a drink.

"How's Boo?"

"Gone to Milan, Redd."

He didn't seem all that interested in the drink. A sudden inspiration fuelled by memories of times gone by and the bombers came into play.

"Redd, do you know where we can get some gear?"

He pretended he didn't want any. I knew this game backwards.

"Redd, like I said, Boo's in Milan, I've got money, let's get a cab and we'll have a relaxing evening."

Within a few short breaths, Redd phoned a cab, we were on our way. I didn't even for a moment pause to reflect that I'd given up. One fix couldn't do any harm. Later, back at Boo's nest, I prepared water for the syringe, then rolled up my sleeve. Opening the packet, I examined the gear with expert eyes.

"Good looking stuff you've got us there Redd."

Then I shoved half the packet into a spoon. Despite not having a fix for nearly a year and a half, I had no trouble locating a vein. Instant hit. Redd had slipped into my blazer, wandering about examining the flat. The fix made me feel dizzy, strong stuff indeed, puking beer into the bogs, overcome with that pleasurable feeling, then sat down in the living room after splashing my face with cold water. In the fuzzy distance, Redd echoed as if in a dream.

"Hey! Are you alright Dan?"

Soon I felt soaking wet, blurred confusion, being hauled around the room, slapped on the face.

"Danny! ... Danny! ... Snap out of it! ... Come on ... I've called an ambulance."

The doorbell rang, me snapping out of it, back into the living world. I went downstairs, opened the door, chatting cool as can be with the ambulance men, explaining everything was alright, the call had been made by a drunk at a party. They didn't argue, this was the respectable Crescent, not a council estate and left. After this performance, I pulled myself upstairs, once inside, I collapsed again into a pinned heap. I woke up early in the morning from a semi-coma. No doubt about it, I'd overdosed. The bombers had saved me, kept me alive throughout my collapse. Still smacked out of my skull, I gazed into the mirror. No eyes, more puking. I saw a dirty crumpled mac laying on the floor, my blazer gone. Redd must have left me for dead, making off with my blazer into the bargain. Redd had moved back with his parents in their flat at King's Cross, so there I went, fuming. About ten in the morning I knocked on their door. Redd, wearing a kimono, a remnant from his Hampstead days, answered the door, letting me in, taking me into his bedroom, coming out with lame excuses.

"But Dan, you said I could swap it for the mac."

I didn't bother to argue, merely handing back his grubby offering, while he surrendered the blazer, looking crestfallen. Leaving after the formalities of exchange, I resolved never to backslide again. On the way out, I'd swear Redd's old man still wore one of those Biba shirts.

CHAPTER TWELVE

Boo came back from the fashion show with my usual gifts. She had a project in hand that involved filming a fashion show for prospective buyers of the new range Daddy's company were bringing out. The video was produced by a friend of Boo's who studied at the Royal College of Art. I found myself forced to endure the tape several times until one day during an idle moment, I viewed the film privately on the video machine, puffing on a joint. Rather than the fashion show itself, I wanted to look at the section that had always been fast forwarded. This part featured the factory up North. Dozens of machinists, mostly female employees, toiled away at their benches, creating wealth for Boo's family. Some wore the very dresses I sold on the rail, discounted rewards for suitable deference, pliancy or over-fulfilling quotas. Boo put in a cameo, wandering up and down the passages, pausing to check finished products. I remembered how I'd always hated the boss's pampered offspring swanning around, doubting if the situation was very much different here. Boo explained to the camera what the employees were doing. I also remembered how she'd cracked up there, having to be brought back home to run her punk shops. But these workers had no choice in the matter, couldn't afford the luxury of a nervous breakdown. Some of the machinists glanced up from their toils as if resenting the intrusion, others demonstrated deference.

"Hello Boo."

A shot of the charge-hand trying to look busy revealed a chain of smoke from a concealed cigarette behind his back. He put on a cheery face amongst the whirring noise of the machines. All this told me more about the reality of the business than any fashion show or shop talk after Boo came home evenings. Factories up North pay lower wages, people slaving away for eight hours or more a day. And here was I, a kept man, going out with the boss's daughter. An outside shot of the factory said it all, more eloquent than words. A bleak building, cross between a barracks and prison. The video gave me more of an idea how much power Boo had, that one day she might be running the whole shebang.

I'd been hanging about more with Mark, or Billy the Kid as he preferred to be called. We decided one Thursday, when I described Maastricht, to go. The very next day, to be precise. I thought what the hell, why not? Neglecting to inform Boo about this decision, I guessed that if I vanished for a few days she'd believe me to be decorating the flat. Friday, I took all the money collected on the rail and left, taking my passport and some bombers. Dropping some early on, by the time we reached the boat we were well off our heads, me going into the duty-free, ripping off two hundred camels and a bottle of vodka. No trouble at all, bombers working their magic. Maybe too well. As we gulped down the pilfered vodka, Mark started to lose control, dancing around the boat like a headless chicken, shouting and screaming. A few complaints must have been registered because upon landing at Ostend, the crew detained us, held for some undisclosed damage inflicted while Mark did his whirling dervish number. They bunged us up in a cabin, confiscating the duty-frees I'd lifted. Neglecting to search us, I held on to the bombers. By midnight we found ourselves undergoing repatriation.

The rail continued but I couldn't help thinking that pressure for gainful employment would be forthcoming yet again, so I made a conspicuous display of visits to the job centre, looking for gardening work. All an act, of course. Justin, upon giving up the opiates, started his own dope business. I saw him intermittently, noticing he'd turned cleaner in both appearance and personal habits. Nothing short of a miracle. The old routine continued. Bomber binges, entertaining Boo and her wooden-headed friends back at the flat, going out with Boo to wine bars, restaurants, movies. We were the happy couple again. Loader now always seemed to be around, which was okay by me, Boo preferring him to the likes of grubby Mark and Justin. And at least, in line with Boo's priorities, Loader worked, albeit spasmodically, at his trade of handyman. Back on the never-ending rail of fortune, I expanded business by going down Ridley Road market, Hackney, with Loader. We'd collapse the rail into sections, stuff the dresses into plastic rubbish sacks and catch the train from Camden Road. Our dresses went like hot cakes in this part of the world.

One Monday before going to Ridley Road me and Loader went for an early breakfast, leaving Boo to be last out of the flat. I'd lost my key and, being one of those written permission security things, we hadn't bothered to get a replacement yet and shared hers. Boo left a note on the door saying where she'd concealed it, usual place, under the flower pots. Loader spotted a figure snooping near the door, reading Boo's note as we returned. Getting closer, I saw it was none other than Mario the Mugger. Not a moment too soon. We were diplomatic, inviting Mario in for a tea. Loader offered a bomber which Mario dropped straight away.

"I see you've been to Doctor Nic then."

Mario joined us for our journey to Ridley Road, managing to get thrown out of a pub after a violent struggle. One pint and the man was steaming, eyes expanded increasing his already manic glare, the kind that signalled danger. We fobbed Mario off with vague promises about seeing him again, whereas we'd decided to steer clear for keeps.

For a while, back home in the domestic situation, I played it cool, doing the rail, placating Boo with my carefully measured charm dollops, on the surface fitting into her scene, which meant doing party rounds. A time of suppressed yawns. At least Loader proved to be more than passing interest, him being quick off the mark, smart and most folks liked him. After a few weeks of self-enforced domesticity, time came for another bomber party. So the following weekend I stayed out with Loader, ending up in Archway with a couple of girls we knew, June and Vi. Loader had use of a car so we rounded off the weekend at Vi's parent's house in Hampstead. Ironically the wheel turned full circle again, this place being opposite Boo's mother's flat. Our weekend of drugs and sex finished, Loader drove me home. Before pulling up in the Crescent, we both looked down to the floor of our vehicle where evidence of our naughty weekend chinked together, an empty Durophet and rum bottle, causing us to erupt into a giggling fit.

On the drive back, I'd had a memory jolt, telling Loader how I'd met the bearded lady a couple of days previously, seen she'd winged herself shaving. I'd also remembered something else, a tale she'd related to me. Clarissa had been living in a flat, sharing with a posh woman near Euston. This woman had been raped a couple of months ago at the Notting Hill carnival. Displaying a lack of common sense, the fool had been lured into a house off Portobello Road to score some ganja. There, she'd been raped by six heavy dudes, the unhappy experience upsetting her to the extent of losing her marbles, taking to painting her ears blue, sort of an association from art school days. Finally flipping in New York, this Cynthia became a resident of Belle Vue hospital. Now their joint flat had become empty, owing to the bearded lady not fancying the prospect of living alone in a block in Somerstown, the place being full of junkies, drunks, squatters and Europunks doing their number years out of date. In other words, this flat was empty, going to remain so. All we had to do would be gain residency, pay the token rent. Only one obstacle blocked the way – the posh Cynthia's mum who had to be persuaded into handing over the key Clarissa had given her. We agreed between us before I'd stepped out of the car that Loader would be better equipped to handle that delicate operation than me. Being in a bomber-induced state of mind, party time looming, I told Loader I fancied moving in there if trouble back home flared up with Boo.

That night I slept on the couch, Boo in a deep sulk. Words were useless. Come morning I phoned Loader. Hours later, we drove to the flat, clocking it from the outside. The place wasn't all that bad, standard thirties council block. Meeting with our approval, Loader drove us straight to the mother's workplace, somewhere in the City, up in the heights of an imposing office building. Communication had been established by Loader that very morning by phone, acting upon information gleaned from the bearded lady. Over the phone, Loader claimed to be a good friend of Cynthia and was here over from business in New York. While Loader strode into the building, I waited in a pub. Loader emerged shortly after, smiling, spinning the key into the air. I knew he'd pulled it off, aided by his best suit, shining grey hair, pleasant bedside manner. He'd spun her a repeat of the yarn crooned down the phone. The mother had been charmed by Loader, who experienced great difficulty keeping a straight face after seeing a photo of darling daughter on her desk. Loader said he'd have recognised it quicker had the ears been coloured blue. Loader reassured the mother with some drolleries masquerading as wisdom.

"Don't worry about Cindy. You can only go so far in the woods, then she'll see a light shining from a clearing. She'll be out in the open soon."

As she thrust the key over into his hand, she gazed into Loader's eyes.

"I do wish Cynthia knew more people like you."

Loader gave her a flash of his perfect set of pearly whites, pegging back the urge to collapse in hysterics. Instead, he promised to look after the flat, pay the rent. We zoomed back to Euston, slipped the key into the lock. Looking around inside, we found the bearded lady's bedroom next to the living room. Upstairs, the other bedroom. The place itself looked a bit of a shambles, everything covered in dust, electricity not functioning. The girls had been more camping than living here for two years. I went upstairs to examine Cynthia's room. Packed with clothes, mostly costumes from a sale, books piled up, phoney tomes on matters artistic, mattresses, duvet plus her works of art, sculptures, oil paintings stacked up in a corner. The living room had furniture piled in the centre. It all looked fairly bleak from outside but under the dust were all the amenities. I found tins of dog food, reminding Loader of something else the mother said. Cynthia had a greyhound named Jock, now in care of the people next door. It would now become our responsibility, small price to pay. Loader looked around, said he could do all repairs, get the juice working again. In all, this place was ideal, it would only take a couple of days graft to get things shipshape. I'd then move in with Loader. One small detail remained. Boo.

I came back to Boo's in the evening. Storm clouds had gathered then Boo's pent-up fury broke loose. She demanded to know what I'd been doing over the weekend. And today. The crunch had come. Despite comfortable living, easy rail money, I felt I'd boxed myself into a corner, become trapped, particularly since Boo had been more clingy than usual. I'd had to endure her idiot friends twittering on about their work and even tired of cosseted visits to restaurants, wine bars. And the stinking now almost totally incontinent dog, naggings, propaganda conveyed in stupid baby talk about me becoming gainfully employed, trying to fit me into her procrustean duvet. I came off the ropes after she'd thrown all the verbals at me, probably trying for a violent reaction so we could make it up afterwards as we'd done too many times. Then the situation would be as before, a happy couple again. I didn't fudge the issue, telling Boo I didn't need her handouts, I'd got myself a flat, there were many possibilities in the air for me, that I wanted to live my own life again. And yes, I was on the start of a divine bender. Boo called my bluff, so off I went with my luggage, all the stuff she'd bought me, clothes, shoes, into a black plastic bag, bound for Euston and glory, Dick Whittington in reverse, leaving the Crescent paved with gold.

I took the blue-eared nutter's room at the top; Loader, the bearded lady's den. We cleared up in earnest, spirit of salts in the bogs, sink and bath until they shone like Loader's teeth. Under dust and rubbish, we unearthed mod cons, most of which were in working order, cooker, fridge, black and white telly. Within a couple of days a real coal fire blazed in the grate alongside hoovered carpets. Home. I threw out the last black plastic bag containing Immac hair remover tubes, a final bearded lady legacy. We took the greyhound Jock from next door, the neighbours turning out to be junkies. Jock never had it so good, best pedigree foods, walks, rug, coal fire roaring. Financially, we were down to a dole cheque each a fortnight. We ate well however, plundering local supermarkets. Our lifestyle appeared relaxed, civilised, playing chess, listening to records, watching the odd good forties movie on the telly. Drugs were the same, washed down with a little drink. Loader dressed up in the costumes. He'd taken to wearing a green cape with resplendent false gold chain, walking into supermarkets, huge carrier bags harnessed to his shoulders concealed underneath. In this get-up, Loader looked like a distinguished stage actor. Meanwhile, I'd stroll into the supermarket with Jock on a lead. Staff and managers would rush over, shooing me and the dog out. I argued while Loader slipped the best and most expensive food into the bags before checking out on the till with a loaf and pint of milk. Sometimes we'd swap roles, Loader holding the dog, me wearing one of Boo's gifts, an Italian overcoat doctored with nicking slits. All the goodies automatically fell into the bottom lining, including whole cooked chickens.

Many visitors turned up at first, including Justin with samples from his new dope-dealing business. Plus the odd weirdo, one in question being the ex-ladykiller Antonio. Now he looked the absolute nutcase, worse than when I'd seen him in the market. Shaved head, knee-high yellow boots, shorts, woolly jumper, tucked under his arm-loads of gay magazines. Loader found Antonio in a bar and collecting strays as a hobby, brought him back to the flat. I quickly drew Loader aside, telling him this fellow had lost his mind on acid way back. As the cupboard was full, we dished him up a feast. Once Antonio had stuffed himself silly, he had the nerve to start complaining, slagging us off for imaginary misdemeanours, raising his voice in that dreadful arrogant matter unique to his social background. This jarred, us giving Antonio the red card. Once we'd turfed the wretch out he returned for his magazines. Tiring of the shrieking outside our door, we finally saw him off with a hammer, stashing the mags in the bog for entertainment or confusion of visitors. I told Loader no more nutters around here please. He wholeheartedly concurred. Who needs them?

Christmas drew closer once again, I hadn't seen Boo for well over a month. I felt I'd escaped suffocation, made a home of sorts. The greyhound-in-supermarket ruse dried up so we quit when ahead on points, staying indoors more, eating less. Without so many goodies, we found our stream of visitors reduced to a trickle. I started to sell some of the expensive clothing Boo had bought me from Paris and Milan, taking what cash I could get, which wasn't much. Apart from clothes and shoes, all I had was a Walkman and camera but I wasn't willing to part with these. We amused ourselves weekends attending all night warehouse parties, our most frequent visitor, June who stayed overnight with Loader, a busy chap who'd also entertain other females during the week. We were poor but having a good time, girls coming over to see me on occasion.

A couple of weeks before Christmas, me, Loader and June went to a warehouse party near the Cross. Here we did the usual, meeting people we knew, having a laugh, right through to the early hours. Sipping from cans, hanging around near the entrance, we noticed the stocky figure of Mario the mugger strolling in alone. Dressed in Farrah trousers and camel coat, Mario glanced furtively around, nodding to a few people. We went over to greet him, bearing in mind we'd blown him out on previous occasions. Mario packed tons of speed so we ended up buzzing, finally heading over to Brick Lane market on an early tube. During this journey, June noticed Mario trying to slip his hand into a few pockets. This freaked her, so she made excuses and left. Come lunchtime, being at a loose end, we invited Mario back to our gaff. Mario had been the perfect gentleman throughout, polite, well mannered and behaved, apart from his abortive dips. Arriving back home, now coming down off the speed, we all felt the need for a drink while showing Mario the place. He liked the costumes and paintings, even knew the bearded lady from various scenes he'd popped up in around the West End. The subject of conversation drifted to our need to relieve the terrible thirst arising from the speed aftermath. None of us had money but Mario said he'd nip out for awhile, see what he could rustle up from the shops. Quarter of an hour later Mario returned after we'd got a fire going, fed Jock and started a game of chess. Pieces scattered as a handbag landed on the board. Looking up, Mario wore that devilish grin. Snatching it back, he emptied the contents on to our ruined game. A few pens, address book, cheque book, two credit cards, little bottle of perfume, tissues and forty quid in cash. Mario flicked through the address book.

"Always good for a bit of blackmail, lads."

The woman's name turned out to be Lesley Watkins, checkpoint number in the address book as usual. Some people never learn. Loader said we'd hit the jackpot;

this name could be that of a boy or girl, starting to practice the signature. Off we trooped to a pub. Once we'd refreshed ourselves, Mario told us he'd snatched the bag from a pub up the road after visiting two other pubs previously. Third time lucky he'd spotted an unattended handbag on a stool, bunged it under his coat then out in a flash. This geezer certainly operated quickly. Many pints later, Mario dominated the pool table, being an excellent player of this game. We asked Mario to stay the night, him accepting readily. I sensed this would be more than a one night stopover. Next morning, me and Loader went through the exercises we'd kept up sporadically since the born again days. Mario regarded himself as an expert in such matters having worked out in the nick. So we all went through the rigmarole together, using chairs. Sit ups, press ups, bicep exercises. Mario had meanwhile had fallen in love with Jock, taking him out for a two mile run.

As expected, the overnight stay stretched into a week. Mario, I'd noticed, was fond of singing his own praises. He'd done everything in the criminal catalogue, robberies, raiding homes, tying the victims up, guns, sub post offices. He'd also beaten up the love of his life, Suzy, kidnapped her. We were, he stated with conviction, his only real friends, the only people who'd treated him right. Mario had no mates, hadn't engaged in sex for a year. I couldn't help feeling a touch disturbed by these revelations, not wanting to be sitting on a time-bomb primed to go off anytime. Loader however, looked upon things differently, impressed by what he considered to be such blinding honesty to us, his friends. Mario proved himself a laugh sure enough, but I couldn't help regarding him as a potential danger. In spite of this, I wasn't scared of him, although I was more than aware he could tear me apart. But all such considerations aside, we were rekindling our bender, this was no time to be jumping off the merry-go-round.

As regards the cheques, Loader had everything down to a tee, dressing up in his good suit with brolly, briefcase, bowler hat. We'd walk down to Camden Town, hitting up a corner shop where Loader went in alone ordering a case of Swan Lager, carton of Benson for Mario, Marlborough for us. Then, as a parting shot, Loader pointed his brolly to the spirits section picking out two bottles of Blue Label vodka. Once the cheque had been signed, our goodies were bundled into a taxi then driven back to Euston. This went on for four consecutive days. Mario also liked dope, so there would always be a stash on hand but the main poison on this bender turned out to be booze. Getting back from the shop, we'd measure up tall glasses, knocking back the vodka in one, followed by lagers then more vodka. Fully steamed, we'd muck about until nine in the evening, head for a pub where we'd pay for drinks with a cheque. Pool was the big thing with Mario. He'd play all comers for money but, should he lose, he'd refuse to cough up, getting heavy with all the poses, screwing his face into grotesque shapes. This usually served as a warning to all but the most foolhardy. Mario also constantly got into arguments with bar staff, while simultaneously keeping a lookout for stray handbags which he called dummies for some obscure reason. Once Mario tired of pool we'd walk to Mornington Crescent, eat in Greek restaurants.

"They never call the old bill," claimed Mario, referring to the cheque books and cards. Mario seemed to be known in some of these establishments where he'd preside over eating matters like the Godfather, ordering bottles of retsina, followed by a mezze for three. By this time, we'd all be well off our heads, departing in the wee hours back to the Range, our name for the flat.

In our chummy mood we renamed ourselves the Family. Each morning after workouts and aperitifs, we'd clean the place before a day's shoplifting. We'd steal alcohol, then food. If boredom set in, the Family might catch an early afternoon movie up West. For a laugh, we dressed Mario up, using clothes from the extensive costume wardrobe, a cheesecloth dress and cap, wig, lipstick, transforming him into an old Greek tart. Outside Euston station, a couple of drunken Paddies got a shock when they accosted him with a 'how are you fixed for the night shift darling'. Mario reminded us about how he hadn't been laid for a year saying he wished he was gay but knew he wasn't. Loader took this as another example of what he took to be Mario's basic personal honesty with true friends. Just when things started to get tight moneywise, once the final cheque had gone, Mario went out and came back with a wallet. Contents, a small address book, twenty pounds cash, cheque book, card and number on a slip of paper. The ex-owner was a doctor. This had been a lunchtime job, in and out of a wine bar. Loader became the Doctor, three of us going on a Family outing to an upmarket Chinese in Hampstead. We piled straight into the wine, guzzling it down before the meal, a large round of courses. Loader dropped some Valium and this, combined with the drink soon had him reeling, coming back from the bog, he tripped, falling down a spiral staircase. Staff dashed over, enquiring whether he was okay. Loader hauled himself up, brushing his clothes.

"It's alright lads, I'm a doctor."

This Doctor persona didn't last long because once we'd pigged ourselves, we staggered into an off-licence where the manager became suspicious. So we legged it, minus cheque book and card. This didn't make much difference though, as Mario just went out later to snatch another wallet or dummy whenever finances were depleted. Mario would get wound up if he failed to manage a snatch, pacing up and down the living room growling. But he'd soon recover composure, dive out into the streets looking for prey.

We had a few girls back from the pub after closing time and it developed into a little party, smoking weed, drinking, records playing. Me and Loader weren't worried about getting laid but Mario felt he'd been too long in the wilderness, attaching himself to a chubby number who'd been leading him on, making with the darlings, kissing his cheek. They sneaked into Loader's room for a while, then Mario came out smiling, indicating his celibacy was about to be terminated. He picked up a bottle, re-entered the bedroom, clicking the door shut, his loony eyes tuned up. One of her friends leaned over.

"He's alright is he?"

Loader reassured her.

"He's the most emotionally honest geezer I've ever met."

I chimed in, aiming for a touch of realism.

"He's a bit loopy after he's had a few drinks."

A few minutes passed then we all heard piercing screams of panic.

"Help! No! Please!"

Loader's bedroom. We banged on the door.

"Open up Mario! What's going on?"

We barged in, smashing the lock. Mario stood, a kitchen knife in his hand, the girl sitting on the bed, makeup running, in tears, her dress torn. We disarmed Mario gently, whispering to him.

"Don't worry Mario, we'll get you laid before Christmas, trust us."

Meanwhile her girlfriends managed to get her out to the relative safety of our hallway. Mario blubbered pitifully, blaming her.

"The fucking cow let me play with her tits and everything. I was down on her, the lot, thought I'd have a fuck when she went mad, shouting and screaming for nothing."

By now we'd sat him down, seen the girls out. We cooled an emotional Mario out, making him laugh, pouring another drink. Later, upstairs in my room, he demolished one of Blue Ear's sculptures, a bust, carefully removing the face, fashioning himself a mask, which he fixed to his head with a string. Then Mario jumped out on me and Loader wearing the mask and waving the hammer.

"Look boys! Now I look like a real rapist, don't I?"

We agreed, to humour him, sitting down to a nightcap of booze and dope.

After this near-miss rape, Mario got himself a bird, one of Loader's old flames, Sandra. She'd lent us her colour telly for Christmas. Bringing it around, Sandra took a liking to Mario, thinking him a real comedian, having already met him when he dressed as a woman. Loader was going out with June, I wasn't interested and Mario happened to be unattached. Sandra went for him, so that night after drinks, he got off with her. Mario felt pleased as punch in the morning, thanking us for helping get him laid, which we hadn't. With tears welling up in his eyes, Mario told us what wonderful friends we were, talking about changing his life for the better.

Loader however, informed Sandra of Mario's instability but she preferred to ignore this, putting it down to sour grapes. Soon she came over visiting him daily.

Christmas Eve, we put our heads together, planning to make an effort to have a luxury seasonal feast, lifting in an area where we weren't known, Edgeware Road. What with the Christmas rush, it would provide perfect cover. We split up at the station. From Safeways Loader hoisted bottles of vodka, stashing them outside under a pile of rubbish. As I watched him at work, I took a whole frozen turkey, stuffing it down the crutch of my loose trousers, waddling out, hunched in my overcoat filled with the trimmings, into the freezing cold. Here I met Mario who seemed elated.

"I've got some money Dan."

"And I've got the dinner."

We caught a cab with Loader back to the Range. On the table we displayed the booty. Booze, turkey, trimmings. But Mario topped us all, one hundred pounds cash, cheque card and book. He'd snatched this from a hairdressing salon. So out we trekked, spending the cash like honest citizens, buying more treats. Loader went back to the corner shop near Camden Town. They had the familiar order together in a matter of seconds, neither noticing nor caring that he had a different name. Back home at the Range, we spent the evening preparing the grand feast. Christmas morning, Mario presented us with gifts all wrapped up in paper with fancy bows. Loader got a funny face kit, myself a plasticine set. Just what we'd always wanted.

We'd neglected to get Mario anything, very much to our embarrassment, so he sat there looking like a sad kid. Mario cheered up quickly enough though, and we even invited some French punks from the other end of our landing to come over, partake of our feast. They swigged our booze, munched the food, stretched themselves out in front of the telly then launched into an attack on our consumerist attitude, taking Christmas seriously. And where was the dessert? Mario blew his top, throwing them out by the scruff of their necks, supported by the rest of the Family. We just stayed in all day, pigging ourselves, watching the usual crap on telly. After Christmas Day, things began to slide. Physical and mental exhaustion set in due to our prolonged bender. Loader went off to stay with June in Archway, leaving me and Mario together feeling as though our party had shuddered to a temporary halt. Even Mario decided the atmosphere felt stale, took Jock, went to stay at Sandra's for a while. Approaching New Year, I sat alone in the flat, telly gone, no money, reduced to stealing drinks again, meditating on my booze habit.

I popped over to Boo's in order to ponce some money and saw she'd roped in a new boyfriend who also lived in the Crescent – Toby, the publisher's son who toyed with computers. He looked a bit like me if you blinked fast enough. I soon had Boo laughing again. Toby was wary, whereas both Boo and Horace seemed glad to see me. I looked a right state in the aftermath of the bender but loverboy didn't notice, the fellow being head over heels about Boo. Later, when leaving, I knew I was still in with a chance, maybe able to return if I played my cards right. But I'd have to invest some energy and effort into this time, as I'd have to turf out loverboy. By now, both Loader and Mario tired of romance. With New Year's coming on, the Family now functioned at full strength again.

The day before New Year's we were all drinking in a pub near Camden fawn, full of biker types. Loader shone on the pool table, beating regulars hands down. A life of idleness does tend to produce a good player. As the games progressed Mario's eyes roamed, finally settling upon a handbag on the cloakroom rail, next to a leopardskin coat. Mario went over to Loader, indicating to him that we were on to something, that a distraction would be required. Loader gave us the wink, continued to play an excellent game. When he'd reached the final ball, had it lined up, Loader went into the bog, emerging a minute later to rapturous cheers, the crowd wild, clapping, whistling, stamping feet. Apart from socks, Loader stood stark naked. Returning to the table, he potted the black. The landlord wasn't having any of it, dashing from behind the bar, hustling Loader out. Argument erupted.

"Come on mate, leave him."

Despite this, once clothed, Loader found himself on the street. Mario had taken full advantage of the confusion, grabbing the leopardskin coat, wrapping he handbag up in it, sticking the lot under his coat, walking out. Back at the Range, we tipped the contents out on to the table. Photos, fake jewellery, money, cheque cards, books. This would prove a shade more difficult, a Henrietta. Loader tried the signature, attempting to make it appear as a Henry. He admitted we'd have trouble with this one but he'd give it a bash.

New Year passed into another drunken blur.

January is usually the most boring of months, for us however, the bender continued, thanks to the cheque book. The Family, with greyhound in tow, took a trip to Sloane Square. We were dressed to the nines, strolling about until we are to an indoor market, sitting down for coffee. Loader went to an off-licence, returning brandishing a bottle of Jack Daniels. Something to keep out the winter hill. This went into the coffee until several pots later the bottle stood under a chair, empty. Mario insisted on another bottle, so Loader patted the cheque book then dutifully left. Half an hour passed, an hour. No Loader. We were realistic, obviously he'd been nicked, cheque book and all. We left, Mario saying he was off to Sandra's for a few days, taking Jock. I decided to head up to the Archway, see June, explain the situation, after I'd completed a task, disposing of incriminating evidence. Back home at the Range, I smashed some chairs for fuel, got a roaring fire on the go, sprinkling it with white spirit, burning address books, photos, wallets, cards, cheque books. I sat, watching photos of other people's grannies, boyfriends and kids burn. In went the dummies. Fuel included some of the paintings, breaking the frame, ripping canvas. This burnt well, the oils producing vividly coloured flames. After warming myself, poking through the ashes, removing charred metallic scraps, handbag clasps, keys, I scooped them up, placing the remains in a plastic bag once cooled under the tap. On the way to June's, I dumped them in a bin. A rushed job but sufficient.

I returned to the Range. The police had combed the place, things looked different. I lay on the sofa alone, gazing up at the ceiling. Now on the speed comedown, the bender feeling hit me. Above all things, I needed a drink. But it was late at night, no money, all possible sources of booze long closed for the evening. I glanced over to the shelves filled with empty bottles, mostly spirits and wine, one hundred in total, past evidence of the bender. I couldn't believe how much I'd got through and how much I needed one now as I rolled up a smoke from fag butts. My head swam as I reclined, everything going too fast, like just before the time I'd cracked up. An idea. I hauled myself up to drain the dregs from the bottles, filling a pint glass, creating a misty pink concoction, downing it in a couple of lusty gulps, sitting down, eyes watering. I needed to get my blood circulating, even if it meant a walk in the bitter cold. Making my way towards Camden, my head swam again. No one about, dark, dead, thoughts rising in a jumble about the last few weeks. Loader nicked, pool in the nude, rapist's mask, Mario the Mugger's dummies. I recalled something Mario told me about what he'd done before meeting us again. He'd hung out in the London Zoo after jumping over the fence near the bridge by the canal, ate food in the restaurant without a penny. He knew this place inside out, every tunnel and corner, bench, animal cage. Mario often told me he preferred the company of animals to humans, claimed to have spent the night with the wolves. This must have been part of his being in the wilderness. Mario said he'd clambered over the fence into their compound one night. Once in, he'd pissed in a circle, the wolves leaving him alone to sit in meditation. He'd even made out the leader of the pack who came over, sniffed him. I didn't know what to believe.

I walked past Boo's. Lights were on but I was realistic, a bad move to go up, I just couldn't articulate anything. Soon I reached Regent's Park, beyond by the zoo, maybe the company of dumb animals might be preferable this night. I climbed over the iron fence, gaining entry into the park, past the scene of my Mother of Turkeys where I'd implored divine intervention. At least I'd kicked the smack habit but now I knew what booze was all about. I reached the wolves who were located nearby on the edge of the zoo behind extensive security. Putting my glasses on, I saw one trotting about, looking like a large Alsation. It yawned, revealed white fangs. I read a sign affixed to the wire: 'These are dangerous animals. DO NOT FEED'.

The fences looked impenetrable but I had no intention of venturing in there anyway. All the same, I bunked in the zoo elsewhere, disturbing some birds of prey. Then, Bethlehem shimmered before me, three huge man-made mountains swathed in golden light, the abode of alpine goats. What with my frame of mind, it looked like an acid vision, a semi-religious experience. Now I stumbled towards my illuminated peaks, past bears sleeping in pits, thinking about joining the penguins in their pool. But January is the worst time to commune with these creatures. Climbing up the winding paths, I reached the base of my mountain, got over a four-foot fence, negotiated a trench. Having surmounted these obstacles, I clambered on to a ridge, feeling that I couldn't give a damn. The goats reared up, hooves skittering up the sides of the artificial mountain. I crawled into the entrance of a cave. Inside, electric lights, glowing alcoves and, in contrast to the freezing cold outside, floors were warm, underground central heating. Here I lay down, bedding into straw, the place smelling of the country. I rolled my coat up into a pillow, crashed out.

Morning, I was hit by a ray of light. Opening my eyes, I didn't know where I was, heating had gone off and goat faces peered at me from around the entrance. A cacophony of sound snapped me back to reality, weird moans, roars, snores, strange bird noises. Covered in goatshit, I wiped my clothes on the walls in a futile attempt to scrape the crap off. Scrambling out, I ran downwards over the trench and fence, past a moaning polar bear. Further on, bison jousted, bumping heads. Over the main fence, on to the canal towpath, walking back to Euston after cleaning my reeking clothes in the water, splashing myself on the face. Heading back to the Range, I knew the binge had all but ground to a halt. I had to do something, leave before disaster struck. Thoughts turned to Boo, home comforts, warm flat, rails.

After getting back frozen to the bones, I took a proper hot bath, then slept, collapsing on the sofa. Early evening, a key turned in the door.

"Mario?"

"Dan?"

I explained everything, when and where Loader would be going to court. Mario told me he had to lay low, stay away, because the police were looking for him in connection with a serious offence. He stayed the night, a miserable affair, sharing a couple of lagers from cans, more dog ends, early to bed, minimal conversation. Rising early, we started to clean up, no exercises. Things weren't the same without the Guv. Sandra came over with the greyhound and Mario couldn't believe his luck when she invited him to move in with her after I'd explained to her about the Range coming to an end. Suddenly the door opened, us rooted to the spot. Mario looked at me, instant worry, us thinking of the police. In walked the bearded lady and Blue Ear's mum. At least the place looked presentable.

"Hello Clarissa! Loader's away on business in Geneva."

The mother looked uneasy, climbing the stairs to my knocking shop. A long silence followed by a scream. I must admit, there was a contrast between upstairs and the domestic bliss of the living room, my place being a pile of the theatrical costumes, books scattered and trampled, a whiff of crusty semen, one of the mattresses half burnt from a discarded cigarette, the stale odour of empty lager cans, half-eaten Macdonalds, hundreds of fag butts. Cynthia's works of art were defaced, ripped, ringed with coffee cup stains. Her sculptures had been dismantled, piled up in corners. This must have been the mother's idea of hell itself. She clattered down the stairs, holding the rapist's mask, barking in the usual middle-class manner when dressing down social inferiors.

"Just who are you? What are you doing here?"

Mario remained silent while I fobbed her off with an improbable story. We'd only been there a day, looking after the greyhound. The bearded lady tried in vain to pour oil on the troubled waters, mother though wasn't having any of it.

"I want to see that Loader as soon as he gets back from Geneva. Cynthia's better now and she's coming back. Tell Loader to see me at my office, just leave everything and get out"

Mario looked visibly upset as she took Jock into her custody, leaving with the bearded lady. Mario departed with Sandra, I realised that staying here would be out of the question if Blue Ears was returning. Even if she granted me permission to stay, I couldn't stand the sound of her voice, which was something like Princess Anne on smack.

At a loose end, there was only one thing to do. Go back, see how Horace had got on in my absence. And check out how Boo was making out with loverboy. I'd give him a cold reading, then make my move. Ringing her bell, gaining access, Boo met me with a pearly white smile, Horace jumping all over the show. Even he smelt better than me as the pong of goat mountain still lingered. Boo introduced me to Toby loverboy again. I shook his hand, felt his clammy pulse. Nervous, he couldn't look me straight in the eye. I glanced at his clothes, immaculate, gold wristwatch, boring, a walking computer manual. I told Boo about the mad scene at the Range, Loader getting nicked, the greyhound. Dalliances with the opposite sex I neglected to mention. Loverboy just sat there dumbfounded as my tales reeled off. Boo laughed again, so I knew I'd struck the right chord. I asked Boo if I could have a private word, before loverboy regained his footing. She asked him ever so nicely to go back home and she'd call him in an hour or so. Soon as the grey eminence departed, I came out with the remarks.

"Exciting isn't he? Real life and soul of the party."

These and other cracks had Boo laughing, near hysterics as I laid it on. Now I made my move, diving on her, pulling her clothes off. She started groaning, me making all the reciprocal acts. We had sex on the floor, doggy style. The animal smell from the zoo, combined with the aroma of countless one night stands and rough living must have been a heady mixture for her. As she hollered, making a racket, I glanced over to Horace smiling. It was as if he knew what was going down as he appeared to wink back. Once my duty had been performed, I checked out loverboy's clothes, slipping into them, then started imitating him while I whipped up a pasta meal in the kitchen, going to town on the bloke, doing his posh accent, talking about finance, the plastic revolution, how easy it is to make money nowadays. I guessed Boo hadn't had much in the way of entertainment from belly laughs to sex over the last couple of months. Later, she telephoned the jug, telling him to come over. When he rang the bell, I'd already posted myself by the main entrance with all his stuff in a holdall.

"Think this belongs to you, Toby. Happy New Year, catch you later baby."

Back again, Danny Boy, Horace and Boo.

CHAPTER THIRTEEN

Loader got out on bail after a court appearance. Conditions were stringent, he had to live with respectable June at her Archway flat. Loader had to chill out and knew it. Mario went to ground in Sandra's Notting Hill bedsit. Loader had been charged with forgery, deception and theft.

I returned to the Range to collect a few bits and bobs. As I entered the flat, standing in the hall, I noticed a silhouette in the living room, seated on a swivel chair. It swung around and there sat Cynthia Blue Ears, back from her vacation in Belle Vue.

"Hello Cindy, what a surprise."

Smacked up to the eyeballs.

"Danny ... What are you doing here?"

That annoying Princess Anne on fifteen RPM accent.

"I know you've been staying here ... None of the bills have been paid ... What about my damaged artwork? You owe me at least a thousand pounds ... "

I stuffed all my things into a duffle bag. She disgusted me. I felt like kicking the chair from under her, booting the inbred head but I left that to the next love in her life. Yet another rich Dumbo who didn't know what month it was, let alone what day.

"Don't worry Cindy, we'll sort it out, no problem. You should give up smack, it don't half cost a lot of money."

She sat scratching. "

What do you mean?"

"You know what I mean. Don't worry about the money, I'll keep in contact. Bye."

One morning at Boo's a letter arrived, florid handwriting, betraying the fact that Loverboy Toby was trying to re-establish communication. I took it into Boo, grinning.

"There's a print-out from the computer here. Shall I sing it or simply read it?"

Boo blushed as I called Horace in for the recital, the missive already removed from envelope. Although she begged me not to read it, I knew Boo was dying for me to get on with my rendering of this pathetic offering. I read aloud the publisher's son's pitiful attempt at a comeback letter, mimicking his plummy accent. He'd tried to ring her but there was never an answer. Could something be wrong. Sad stuff indeed. It finished with a minor flourish.

"Have the curtains drawn? Have the lights dimmed on my Juliet? Are the roses dead in our garden? I love you, please phone, please."

It ended in telephone numbers. I thought his twenty five watt bulb had blown, then started taking the mickey.

"Has the prize marrow in our allotment been chewed up by a stray donkey …"

Once she'd stopped laughing, telling me how dreadful I was, I re-read the section.

"I feel I've lost something dear to me, I really must talk to you, please return my calls or write. There is no cure for a broken heart."

He was gone on Boo for sure. Men were like that over her. The pest continued to phone her at work, Boo ringing me back to complain, informing me that he would be coming around to the flat at six. I said not to worry, I'd sort him out, give him back his remaining stuff including Christmas presents, tell him I'd come back for good then goodbye. Toby turned up, dead on the hour, ringing the doorbell. Instead of Boo's pearly whites, he got me sticking my head out of the window, wearing a dirty vest. I greeted him downstairs, opening the door. He'd dressed to kill. Pointed white shoes with buckles, blue sharkskin coat. It looked like he'd been cooking under a sunlamp, stank as if he'd bathed in aftershave. I leaned across the door, fag hanging out of my gob but also wearing Boo's silk Kenzo pyjama bottoms. He stammered.

"I thought … I came around to see Boo."

He slipped something back into his pocket, it looked like an offering, contained a jewellery box. I did him a favour, wised him up.

"Don't you know? Me and Boo are back together squire. I've come home. Here, I've got your gear, some of the stuff you left behind."

I handed him the bag with his remaining possessions.

"Oh, and by the way, Boo don't want no more calls. Well, I think that's taken care of everything. Catch you later."

He walked dejected down the stairs, me clicking the door shut behind him.

"Adios amigo."

Through the fish-eye lens, I saw him shutting out the gate, into the Crescent. I couldn't help but reflect, these rich boys didn't know how to write a letter, handle women or even argue with a determined fellow like myself. So much for their much-vaunted education and supposed superiority.

Didn't take long for the magic rail to make its reappearance. Traders down the market were glad to see me back in action again. Sometimes Loader would pop down to say hello. He felt worried for his old girlfriend Sandra now that Mario lived with her. Loader wasn't on form but soon enough he trotted along, going for drinks with me after the rail. Loader was keeping himself busy back at June's, rewiring, plumbing, decorating. Boo, meanwhile, put in extra hours at work, not usually getting back until eight, while I'd have finished by three at the latest. This gave me plenty of time to play around in the bars. After exercising the mutt I'd hit those bars with a vengeance, justifying my behaviour by saying well at least I wasn't sneaking away to get heroin. Instead I'd developed a crave for booze and the surrounding ambience, playing the jukebox, football machines, pool, flashing the wad. And meeting more women.

In one of the bars I frequented I'd noticed a nice-looking small bird with a sultry Latin look. Middle-class, of course. I soon managed to nudge aside the current boyfriend after figuring out her long-standing relationship was on the rocks. I'd always been a good one with the advice. Miriam said she liked old movies, so I regaled her with the silver screen classics, me acting out and imitating the parts. One afternoon the inevitable invitation to her home came, so off I went, clever enough to know not to steam in. I'd play the mature gentleman, go back to Boo later, someone I'd neglected to tell Miriam about. Her house stood in Camden Road, close to the tube, five minutes from the Crescent. Inside the building reminded me of a maze, us having to negotiate past offices, up flights of stairs that led to yet more flights, out into Wendy house apartments, plenty of space, connecting rooms. Miriam mentioned she had a small room available, next to hers by a remarkable coincidence. She only paid the ridiculous rent of six pounds a week, leaving me to marvel yet again at the almost supernatural ability of these types to obtain the best deals for next to nothing. Another Camden housing co-op. Miriam told me the other residents were a young doctor from Rugby in his early twenties and a woman named Leonora. I didn't like the sound of him one little bit, particularly when Miriam filled me in on some details. I looked at his social conscience posters pinned to the walls. Solidarity. Pictures of Belsen 'Never Again'. Couldn't help making a few remarks.

"Here Miriam, you're Jewish, I bet you don't want to come home to this depiction of mass genocide. Solidarity, a bloke spouting on an orange box."

Miriam told me he liked The Smiths, often played them full blast. He pulled the nurses, fixing them up with his single speciality, cauliflower or onion bhaji followed by a trip to his room. I got the picture. He'd split up from the real boss of this house, Leonora double-barrelled wonder. Miriam had already told Leonora about me, what a wonderful entertaining cheeky chappie I was, but she didn't like Leonora all that much. Miriam herself didn't stay there all the time as she half lived with her regular boyfriend, Dominic. Now however, with the growing rift between them, she stayed here in Camden Road more often. I wanted to meet this dynamic duo, Young Doctor and Leonora. Although a stay for the night was on offer, I just pecked Miriam on the cheek. Returning to Boo, I told her I'd be over at Loader's more often, helping him out because he'd been having some trouble in the mental department, pressure of being remanded on bail.

I'd only been back with Boo for a couple of weeks and here I was playing away games again. I guess monogamy didn't constitute part of my psychological make up.

Having the rail enabled me to afford the cost of conducting affairs, seeing Loader, Justin and Billy the Kid, standing them drinks. They all saw me in the bars with Miriam. Mark and Justin watched me with growing envy. Especially Justin, who hadn't been laid since Hitler was a corporal. As a good player of head tennis, I soon found out Miriam was an only child, her ideas came from boyfriend Dominic, that both were cheating on one another. I decided to consummate my part of the two-timing angle, so I suggested one quiet afternoon in the bars why not go back to her place, play some records, get some cans in. So late afternoon, I got laid, had a cigarette and met the other residents, Leonora and Young Doctor. Leonora looked exactly as I'd imagined her. Fuzzy hair, piggy-eyed, double chin, making her look like a cockerel, uniform of baggy clothes. Leonora had a skin problem, I'd already been through the bathroom cabinet, seen the Tetracyline tubes. I'd never clapped my eyeballs upon such yellow heads since my wormy bad trip up in Hampstead. Leonora appeared confident, yet underneath I detected apprehension. As for the other half, Young Doctor, I could tell he still adored cockerel chin who was now going out with some Gunga Din. Young Doctor was the mousy type, silver rimmed specs, one of the most contrived people I'd ever met. For some unknown reason Leonora liked me in her patronising manner, impressed by my verbal trickery and happy-go-lucky routine. After some light hearted banter with the duo, Young Doctor found himself retreating from a barrage of insults. Into his room alone, slamming the door, on went the 'Smiths', full blast. I made only one comment to Miriam and Leonora.

"I'm a bit too old for this sort of thing."

Then left, back to Boo for the evening.

At home, my spirits up, I amused Boo all night. This however, soon changed a couple of days later when a mood-swing induced by black bombers came on. These swings were now dangerously unpredictable. A mellow mood, good listener or talker could in a flash be transformed into headbanging, shouting and the odd bout of fisticuffs. I felt strange, a combination of confidence allied to the desire to self-destruct. So I told Boo I'd been in deep meditation, thinking about getting my own life together once again, spinning her the line that I didn't want to be strapped down, had to expand intellectually, talk to people about art and literature. Boo wasn't fobbed off, this time delivering her own bombshell.

"It's that Miriam girl, isn't it?"

Some invertebrate, probably Justin, had put the bubble in. After this I expected the inevitable explosion. Instead, much to my surprise, Boo came out with sympathy and understanding, she'd do anything to accommodate my whims.

"I'll give you your own space, Dan. I've still got some dresses. I'll let you do the rail if you like."

Very much indeed. I couldn't believe my good fortune. I'd landed a version of freedom. Being generous, I traded off, promising I'd visit often, make sure to keep the fluff off her needle, keep her happy. Over the next couple of days, pleased as Punch, I started moving my gear over to the room at Miriam's.

I soon settled into the little room, Miriam impressed by my overall demeanour, patter down the market, easy manner with the multitudes and bar room philosophising. Miriam herself, between parental handouts, worked colouring animations that were broadcast in advertisements on commercial television. This resulted in her being out of the house early along with the others, allowing me to take my time combing the place for money, searching drawers, clothes, behind the sofa, inside pots and tins. Once cash had been found, I'd drop some bombers, go to the bookies then head for a bar. Miriam joined me early afternoon. Usually, after another boozing session it would be back to her bed. I'd previously told her that I'd gone out with Boo years ago, so Miriam thought I had been at a loose end. It wasn't as though Miriam was exactly honest herself, I knew my place in this household in relation to her – court jester, bit on the side. Miriam's boyfriend, Dominic, was a mister meaningful who played bass guitar between inheritances. A total bore. Miriam told me she'd been going out with him for a long time but didn't know how to end it all. Truth was, she wasn't sure. Dominic, apart from being a boring twit, tried in vain to humiliate me. He used long words out of context, thinking me to be dead ignorant. I'd smile, strum a spare guitar, then he'd have a bash, playing complicated chromatic scales rounded off by dextrously plucked arpeggios. After his admittedly technically brilliant rendering, I'd pluck it back again, launching into a song, playing the instrument with little else. Any audience always appreciated my act as singing and strumming always beats the accomplished soloist hands down. Dominic, of the usual limited perception, thought I was screwing a local barmaid, something more on my level. We kidded him along on this one whenever he enquired into her well-being, me giving him the wink and nudge.

Living with the creepy duo proved to be more of a strain than originally envisaged. Young Doctor cracking snide remarks, disparaging comments about my lack of formal education and accent. I held my fire, marking time, catching up his minus doomsday points. I carefully observed the slimeball bringing home the nurses. The smell of onion bhajis would greet me coming lack from the bar, along with a nurse vanishing into his room, dreadful music blaring out. Leonora was undisputed Queen of the castle. I found her repulsive to look at, an eyestrain. She'd strategically place herself near to the bog, doing some household chore or other on her mornings off. I'd have to negotiate my way past a hideous sight like her ironing in her knickers, wrinkly legs on prominent display. This, I presumed, was meant to be a turn-on. When I'd return from the bog, she'd woffle on, any old excuse for a conversation, me avoiding any signal that could be misconstrued, careful to evade the slightest physical contact as I slipped past ensuring no accidental frottage.

Settled into my new base of operations, Loader came up for trial. Open and shut case, nine months. Shortly after this, the phone rang. Mario the Mugger, emerged from the love nest, someone had passed my new number on. Having the whole day to yourself can be boring with little or no money, you'd hang about with anyone who had a bit of dosh and who'd spend it, so I met him down the road. Although I felt a touch uncomfortable, the lure of money for drinks seduced me. Mario rattled out a story over the first pint about how he'd been living in Notting Hill with Sandra but now he'd met another girl, a Latin American.

"All these birds round there fancy me Dan, I can't believe it's happening."

Neither could I. How could women be so stupid? I told him about Miriam, gave him my address. Sure enough, next afternoon, the bell rang. The house being empty, I let him up. Mario was loaded, cash, cheque books and cards. He'd been up to his monkey tricks in the zoo. Mario looked around, furtive glances, places where money might be stashed. I assured him that I'd ready checked out every possibility. For the next few afternoons, we were out drinking together, most of his dough going on expensive shorts. Mario still couldn't hold his booze. One pint and his eyes would go funny. From then on, he'd be dangerous, offering people out, doing tills, stealing blatantly. With anger stewing away inside, I didn't fancy joining him in the Pentonville Hilton. Mario's afternoon conversations were predictable, one track, about himself, what he'd done, was going to do, what a tasty geezer he was. People started avoiding me in his company. Between rails I found money scarce, even raiding the common kitty for twenty pounds. The phone rang again. Mario. Had he any money?

"Of course I have!"

So I met him in a pub off Parkway, where he waited with two pints, pool table set up. Mario's flip-flops were broken, he just stood there barefoot, pondering over what sort of present to buy the Latino, cheque book at the ready.

"Perfume? Flowers? … I know! A cuddly toy!"

Barefoot Mario marched straight over to a nearby toyshop, returning with a giant teddybear which he parked on a pub seat while getting the landlord of the establishment to cash another cheque. More drinks flowed. Later, we ended up walking down the street, Mario still barefoot, raving, barging into people, clutching the toy like some monster toddler. Collecting my senses, I managed to detach myself from his company. Later that night, he turned up at the house asking what had happened to me. I commented upon his new shoes and he forgot my disappearance, describing how the Latino girl loved the cuddly toy, how he was well in with her now. Sandra had moved into a housing co-op flat at Swiss Cottage,

Mario fancied moving with her, somewhere to rest up, watch the telly after a strenuous day's stealing and drinking.

I kept up the double life, some nights staying over at Boo's performing horizontal duties. Miriam thought I slept over at Sandra's. During this time, Justin moved into a tower block flat. He was now doing alright for himself selling dope, plenty of customers, going up a couple of steps. Sandra came over to him, scoring for Mario who liked a blow in the evening. But soon the man himself turned up to score, making Justin nervous, cursing Sandra under his breath for giving out his address. The inevitable followed, with Justin coming home from the pub finding his front door booted in. Mario sat on the bed brandishing an iron bar, the place thoroughly ransacked. Mario didn't beat about the bush.

"Where's the money?"

He left with three hundred pounds and two ounces of draw. After this incident, Justin installed a fortified door. Hearing of this, I thought that things were getting out of hand, this feeling reinforced by a visit to Sandra's new flat. Mario took me and the pouting Latino girl along. As soon as Sandra opened the door, her face dropped. I noticed her black eye. Mario just pushed his way in clutching a bottle of brandy like he owned the place, told Sandra to shut lip, fetch glasses as he was entertaining guests. Sandra looked a nervous wreck, trembling as Mario poured out a couple of measures for me and the Latino. He downed half the bottle in one, which soon had him reeling, off his head. Mario started on Sandra, pushing her about, shouting, telling her she wasn't fit to be called a woman, a whore, an old slag, while bending down to peck the Latino on the head. The Latino smiled like this was normal behaviour in her neck of the woods as Mario bellowed at Sandra.

"This is what I call a real woman!" He pushed Sandra against a wall.

"You're fucking nothing! And look at this! The glasses are dirty!"

Tired of this abuse, Sandra tried pushing him away. At this feeble sign of resistance, Mario launched into a violent attack, slapping her across the face, screaming the place looked a mess. I intervened while the Latino still sat there gushing over the heroic Mario. I pulled the beast off Sandra and he turned on me, flaring nostrils. I backed into the kitchen, Mario breathing in my face, fists raised. I told him to cool it. For my troubles he swung a punch, me ducking, the blow striking the top of my noggin. Mario picked up a knife, this surely was the end of Danny Boy. I'd only joined the other two to see if Sandra was right. Mario's eyes were red, demented. Total madness. I shouted for the final time.

"No! Mario! Put it down!"

He seemed to snap out of his blind rage, throwing the knife to the floor. A look of sudden despair swept over the manic face.

"What am I doing?"

After some hesitation, Mario turned his attention back to Sandra.

"And you've even got me hitting Dan!"

Things calmed down, Mario and the Latino sleeping in another room while I sat up all night with Sandra. As we listened to Mario's nocturnal howlings, Sandra told me she didn't know the way out of her predicament. She had a nutter on her back. Sandra confided to me that she was going to the police. I warned her that the law didn't interfere in domestic troubles and besides, it wouldn't go down well with Mario. I also had my own skin to think of, but in the morning, before sneaking out, I arranged to meet her later in the nearby library where we could discuss the situation in a less hostile environment.

The afternoon rendezvous failed to synchronise, unlike those meetings in forties movies. I later found out that as I sat waiting in the reference section, Sandra paced up and down in the general library. I wouldn't see her or Mario for a while, deciding the best method to accomplish this might be to get away from it all, take a break somewhere. As an incentive towards this, Loader got sprung from jail after playing the loony card. The courts hadn't taken his psychiatric record into consideration, so they released him on probation. He'd been convalescing at June's, keeping away from Mario, who'd in the meantime had badly beaten up one of Loader's friends for foolishly drooling over the Latino. Mark also resurfaced, explaining to me that, as Billy the Kid, he was going home, back to the USA, his previous life's roots, dressing now like a downmarket Roy Rogers. I played along with these fantasies, especially since he wanted someone to live in his Holborn flat, looking after it, cashing his housing benefits, putting the money into an account to pay for the premises plus some other complicated financial arrangements. A few pints later and I was the man. All formalities were completed over a couple of days, him giving me the key, the place mine whenever I wanted it, no hurry to move in as he'd be away for a year at least. Mark, in the interim period, would move in with his girlfriend. All these negotiations meant me spending time with Mark, but after Mario this provided light relief.

As I accepted Mark's offer, time ran out in my new home. Apart from enduring Young Doctor and Leonora, I had to put up with the droning bass player Dominic. Miriam finally broke the news about our extra curricular. He accepted everything passively, having no choice in the matter. He retained enough cunning to play nice guy Mr Understanding, calculating that she'd be back once her fling with me petered out, Danny Boy being nothing more than a distasteful passing fancy. Young Doctor came on strong with the superior remarks, graduating to practical jokes, schoolboy style, whisking the chair from beneath me as I sat at the table. Confrontation wasn't going to be long in the offing and I wouldn't be joking.

Two days later, I paid a visit to another doctor, Nico. By the afternoon I'd tanked myself up with three bombers plus downers, hitting bars for lubrication. Miriam met me later, bringing along a couple of her creepy pals, same league as Young Doctor, engaged to be married, working in housing co-ops wangling places for their wealthy compatriots. I steamed in, insults, piss-taking. They left quickly. Miriam took the wise precaution of splitting. She could see me working into a violent frame of mind, eyes popping. Some of the Mario had rubbed off. I decided to consult Young Doctor, his bedside manner needed improving, so I stormed back to base, out of my nut, adrenaline pumping. As I dashed upstairs, eager for the fray, Young Doctor poked his head out, greeting me with an admonishment.

"Thank you Danny for polishing off my onion bhajis."

I barged into his room, flaming, threw a table against the door, sitting on it, barring exit. The arrogance vanished, Young Doctor's bottle dropped.

"There's going to be a few changes around here doc, starting with this room. It's mine now; I'm tired of living in the matchbox."

Young Doctor sat glued to a chair, blubbering. "Danny for God's sake … please don't."

He tried to rise, I pushed him back down, producing another chair.

"Try pulling this away!"

I smashed it over his collection of African sculptures, broke some Peruvian masks before shoving a chest of drawers into the wall.

"And this can go here!"

Young Doctor sat there, bleating. I delivered the body blow I'd been saving for just such an occasion.

"I know all about you. I've been looking around the house when you've been away, going through your things, doing some investigations."

I lit a cigarette, resuming the verbal attack.

"Who do you fucking think I am? One of these Downs Syndromes your daddy employs in his sweatshop in Rugby Town? That's where the family wealth comes from, that's how you could afford the education to be a doctar, isn't it?"

Tears flowed.

"I'm beginning to like this room already doc. I'm gonna enjoy living here."

I purposefully opened the window, fully breathing in the fresh air. "Ah, that's nice! These'll have to go for starters."

I ripped down the posters, clutching one with a Jewish kid behind barbed wire.

"I ain't one of your retards mate. I know what you doctors got up to in Auschwitz and Dachau."

Tore up his foreign brochures.

"Don't like these either. Just to show off to your fat nurses the places you've been to."

Young Doctor tumbled from his chair, in bits, falling to the floor, adopting the foetal position, begging to be left alone. It was like a schoolboy bully scenario, me nearly feeling sorry for him. Before I had time to develop pangs of sympathy, I pulled out a large knife he kept displayed in a sheath. It gleamed as I juggled it in the air, catching it on the downward spiral, my hair on end. I plunged the knife into the door, full force.

"Doc, I want you out in an hour, otherwise I'm going to come back and kill you."

I slammed the door, then returned within seconds. He lay an the floor gurgling. I kicked his record player to smithereens.

"And I hate your shitty music too! Remember, out. Back in an hour, got it?"

I departed into the night.

After this drama, I immediately moved back in with Boo that very evening. She showered me with gifts, male perfumes, clothes, good food, wine. This went on for the better part of a week, while Saturday saw the rail resurrected.

She asked if I fancied going to Italy for yet another holiday. I declined, finding the idea of having the place to myself, getting laid, stoned, friends around minus Boo, a far more attractive proposition. I didn't see Miriam again, receiving a letter explaining how she'd got back together with boring Dominic, moved to Ireland with him. As for Young Doctor, he'd ventured back, having disappeared for three days. With Boo away, I spent the next two weeks in the usual razzle dazzle manner, her returning without duty-frees or prezzies. Although Boo behaved normally, I sensed that she'd met another fellow, probably someone amenable, younger. After a few days' hesitation, I popped the question, her answer confirming suspicions.

"Looks like I'd better move into Mark's flat at Holborn then, doesn't it?"

We both laughed, no rancour involved.

"Yes Dan, I suppose you'd better."

End of an era. At least we'd split on amicable terms, Boo hinting I could trundle out the odd rail now and again. Nothing to do except pack my things for the final time, keep in touch. It all seemed part of a logical progression, didn't worry me in the slightest. Inevitable but the good life would take a dive. Still, I'd always made out alright up to now but this time I'd be living on my own, another new challenge.

CHAPTER FOURTEEN

The flat, centrally located in Theobalds Road, lay above an Italian restaurant, entry gained by a side door next to a bookies. My new drum sat plum on the top floor. Opening the door, first thing encountered, bogs and bathroom, were covered in brown grime. Mark had never been known for his sense of hygiene, phone books lay piled up, Mark's toilet paper. Past this, the kitchen contained a locker and fridge, both bonded together by years of accumulated grease. This kitchen also boasted a small table and a couple of hard chairs. Floorboards were bare. The only other room overlooked Theobalds Road. It stank, reminding me of the smell in a police cell, only furniture here being a bed constructed from two sofa seats placed together which ,with a filthy carpet and large cracked mirror, made up the entire contents of the living room. An electric meter stood in splendid isolation, broken from Mark fiddling it. I felt excited despite the place looking like a dosser's knocking shop, having a real home of my own for the foreseeable future, at least a year, so therefore secure. I moved in a few things from Boo's, including an old flickering black and white telly, kept the sofa tops and warmed the gaff with a couple of fan heaters. Like Mark, I fiddled the electricity.

Mark stayed in town for the time being, living down the road at his girlfriend's. He felt entitled to turn up every couple of days, snoop around, help spend my dole money. I'd return his visits, easy enough as the girlfriend worked. I kept wondering when Billy the Kid would return to his spiritual homeland but knew he'd eventually go. For the first few weeks, I lived it up, going up West, a mere few minutes walk, diving into all night bars where everybody knew me, selling bombers. My sex life took off, a real bachelor lifestyle. Loader split up with June, shared a flat with another guy in the heart the West End, so he also found himself indulging that same lifestyle. Back in my new home I didn't bother much with cooking, living out of chip bags. Doing the odd rail helped bring in a bit of cash now and again.

Boo had already ensconced her new lover into the flat, rolled out that procrustean duvet. I found myself surprised by his youth, a mere eighteen, an Italian named Enrico. Although he looked like a peasant fresh from trampling grapes, Enrico in fact came from a fairly wealthy background, his parents owning land and a wine press somewhere near Florence. He didn't speak much English but seemed willing to learn. Boo didn't appear embarrassed at having such a young fellow in tow who couldn't speak much of the lingo. She positively beamed, so I knew I could hit her up for more dresses. I got on fine with Enrico, playing guitar, teaching him some English. Being up at Boo's struck me as rather strange. It seemed like I'd never lived there, what with the almost overnight changes. The picture of me by the bedside had been replaced by a soft focus number of Enrico, who'd become the new dog walker. By this time, Horace was totally incontinent, virtually toothless with bald patches, hobbling along, a ball of rancid fur.

Christmas rolled around again, the time of year that always acted as a pivotal point. I guess it stemmed back to when I was a kid, the only time apart from your birthday when you ate well, got presents. Back in the flat, after my initial burst I settled down a bit, life assuming a less hectic pace.

I continued visiting Boo and Enrico, without overstaying my welcome. Boo liked her dope, Enrico didn't mind a smoke himself. I scored for them but after a while, introduced Enrico to Justin, getting him to drive me there in Boo's car. Justin spoke Italian, his father had been headmaster of an exclusive private school in Rome. Justin also continued to rise in the world. Thanks to dealing, business had taken off, trappings to prove it, stereo, colour telly and video, clothes, phone ringing all the time. Like many dealers I knew, his social life revolved around the business, him hanging out with a younger clientele but he still wasn't getting any sex, thinking of going to Thailand with Loader. I couldn't help slipping in a remark.

"That's a long way to go to get laid."

He smiled in agreement. Enrico got on well with Justin, glad to hear his native tongue. I helped Enrico with the London language, swearing, slang and the like. By now, the only way I could get a rail together was to go through her new man, who'd already been lined up with a job with one of Daddy's partners at a subsidiary, driving, loading cloth. After cultivating Enrico, I asked Boo if I could do a yuletide rail, what with her also needing cash for ready spending money. She agreed, otherwise I'd have been stony broke for Christmas.

Just after New Year I bumped into Miriam again, back from Ireland, now living with Dominic in his flat down Tufnell Park way. Miriam appeared reluctant to converse, my explosion and resulting death threat against Young Doctor probably having something to do with it. I soon managed to get her laughing about the whole episode on the way back to my place. By then, it had a slight nautical flavour, looking like a ship's cabin, little chairs, black and white telly. After aperitifs, the inevitable. Only this time I couldn't get it on, in spite of desperate fumbling attempts on my behalf, it was a no go. Maybe I'd been drinking too much, perhaps this could be after effects of bombers. Following this exercise in frustration, Miriam left, after arranging to call around sometime later that week. Of course, she never showed up. Back to the bass player for a living death of boredom.

However, before I had time to ruminate over this, out of the blue, the Dutch bird Marie turned up. When Marie came over to the new gaff she wanted me to make a go of it, started by bringing over kettles, cutlery, cups, giving the impression she fancied staying with me for a while. First day I'd met her, I was on the last of my bombers, therefore in sparkling form. But a pattern had established itself. After the bombers were finished, I sank into apathy, dozing off all hours, plus impotence punctuated by boozing. Several abortive attempts at carnal entertainments saw me simply giving up, preferring coma. So Marie felt pissed off, departing to stay with Lenny and girlfriend in West Hampstead. As a parting shot, she told me to come over, visit her in Holland when I felt more together. I just mumbled yeah sure from the sofa tops.

After these non-events, isolation crept in, people no longer coming over to see me, the forgotten man. No telephone, little, if any, money, fiddling the electric, bomber comedowns lasting a week. I'd stay huddled between two fan-heaters, laying on the sofa tops, recycling fag butts, watching the box. My black and white telly triggering bouts of melancholy, football in monochrome, banging the set to get a decent picture, reminding me of those less salubrious days of childhood. I missed Boo's place. In the past I might have wheedled my way back. Now it had all finished, realisation hitting me at long last, no more easy ready money as she had the live-in, working lover. The honeymoon period with myself played out. I had to survive somehow. At first, I hit the supermarkets run by Indians and Filipinos in the local area, soon increasing my radius. I'd steal anything that could be put into an oven and tinned foods, chocolates, booze, these obtained by quick in and out jobs. Once, I lived on smoked salmon for a week as I'd managed to scoop up eighteen packets in one go. My nicking coat started to look a bit threadbare, at a casual glance though, it still retained vestiges of respectability. I'd fallen into debt at the local newsagents owing to my need for cigarettes which are next to impossible to steal. By now, Billy the Kid reached New York, sending a postcard telling me to keep up payment on the rent. So far, I'd made a couple of instalments, nothing more.

Sitting alone one evening gazing at the flickering black and white, a voice roared up from below in the street.

"Danny!"

Mario had returned. By now, being skint and increasingly isolated, I let him in, glad to see a face. He trundled up with a bike he'd stolen from around the corner. More importantly, Mario had a cashpoint card. Owing to the bare cupboards, empty ashtrays and lack of liquid refreshment, Mario must have instantly figured I was broke. Straight away he offered to take me out for a drink which I accepted. Then down to Chinatown for a meal. Mario now lived with the Latino, had saved up money to visit Brazil with her. He wanted to go live in the jungle, an appropriate choice. Mario had been up to the usual but the Latino tried to steer him on a narrow path, persuading him to attempt gainful employment, the whole thing having a familiar ring to it. A week as a waiter until he assaulted a customer, courier work for a couple of weeks on a stolen mountain bike. Basically though, all appearances aside, Mario visited the zoo and other thieving haunts between intermittent employment. By evening's end and a brawl in the pub, I made it home alone. Mario said he'd call up sooner or later before going away, thinking I could just about handle that, my safety clause being his actual departure. Besides, all this broke the stultifying monotony of being skint.

The only visitor I got now was Mario. He had money from the usual sources. Knowing I was skint, he counted on me to accompany him, a captive audience using me as a sounding board, hardly anybody else could stomach Mario even in homeopathic doses. His favourite stomping ground turned out to be Portobello Road. Here he'd kick off in a bikers' pub, buy a gram of speed. We'd snort half each, drink, hog the pool table. Following these preliminaries we'd go slightly upmarket to the Warwick pub, which boasted a more trendy clientele. Here, Mario derived a sense of bullying superiority, lording it over them, playing an altogether different tune from the previous pub. I found it difficult to match Mario drinking. He could, with the assistance of speed, knock back ten pints. Mario certainly had a reputation of sorts in the Warwick because after half an hour the place would empty. Another place to booze was the West End where he knew a few small-time villains and prostitutes. I still knew a few trendies here where Mario did some of his dummy grabbing, so people who'd wised up would be falling over themselves to avoid him and I started getting fluffed out into the bargain. They'd started pairing me off with him. Word, however, spread. The mugger was going away to South America. Things changed overnight. Instead of places becoming vacated, people were coming over, cravenly shaking his hand, wishing him luck, generally queueing up to crawl and debase themselves in front of the bullyboy. You could have been mistaken for thinking Mario was emigrating for keeps.

One boring night after a few solitary drinks, I decided to go over, visit Boo. She was alone, Enrico had gone back to Italy for a couple of weeks. Boo herself had just returned from Japan. Her position in the family hierarchy continued to rise. She seemed glad to see me, showing off all the stuff purchased on her visit, taking me into the bedroom to exhibit contents of her new wardrobe. I noticed a fancy sweater, asked if I could have it. Boo laughed, politely refusing, this one cost her over five hundred smackers. And there I stood without the bus fare home. As she popped into the loo, I noticed something else, her handbag on the bed. More than a mere touch of Mario must have rubbed off because soon as that bog door clicked shut, my greasy mitts dived. First thing I came into contact with as a little wad of large yellow banknotes, ice fresh and crispy. I held them, adrenaline pumping. Japanese money, always worth something. Hearing the toilet flush, I skimmed half off the wad, placing it double quick. Now I had money I didn't fancy hanging about too much, had to get it changed up. Straight down to the nearest Bureau de Change. Handing over one of the notes, I got back eighty-seven quid. Couldn't believe my luck, having another seven. Off to a supermarket with an off-licence, grabbing a load of food and booze, paying for once. Next day, over at Mario's, he was off in a couple of days, exchanged some pleasantries, bunging him fifty pounds spending money for his trip, telling the lie I'd won on the horses.

Armed now with cash, I zipped over to Hornsey Road to get more bombers, pay off my debt to Doctor Nico that I'd run up as of late, owing him oner. If I paid him off now, I'd be good for tick in the future leaner times. The surgery now resembled an adventure playground, full of juveniles, addicts young and old, various shades of lads. The Doctor was dishing out DF118s, Codeine-based opiates. By now, I'd established a chatty routine with Nico, something akin to seeing a barber. How's the wife, I see Chelsea won last week. Paying my debt did my rapport no harm. Back at the flat after Boo's money had disappeared on a week-long bender, I didn't bother to take stock, weigh up the possibilities. There weren't any. Only further degeneration and decay. I neglected personal hygiene, not shaving for weeks or washing clothes, me remaining in splendid isolation, venturing out to steal food and drinks from supermarkets. My only bursts of activity coincided with arrival of dole cheques, visits to the bent doctor. Money soon went after hitting student bars in search of cheap drinks. Sometimes when skint, I'd drag myself to the library across the road, browse through a few film books. Things were well on the downward slide. I only existed. No visitors, only plenty of time to reflect between fan-heaters about the old days at Boo's, being a kept man, money always, holidays abroad, nice clothes, the rail, social life in Camden. I'd given up on the libido. It wasn't even a case of not being able to get it on, desire itself had burnt out. Now I began to worry about the future, what lay in store for worthless me? The flat wouldn't last forever, rent arrears were piling up, unpredictable Mark might be back anytime. Things may deteriorate further. How bad, I didn't know but I began to recall my previous madness, the loony bin. Whatever the future, it isn't something to look forward to. No rich girlfriends. No girlfriends of any description. Nor, unlike many a past acquaintance, a nice convenient inheritance to bail me out. Something had to break this downward spiral before crack-up. Anything.

Skint, impotent, too apathetic to even visit Loader or Justin, I became a semi-recluse, a virtual hermit. I'd run out of fly spray, washing up liquid, bog paper. One morning, like most mornings, I lay listless on one of the sofa tops, staring at the ceiling, it dawned on me I'd sunk into that dire miasma that I'd faced after my youthful spell of madness and incarceration. A loud honk on a car horn, a shout of my name, shook me out of contemplation. I couldn't believe it, recognising the voice immediately. The mugger. Whatever happened to Brazil? The jungle? I peeked out the window. There, on the pavement below, a sun-tanned figure paying off a taxi driver. I shot downstairs, my first visitor for months. Mario waved his entrance fee, a fat wad. Never had I seen him looking so good, he'd been working out, thin at the waist, muscled shoulders and chest. I couldn't help thinking there would be a lot of disappointed folk in pubs around Notting Hill and up West. First thing Mario did was comment upon the state of the flat, then myself. He lectured me about my living conditions, opening the windows to liberate flies, picking up a rag, wiping dust off the telly screen.

"Dan, what's the matter with you? You've let yourself go."

Mario walked over to the sink, balking at any further improvements as wildlife crawled on the greasy plates.

"Fuck this Dan, let's go out now and have a breakfast."

He knew I'd jump at that one. I hadn't eaten breakfast in a café for an age, so I was game. Mario suggested that I clean, myself up. I took a whore's wash, face and armpits, followed by a feeble shave.

No messing about. Traditional English breakfast. I enjoyed this more than the flashiest joint I'd ever been to with Boo in Hampstead. Fried slices, tea in steaming pots, eggs, bacon, sausages, mushrooms, tomatoes. Between scoffs, I asked Mario what happened, why the early return? He was evasive but it seemed to me they'd spunked the money on high living. The girlfriend didn't want to go into the jungle but Mario swore he'd return, explore the interior next time, this having been a trial run. Now Mario was back, brimming with confidence, raring to go. Outside the café, he posed, showing his muscles. True enough, he'd toned the body, cultivated a radiant tan. But that face. Squashed up broken nose, eyes popping from his skull, giving him that manic glare. His forehead resembled a roadmap, with a curly black barnet receding. I could see patches of scalp shining through. From his left nostril to the top of his upper lip, a scar. Another tramline ran down the chin to throat. Mario's face was a jigsaw. Finally, his ears were mismatched, one cauliflower, the other normal. Mario told me he'd been thinking about going to Hollywood.

"Maybe I'd be the new Tarzan."

Looking at him, I thought the closest he'd go would be to audition for a gorilla suit part. Opening time arrived, me dying for a drink. I felt glad for even this company and, of course, the treats. We spent most of the day drinking, then he dragged me down to Portobello. Alarmed faces emptied from the bar in ten minutes flat, watching them leave as Mario got in the first round. Back to square one. Mario became intoxicated, me finally leaving him flexing his muscles in front of a jukebox after he'd downed his customary ten pints. I made excuses, ponced the fare back and left, Mario's ego so tripped out he failed to notice my departure. I had the feeling he'd be calling up next day though.

Early next morning, the street reverberated.

"Danny!"

I let Mario up again, noticed the look of distaste as he surveyed the flat, telling me he wanted to do me a favour, help me get together, starting with the flat. Once we'd downed another café breakfast, we returned, Mario getting down to the tasks, closing doors and windows, spraying the rooms with flykiller. We left the flat for a while, allowing the chemicals to do their job. Went shopping, Mario purchasing bog roll, washing up liquid, bleach, toothpaste, J-cloths. He even pointed something out along the road.

"Look Dan, a laundry."

Back inside, Mario started to clean the Augean stables while I sorted out the washing up, brushing aside dead flies. Clearing up the dump represented a full day's working up to a fair old sweat, so evening began with another trip down Portobello. Before that, however, Mario ensured that I was scrubbed clean until I gleamed, then my filth-encrusted clothes were taken to the laundry. I must admit that I felt much better after these transformations, but deep down I suffered from foreboding, wondering how I could eventually elbow him. I sneaked off again once Mario got plastered and started picking fights with other drinkers.

Mario laid off with the visits for a couple of days, turning up with female company, the Latino, one afternoon. I suspected that he'd spruced both me and flat up to show her he had a friend in this world. They sat on the sofa seats, Latino acting pleasantly, chatting away, proud of Mario's manly image. Remembering how she sat there virtually applauding Mario's brutish behaviour towards Sandra, I still thought she hadn't figured out how dangerous he was, that she'd been juggling with tubes full of nitro-glycerine. With her long dark hair, middle age creeping in, the Latino looked attractive enough. We around smoking joints.

A pattern of sorts established itself, Mario calling over in the morning every other day. He had some talent as a cook and took to bringing food for breakfast, preparing it himself. The money supply, as always, came from hole-in-the-wall cards, taken from dummy snatches. When desperate, he'd mug people, mostly older geezers or wimpy student types. This he called working. We spent most of these days reminiscing about our old fun days at Euston, him still missing not having Loader about. Another topic of conversation was Mario's love life. Somehow I suspected he rubbed in the fact I'd become, for the time being at least, impotent. He waffled on about the holiday in Brazil, me having already read between the lines. I'd surmised well. He'd enjoyed sunning himself, wanted to proceed with his crack-brained scheme to live in the jungle but spent most of the time in Rio on Copacabana beach. Mario played the honeymoon trip, feeling alienated from the population, unable to speak the lingo. I doubted whether Mario attempted to exploit his criminal talents there, so he must have behaved like a good little boy. After a few weeks of this, he probably wanted to return to London. I endured all this only fortified by the main incentive, booze. This dragged on for three weeks before the inevitable big drama.

Instead of the long bellowing roar, a short strangulated "Danny" drifted up in the morning air. I sensed something was amiss, having a sneaking feeling it involved the Latino. A distraught Mario climbed the stairs, head hung low.

"I don't know why I did it."

"What's wrong Mario? What's up?"

Mario dubbed out his fag, lit another.

"What did you do Mario?"

He gulped. "I beat her up."

Suspicion confirmed. I had to play this one with Father Confessor understanding.

"What was it Mario? Wasn't a knife was it?"

Silence, followed by a mumble. "Bicycle chain."

Mario buried his face into hands, cigarette sticking out.

"Fucking hell man, is she alright?"

He became agitated.

"I dunno Dan, I dunno."

I fixed a cuppa.

"How did this all come about Mario?"

In between slurps, he told me about how they'd got drunk at a pub down Warwick Avenue. I pieced the story together, allowing for my own interpretation. According to Mario, she'd been flirting with men in the bar. He became jealous, probably aided by drunken flashbacks of Brazil. But this time they were back in London, his manor, brooking no funny business.

"I told her Dan, didn't I? Wait until I get you home."

Mario's thought for the day must have sobered her up a touch as he marched her home from the pub. In the front room, he unexpectedly wheeled the stolen bike in, confusing her.

"Mario, you're not going are you?"

He certainly was. Off his head. Slamming the door shut, he demolished the bike, smashing it up. The chain fell loose, Mario wrenching it from the frame, smashing it into her face. As she instinctively crouched on the floor, covering her torn, bleeding face, the maniac belted her full force on her neck and back. Mario then threw down the chain, kicked her prostrate body. He claimed to have snapped out of this, saw the horror, including bloodstains streaking walls and ceiling, then ran away like a coward and walked the streets all night. What could I say? I knew she wouldn't go to the police. If anything, she'd disappear, go to a friend or relative. Only one thing left for me to suggest.

"Come on Mario, we'd better go for a drink."

Into the nearest bar, ordered drinks, sat outside. Mario sunk into repetition.

"Why did I do it?"

Then silence. Glasses emptied, Mario withdrew into himself, me having to ask him for a five to get more drinks in. Without even looking at me, he pulled out the money. By our third pint, Mario spoke only two sentences.

"Dan, you know something? There's solace in drink."

No sooner had he uttered this profundity, Mario then burst into tears, shaking violently, sobbing uncontrollably, such sensitivity. Having no time to think, I had to place my arms around him, manly fashion.

"Mario, don't worry, it'll be alright, things'll work out."

Cold realisation hit me that moment. I'd taken him on board now. Bad boy that I was, what had I done to deserve this? He'd be staying for more than an afternoon weep. There'd be more trouble. My only concern, thinking ahead, how can I rid myself of him?

That night we divided the sofa tops, creating two beds. Next day, the machine swallowed the card but Mario still had some cash. He was in a confessional mood, deeply remorseful, telling me he'd probably never get back with her. To divert the subject somewhat, I light-heartedly dropped the suggestion that he should pen her a letter, telling how sorry he was and that in tune with the previous day's tearful conversation in the pub, that he'd decided to give up booze for keeps. This I felt, would keep him busy for a while. I'd also harboured a suspicion that he didn't only miss her, but needed an operational base with home comforts. Mario beavered away at the flat, creating a basketful of waste paper until this final product sat on the table, ready for posting. The contents were brilliantly manipulative. Rather than being written by the devil, it seemed as if Father Mac himself had composed it. After the formal apologies and violin stuff, he got to the root of things. Drink was to blame. He admitted to being an alcoholic, was going to seek help for his problems, now desired most earnestly to come off the demon drink. He was presently staying with his 'friend', giving my address in case she'd forgotten. Mario wanted to meet up with her, just one last time to say goodbye. Once the letter had been dispatched, I suggested going for a drink before we lay further plans. All of a sudden, Mario came over righteous.

"Look Dan, I meant what I wrote, I'm jacking it in."

As if by magic, he drew out a leaflet which he handed to me. 'Do you have problems with alcohol? Do you drink in the morning? Do you need a few quickies prior to a social engagement?'

Mario lectured me. Now, it seemed, I too had a drink problem because I could answer 'Yes' to any of the printed questions. I knew now that he'd be riding two wagons simultaneously, expecting me to take part in the circus. I liked drink, no question about it, but apart from obtaining it I didn't think I had too much of a problem. Unlike someone else I could have mentioned. Mario told me he would now be attending Alcoholics Anonymous meetings. To confirm this, out came a card, details, locations of meetings in the area.

"I mean it Dan, I'm gonna get straight, get back with her."

In his own twisted perverted mind he may have meant it, but I didn't half fancy knocking back an ice cold lager there and then.

That very night, I chaperoned Mario to an AA meeting in the West End, about a twenty minute walk from my place, past scores of noisy enticing bars all lit up. The meeting was held in the basement of a church. These were mostly men, older, mid-forties. I felt like a twelve-year old. Mario looking older, fitted in better, knew a couple of geezers present, small time ageing villains whose wives had left them. We sat at the back of a semi-circle of chairs. Like NA people, they told their stories. Broken marriages, lost jobs, brawls, declining fortunes, jail, sleeping rough. After a turn from a reformed character, people put their hands up, introducing themselves.

"Hello, I'm Tom and I'm an alcoholic."

These guys spoke with slurs, as if drunk, despite being stone cold sober. Burnt out, the spark having long since departed. I endured one of the longest hours I'd ever experienced, passing the time eyeing up a tasty looking forty year old blond woman who seemed to enjoy the members' gloating. When, mercifully, the meeting ended, Mario talked to the geezers he knew. Then, much to my embarrassment, we all held hands repeating, with Mario grunting, the Serenity Prayer. Later, I found myself forced to drink coffee in a nearby café, listening to further maudlin tales of alcoholism. My heart sank, I knew we'd be doing this every day for an indefinite period.

Come morning, we rose to another coffee and a stroll to the university complex. Here, we played snooker, Mario demonstrating his skills. This was different from pool, more tedious, as even Mario found it difficult to pot balls rapid succession. After a couple of games, we sat on the lawn in the sunshine, Mario eyeing up student's bikes, remarking that a bolt-cutter would come in handy. I wasn't interested in getting a bike as I weren't on a born again fitness fanatic trip. We queued up in the students' canteen, collecting a food tray, bombing out under the rail, by-passing the till. Mario read in an alcoholic pamphlet that once you'd eaten a full meal, the need for drink is less pronounced. We split up, me heading back to the flat. I'd come to an arrangement with him concerning the key, which we concealed behind a loose brick near the door framework. It had proved impossible to obtain a duplicate, needing landlord permission to have the key cut by a specialist security service.

I felt glad to get away from Mario for a few hours, home by myself, away from the incessant chatter about he, Mario, going dry, various other facets concerning himself, what a great guy he really was and how he'd eventually get his bird back. That afternoon, Mario turned up on the doorstep, mountain bike beside him. He shouted for me as I had the key, part of the arrangement being that whoever was upstairs would retain it, letting the other in. Downstairs, he showed off the bike, nicked from the university. In a holdall over his shoulders pair of bolt-cutters. As Mario wheeled the bike into the narrow hall he informed me that he'd gone to the trouble to steal another bike, hidden it just around the corner. So I'd be expected to join him on cycling excursions. Evening, back to AA meetings. Although these meetings were supposed to encourage you from the demon, these constant references only stoked my thirst. A couple more meetings later, even Mario started to give out indications of boredom and could see I wasn't the slightest bit interested, finally accompanying me to the pub where he sipped a coke as I downed a cool refreshing strong pint of lager.

Putting up Mario felt like serving a term. Even the living room took on the appearance of a cell. The sofa tops were placed apart, one apiece next to a window, dividing Mark's regulation type blankets between us. Mario placed a chair next to his bed, upon which he folded his clothes, a couple of jackets dangling on hangers perched on top. We also had a small headlamp each. Evenings were spent watching the flickering telly or reading if I wasn't out boozing. I'd helped create my own prison, run out of money and friends beause of Mario, who now also controlled the purse strings. To make matters worse, I had to go score blow for him, as he required something to replace the alcoholic crave. Getting stoned with Mario represented a real chore and a half, subjected to endless monologues.

I exercised an anthropological prerogative, piecing together something about his background. First of all, his name was phoney. Mario wasn't the slightest bit Mediterranean, hailing instead from a seaside resort on the South coast. I'd come across this phenomenon before, someone more Cockney than a genuine Londoner, all put on. Owing to time spent inside, living in town, mixing with the indigenous population, he'd cultivated the accent well. I also noticed he spoke in deeper tones than his natural voice, which only emerged whenever he became animated, talking about himself. Mario hailed from a middle-class background, but had been thrown out of numerous schools before graduating to borstals. He'd been kicked out of the family home after beating up his stepdad, mum and probably granny. Mario did more time, drifting to London, tried to become a villain in the West End, failed, emerged as a punk, dying his barnet, stealing all his clothes from the top shops in King's Road. He continued with his bullying ways, picking fights at gigs, robbing people in the toilets, the odd prison spell for theft or assault.

Mario, however, was no moron, which made him even more dangerous as he possessed an over-active imagination combined with animal cunning. He'd read a lot, result of being locked up. He semi-digested quality newspapers, listened to Radio Four and the Home Service, so he did have a smattering of knowledge about the outside world. A petty operator like Mario often talked about climbing a couple of rungs higher up the criminal fraternity and, of course, boasted of big important jobs already committed. Or claimed to, at least. Jail memories I found excruciating. How he'd been a baron, that he'd always got hold of dope inside, what a big man he was and how he'd get fit inside, working out against a background of Greek music on the radio, perfecting his pseudo-Mediterranean image. And now here was I, the new cellmate.

We had to support ourselves. For the first time in his life, Mario signed on, using my address. The larder had to be filled so we'd go on lifting expeditions to the nearby Safeways. I wasn't really on a shoplifting buzz but, eating his food, I felt obligated to contribute. Mario would nip inside while I awaited him on the concourse, me feeling drained after watching him working out on his morning sit and press ups. Mario would normally be in the store for about twenty minutes and then emerge with a manic grin carrying a large box on broad shoulders, filled to overflowing with steaks, oven chips, all the good things. I'd trot along behind him, back to base, then fulfill my part of the contract, scoring blow on tick. Mario whipped up eight course dinners after a smoke. Once the food settled, he'd suggest going down Portobello. Should I demonstrate the slightest sign of reluctance, he'd dig me out, saying I wasn't in shape. Cycling about on the stolen bikes, I once again realised how cut off from everyone I'd become, peddling alongside Mario, who mounted the superior bike, my mind drifting back to life with Boo, how everything had been so easy. Sometimes I'd give him the slip, double back to the house, hide the key, just to be alone for a while, get some rest from the maniac.

Mario soon tired of being skint, reverting to his old trade, handbag snatching. Now he had money and cards, I found my life more regulated. We'd stroll into the West End, him fancying a movie. So I'd have to sit through a load of trash that reflected his mentality, films about muscle-bound heroes single-handedly winning wars or conquering the universe. When Mario was on a movie buzz, I'd have to suffer four in a row. This was no distracting escape for a few hours as movies should be, more of a prolonged torment. I felt as though my brain had begun to disintegrate under the torrent of bullshit, obsession in the extreme about how he, Mario, was going to get a job, how that would impress the Latino. But he stood in a quandary. Why hadn't she answered the letter? Helpful as always, I suggested that maybe he should phone her up. A weird glow illuminated his eyes.

"Great idea!"

Next morning, I again managed to give him the slip, stepping into a pub for a drink, spend the last of my dole cheque. Mario found me. Was there no end to this?

He sported a new haircut, seemed over the moon.

"Dan! Great news! She wants to see me! It worked!"

My opinion of the human race reached an all-time low. How could anybody be so stupid? Despite the unfolding of another probable catalogue of pain, I sensed the pressure might be off me now he'd transferred his interests elsewhere. I could afford to worry about other people, in particular those I thought were asking for trouble.

Mario now vanished for a couple of days. This absence itself said more than anything about the idiocy of the woman. She'd obviously fallen for the changed-man routine, assisted by his props, AA leaflets sticking out of his jacket pocket, a teach yourself Portuguese book tucked under his arm, flowers. He'd told me he was going to buy her a kitten, so even this corny old trick worked. He now called over, ecstatic as he related to me about how he'd got back with her. My ears pricked up when he announced he'd be moving back, that he'd come over to remove some of his stuff. Mario proposed a celebration drink. As for me, blood pumped with excitement, relief and joy which I had to conceal. Sure, I needed a drink. The transformed man now sunk a couple of pints. Mario finished his supping, then asked me if I fancied a drink tomorrow, to which I replied that I'd see him next day. I thought I could just about handle that as I planned to slowly slink away to the sidelines then dash out away from the playing fields.

Midday, the shout aroused me from the now joined-together sofa tops. I'd already eradicated all signs of the mugger from my flat but he never noticed as he stepped in, arms entwined with the Latino. Both smiled as if nothing had ever gone wrong. Once I clocked her, my jaw hit the floor. Mario had made her change her appearance. Instead of looking like a secretary, she wore a denim suit and leather jacket. He'd also persuaded her to cut off most of her hair, dying it blond, making it fuzzy. This hadn't done her any favours, what looks she once had were gone. The Latino now looked like a chimp who'd come out of a snowstorm. I couldn't help it, maybe the whole thing was so absurd. Then, once I'd calmed down, off to the pub, games of pool, drinks. The born again non-alcoholic phase had been swiftly jettisoned.

I knew that I wasn't entirely free of Mario yet, merely working my way towards it. He still persisted in calling over, with and without the chimp. She'd got him a job as a waiter through an agency, so he felt entitled to parade his straight credentials before me. This conversion didn't last long as Mario lost his temper, assaulting the manager. The Latino didn't like him using stolen credit cards, preferring what she called honest money. When alone, Mario bored me rigid with tales of his rehabilitation which I knew to be all self-delusion. Mr Wonderful was even considering becoming a dad. Listening to this drivel, I once again reviewed my situation. Thanks to my hermit period, but more thanks particularly to Mario, everyone had given me the widest berth. I'd all but lost contact with the world outside. No one came over or even stopped in the street for a chat because of Mario. I comforted myself that I'd slip from his grasp, not quickly enough for my taste though. How could I make that final break without becoming engulfed by the inevitable eruption? I'd troubles of my own to consider, rent arrears piling up like a Third World debt. I'd been cashing all the rent cheques and, what with Mark due back, sooner or later I'd have some explaining to do. But how to finally shake off Mario? That was the question in hand. I got in contact with Loader who came over to give me assistance fixing a door. The flat certainly was getting into an advanced state of disrepair, superstructure beginning to crumble. I gave Loader the low-down about my Mario saga. He understood the situation only too well, advising me to blow him out pronto. More easy said than done. Trouble was, I just couldn't see a way out. It felt like being married to a nutcase.

As fate would have it, next day a shout bellowed up from the street.

"Danny!"

Mario again. I went down, opened the door. He stood there, eyes popping.

"It's happened again! I've done it again! Beaten her up!"

Her misfortune represented my opportunity. It was now or never. I let him have it.

"Look Mario, I can't handle this anymore, I've had enough. It's doing my head in. I think you need help but not the sort I can give you."

Mario stood outside, head bowed, acknowledging me to be right and that the party, here at least, had finished. All the same, he used a door-stepping technique to gain further entry.

"I've got a dole cheque coming soon through this address."

I told him I'd give it to the geezer in the restaurant below, collect it without bothering me. I'd had enough, thank you very much and closed the door on a forlorn Mario. As that door closed a tremendous wave of sheer relief overcame me. I actually trembled walking upstairs. Had I really rid myself of him at last or would he be over next day, maybe next week, alone, with the chimp, perhaps pull a 'chance meeting' on me? Precautions had to be taken to ensure the disease didn't creep up again to overwhelm and destroy me. Off to Loader for advice. After all, I'd blown Mario out as suggested. We put our heads together over a pint, arriving at the conclusion the best course would be to write him a letter, leave it with the dole cheque. Something final, absolute, beyond question. We penned a modest composition, keeping it straight, minimal, no toeholds provided. Short, sweet, to the point.

"Dear Mario. I can't see you anymore. It's all a bit too much, I just can't handle it. I think you need professional help but I can't see you anymore. Goodbye, Dan."

When his dole cheque arrived, I tacked the note on with an elastic band, handing it over to the man in the restaurant, then hovered in my flat above for a few days. His dreaded shout never materialised. This nightmare had ended, he finally got the message. Mezze for one.

CHAPTER FIFTEEN

No Mario, giro plus bomber script coming up meant I had reason to celebrate, taking the trip up to Doctor Nico. His place continued on the downward slide, waiting room chock full of druggies, mostly young smackheads off the estates who'd come for Methadone, DF118s or Valium. The waiting room was a Babel of worried-looking people itching for their prescriptions. It no longer resembled a doctor's surgery, more of a junkie's convention. This wouldn't last forever, sooner or later the authorities would twig it. I needed Durophet to give me energy, allow me to get out, circulate, try to resume some sort of social life. Armed with bombers and dole remnants, I hit the night spots with Loader to pick up threads.

Loader was still saving up for his trip to Thailand with Justin and had also invited half the world and their problems along. He claimed he'd be able to sort everything out, no trouble. A Mario residue still clung, his shadow haunting me. Every now and again I'd think I'd seen him pedalling away in the distance or coming out of a shop. It all turned out to be products of the imagination. People gave me the cold shoulder at first but it didn't take all that long before they realised I was no longer associated with the devil, so things started to perk up a bit. I supported myself the only way I knew how, lifting from local supermarkets, not bothering much with cheap stuff, deciding that if I was going to steal and suffer the consequences I'd only nick luxury foods. No can of beans for me if I felt peckish, only the best. Summer and autumn had passed me by in a blurred whirl, what with Mario blotting out the sun. Nevertheless I felt better, despite a tendency to lean more on booze.

I bumped into a girl named Karen outside Safeways in Bloomsbury just after I'd been doing a spot of lifting. I'd met her before, through friends, and she knew a lot of the folk I'd hung about with in bars a couple of years previously. One of them being a black bass player, her having a coffee-coloured kid about two years old, so it didn't take long to guess the father's identity. This fellow I remembered as a Romeo who knocked off other women and already had a couple more kids on the go. Before I knew it, I was back at Karen's place in the Bloomsbury Centre, a spacious council flat for a one-parent family. With me living down the road, we were practically neighbours. The place here was miles better than my gaff, warm and a colour telly. The kid liked me, so I played a while with it. Karen seemed pleased by this, making me a cup of tea, rolling a spliff. In a couple of hours I'd worked out that her folks disowned her because of the child, most likely owing to it not being lily white. It's father came over on the occasional visit to knock Karen off, the kid on his knee for an hour. Karen was lonely, skint and I stayed the night. Unfortunately, once again, I failed to deliver the goods, much as I wanted to as Karen was attractive and willing. Booze and pills were taking their toll. As the festive season tuned up I fancied, as I usually did this time of year, something approaching a home environment, a mini nuclear-family buzz even. So I arranged to see Karen again, possibly I might even succeed in stoking the flames of passion provided they hadn't already been extinguished by seasonal excess.

In the evening I'd be over at Karen's, always packing food nicked from a supermarket, maybe a small prezzie for the kid. My cooking number, demonstrating culinary skills had Karen impressed. Romance could have blossomed, we teetered on the brink, but when it came to lovemaking, I couldn't deliver. Perhaps also my inability was related to a psychological probem, not knowing where I stood in the world, lack of confidence, no goal, after effects of Mario, no money, owing tons of rent, Mark coming back any time, being a virtually worthless unemployable drone. Never mind. A drink, two would always cheer me up.

Early morning, a couple of days before Christmas, I went over to Karen's, told her I'd do some seasonal shoplifting, we'd have a really good traditional feast and holiday together. I'd fix everything. Later, I popped into Safeways by myself, commandeered a trolley, pushing it through the hordes, putting all the goodies into a box placed on top. Turkey, stuffing. sausages, pudding, tins of biscuits, boxes of chocolates. Soon, the box filled to overflowing. No one noticed as I left the supermarket carrying a laden box crowned with fancy Christmas crackers. I'd already picked up a discarded receipt, tucking it into a prominent position, allowing it to flap from the box. This I felt to be proper, no messing about lifting. A staff member helpfully opened the door for me as I walked out, then heaved the booty to Karen's flat.

I needed a drink pronto. Karen didn't have any booze in the house so dived into Safeways off-licence. Here, I grabbed a crate of bottled lager, strolled out ending one of the best lifting runs I'd had for ages. It blew Karen away when I arrived back with the extra cheer. Strangely enough, after all this effort, Karen started acting weird, seems that she didn't like me steaming into the crate, telling me that I couldn't just move into her flat, behave as if the place were mine. All I'd done was bring up a change of clothes, towel, razor and sounds. Far as I was concerned, this would just be a holiday type amusement for a couple of lonely isolated people. Instead, Karen got snotty, gave me marching orders. I wasn't going to get into a futile argument, maybe Karen just felt tired, what with the kid howling and screeching. Wanting peace, to relax I departcd without uttering protests.

Christmas Eve, late afternoon, I stood back on Karen's doorstep, thinking that now she'd had time to straighten out, I'd have plenty of good food, drink and company. Ringing the bell, the letterbox flapped open, a spiteful, almost loony voice screamed out.

"Piss off. Go away!"

I just rocked on the spot, flabbergasted, then heard a crashing noise. Gazing into a courtyard below to the source of the racket, I saw my personal property scattered. She'd loaded up a bin-liner, chucked it out the window. There wasn't any kicking in the door or pleas through the letterbox. I philosophically regretted investing my energy and efforts into providing her with a happy Christmas feast, spun on my heels, grabbed the bin-liner downstairs. Back to Holborn for a bleak Christmas without trimmings, just a few hurried snatched cans of food and bottles from the only supermarket trading at this late hour.

After an indifferent holiday period, I felt I'd had enough with people for the time being, rekindling the hermit flame. TV bailed me out, breaking up the day's shoplifting for my modest needs. I saw Loader but, being skint, it was no fun listening to his plans for imminent departure to sunny climes. Things weren't improved by Mark threatening to come back. Debts loomed large.

One morning a surprise, a handwritten note stuck to the door, bearing my name. The old ticker missed a beat. Could this be a Mario missive? Finally summoning up the courage, I read it. Enclosed, a phone number and, to my delight, Betty's name. She'd been in the area, tried to look me up. I rang her, arranging to meet in happy Hampstead where we used to drink together. In the back of my mind I wondered if possibly there may be a chance to see if my impotence had subsided. Certainly Betty sounded glad to hear from me.

Loader meanwhile departed to Thailand along with Justin and the rest of their swollen entourage. I didn't know how long they'd be away but that was of no concern to me, having enough on my plate, what with Mark back at an unspecified date. Down then to Hampstead. Just as I arrived a car pulled up, Betty stepping out, greeting me. She looked different, short haircut, sallow complexion, badly disguised with layers of make up, still trying to look glamorous. Immediately, I spotted tell-tale signs, she had a habit. Then came the shock, for who should prove to be the driver but none other than Redd. In spite of him being clean-shaven, scrubbed and well-dressed in comparison to myself, I wasn't in need of extraordinary powers of deduction to see a gear-orientated relationship stood in front of me. Supping a pint, conversation at a minimum, Redd hadn't changed. Phoney accent, over-protective with Betty, draping himself around her as if to ward me off. Some date this. I tagged along with them to an appointment, me and Betty waiting in the car, Redd going to score the smack. Conversation didn't exactly flow. Half an hour passed before he returned, then drove to their current domicile. They were sub-letting a council flat on the Regent's Park estate, a bare depressing dump, sofa, television, silver foil everywhere. Soon as they got through the door, both came alive. Anticipation. Talking incessantly, they prepared the foil, not even bothering with the preliminaries of burning off impurities. Straight on to foil, gear piled up in a little mountain, burnt until it ran down like sludgy oil, chasing the smoke up and down using tubes to inhale. In between prolonged snorts, they offered me a go. I declined, making excuses. Now they ignored me while watching the news. This was the last thing I needed, a junk scene. I rose from the sofa, them hardly noticing me as they nodded out. I mumbled farewells, departed, thinking about the fine state of affairs that the only bird who'd got in contact happened to be a junkie with Redd in tow.

With spring coming around again, nothing spectacular occurred. Same old routine. Signing on, nicking food and drink from supermarkets, visiting Doctor Nico, dreading Mark's return. Even now, I felt one step from dossing on the streets. A shout from below roused me, a voice I hadn't heard for a while. Mark, back from the States. Even before I reached downstairs, I knew Mark would be planning to sell the lease on his flat, collect all the back rent. Mark looked exactly the same, a mess. He strutted around the flat, moving the few sticks of furniture, the place no longer mine in any sense of the word. Mark even removed a couple of posters. His first enquiries concerned the rent, forcing me to confess I'd been lax on payment. Mark calculated that I owed him a grand, this amount being a fortune with fifty pence in my pockets and no prospects. I avoided a screaming incident by convincing him I'd go to Boo, get a couple of mega rails together, raise the money. He asked for the key, leaving me feeling good as homeless. This resulted in me sticking close to Mark as he toured town, celebrating his return, visiting old haunts. Mark worked as a pushbike messenger in New York, had been run over and was in the process of suing the city. He drank like a fish, standing between smack habits. Not having much cash, he began to pester me about putting in my request to Golden Goose Boo. Mark treated his captive audience to an exposition on the land of the free, greatest place on the planet, raving on about such riveting subjects as how cheap everything was over there. Everything in America seemed bigger, as were Billy the Kid's mystical meanderings. I had to see Boo as Mark laid on the pestering guilt trips in generous dollops.

I rang the Goose's bell. Enrico let me in and poured me out a few drinks while I told Boo about my financial plight. She was well aware where all this was leading, so after a few social niceties, I popped the question. Boo made an offer I wouldn't refuse provided I hand back some of the cash. Deal. Next day, not wishing to waste any time, I went over, collected two fat bagfuls, wheeled the rail out. Being Friday afternoon, I did roaring trade, an uplifting experience, raking in the dough, sickening to know I'd have to bung it to Mark. Just before I jacked it in, he came down the market. I handed over four hundred, repeating feat again Saturday. I retained some of the money, Boo's percentage dutifully dished out. This had me thinking that maybe I should start tapping the Goose for more golden eggs, suspecting hard times approached.

Living with Mark meant sharing a cell with a tramp, beds once more divided, alien odours beginning to dominate. Incentive for rubbing shoulders in such select company diminished by the day. I had to procure accommodation elsewhere, options zero, as dossing on people's floors became preferable to Holborn.

With Mark making serious noises about selling the lease, my tenure at Holborn looked all but finished. Staying there proved a pain, sometimes unable to get in at night if Mark crashed out or slept elsewhere. I'd be forced to doss in Red Lion Square on a bench, occasionally clashing with gentlemen of the road.

"You can't sleep here laddie, that's Big Jimmy's place!"

Lucky for me it was spring, unusually warm. Mark himself felt pissed off with living at Holborn, expressing this with anti-social behaviour, trying to nudge me out. I caught him throwing out some of my stuff, which led to a blazing row. We saw the futility of it all, cooled down, agreeing to go out for the day together, get away from it all. Mark suggested we visit an old girlfriend of his who had at least twenty years on me. I couldn't imagine Mark as a toyboy but decided to tag along. On the journey to Fulham, Mark told me about her. Anna was an ageing divorced actress who'd gone down a peg or two, lived in a spacious council flat. Anna greeted us in regal fashion. The flat was certainly large enough, a couple of spare rooms, her children having grown up and left. Anna herself looked quite masculine, talking in actressy tones. She remembered me from trendy parties of long ago. As Anna sat there, chattering away to Mark, I explored the flat. Theatrical memorabilia, the odd oil painting, good furniture, relics from the past. Contemporary, down-at-heel circumstances revealed themselves with an empty fridge, coat hanger aerial on the TV. Anna was also a juicer, that much I deduced from the pile of empty bottles. During our *tête-à-tête*, I nipped out to the off-licence, lifting a couple of bottles of wine. We ended up drinking in her flat. Anna was glad of some company, ragged as it was. She offered to put us up for as long as we fancied, me and Mark giving each other the wink, thinking of Holborn, now planning to settle in for a while.

Being a welcome guest was a pleasant change of affairs. Anna, although on the rock and roll, also had a modest private income, all her money going on booze, cigarettes and a morsel of food. Anna owned a chess set of massive dimensions, traditional wooden carvings, King and Queen almost a foot high, board the size of a small table. I laid the pieces out but neither Mark or Anna knew how to play. However, other forms of entertainment were forthcoming. Films on the telly with Anna and me talking endlessly between movies about stars and directors of yesteryear. Some nights me and Mark went up West to the bright lights, although drink usually kept us firmly anchored in Anna's flat. She even had foresight to lay in for mornings. And took Valium.

In that big bad world outside a general election was in the offing, Maggie's third term coming up. The three of us went into a nearby school fête one Saturday afternoon, where the main political parties ran stalls, playground festooned with rival propaganda. We left Anna, a fervent Labour supporter, arguing with some chinless Tories. As a guest, I'd always had a thing about paying my way best I could, so when we arrived at a supermarket, I told Mark that I fancied diving in, getting a box like Christmas. Inside I glanced around. Lazy Saturday afternoon shift. Perfect timing. Placing an empty box on a trolley, began the task of filling up, soon having it packed to the brim, jammed tight with food and drink. I always checked out price labels. Only the most expensive meats, cheeses and wines. Sheep and lamb syndrome. I slipped past the pay clerk, out in a twinkling. Mark, who'd remained outside, greeted me and I dashed around a corner, box high on my shoulder. We returned to the fate worse than death, plucking Anna from the cut and thrust of politics. That evening, we enjoyed a huge blow-out meal, Anna amazed at my feat, Mark trying to claim credit for keeping watch. Later, through a haze of drink, cigarette smoke and bloated bellies, Anna started getting a mite frisky, hinting that maybe I should join her in the bedroom for 'a chat' about movies. Fortunately Mark looked out for my interests, or possibly he felt jealous. Nevertheless he saved me any embarrassment, hustling Anna into her bedroom himself.

Days passed. We still hung about, a decision arrived at to watch election results at night on the telly, Anna absolutely convinced Labour were about to romp to victory. Not being a political animal, I decided to enliven proceedings with another box. Me and Mark went down to the King's Road after dropping Anna's Valium during a liquid breakfast. Once there, I saw a Safeway, telling Mark to keep watch, stay outside. In I went, oblivious to everything bar filling a box, casually throwing everything in as I wheeled the trolley. Joints of succulent beef, small frozen turkey. Approaching the drinks section, I thought I recognised a familiar face. Shrugging, I loaded up with port, brandy and champagne, ambling out box on shoulder, making for the exit. Once outside, I found myself confronted by familiar face in the company of about ten aproned staff, blocking all avenues of escape.

"Right, clever Dick. You're nicked. Would you mind coming along with me?"

Thanks to the Valium, I didn't even mull over the situation or make with some cheek. They marched me to the back of the store between familiar face and a burly staff member. Glancing up at a security lens, behind me, in their aprons, walking abreast like an army of freemasons, the staff. One carried the box, grave ceremony written all over him. They shoved me into a small room, sole furniture a table and a couple of plastic chairs, reading out a list of contents. Quite impressive, I'd been busy in those few short moments. They left me alone with one person guarding me, a hulking black guy who told me that it needed plenty of nerve to fill the box, thinking it a pity I'd been nabbed. He told me familiar face was the new manager, first day on the job, leaving me far from pleased to have been instrumental in helping a future promotion. A beat copper arrived, handcuffed me, dragging his prisoner to the police station over the road. They charged me, locking the cell door, so I bedded down for the night, thinking if you're going to do anything naughty, be straight. A deep peaceful sleep followed, care of the Valium. I awoke early next morning. For once, I found the breakfast fare edible, all the coppers in a good mood, whistling as they unlocked cells, giving out with witticisms. I guess the Tories must have won the election. Anna would be upset but maybe the magistrate might be feeling happy. Even the prison wagon driver warbled operatic arias on the bumpy journey to court. Once inside court, I collared a duty solicitor, giving her instructions. Guilty, but an aberration, I'd been a good boy for many the year, on the verge of getting a job. She couldn't believe the result after the formalities of a trial, conditional discharge for a year. Lucky for me the opposition hadn't triumphed. Back at Anna's with the last results coming in. She broke out the breakfast drinks, crying her eyes out. We'd been there a fortnight, time to get back to Holborn, worry about my lack of housing prospects.

I hung on in the shabby dump, nowhere to go, turning in the odd night kipping in the Square or snoozing through all night movies at the Scala, King's Cross. One sunny afternoon both me and Mark sat outside a pub on benches, no money. As if from nowhere, Loader and June appeared. From their cheery faces, back together again. He'd only just arrived back, handing us fifty quid each. This put a different complexion on things. After hearing Loader's tales of Asia we piled on to the tube, sinking our final cans, heading off to Anna's. Loader looked fit and well, like an American forestry worker. Mark talked about going back to the States, another reminder of my housing plight. I just listened, getting stuck into the drink at Anna's. June left early, Anna and Mark closeted themselves in her bedroom, while me and Loader played chess on the monster board. Loader now seemed distant, his mind drifting off elsewhere, letting out little signs, me putting this down to jet lag. After a drawn out game, felt tired, climbing into a spare bed, leaving Loader in the living room with blankets. During the night, I had to get up, take a leak. Loader paced up and down the living room, fully clothed, me asking him if he was okay. I returned to my slumbers. Morning, liquid breakfast, after which we three decamped back Holborn. Loader smoked endless joints, me noticing him going into a visible depression before our very eyes. As time dragged, one topic proved to be of interest during our conversations over cards. Loader told me of an empty squattable flat going in the Barnsbury Estate near Chapel Market. Taking a mental note of the address, deciding to go over next day, check it out. Departure time, late at night, saw Loader in what seemed to be a near catatonic stupor, like back at Maastricht. Mark agreed with my diagnosis, both thinking Loader might be out of commission for a while. Last we saw of him that night, he shuffled off back to June, mumbling. I could have escorted Loader, made sure he was alright, but I had to think of myself, getting a good night's kip to be up early morning for a special task.

CHAPTER SIXTEEN

Bright and early, over to see the flat, located on the eighth floor of a nine storey early sixties block, I took the urinal lift upwards. This flat stood at the end, entry from a shared outside balcony. I looked at the place from outside, peeking through the letterbox. Bare empty rooms, a few scattered circulars. Being Sunday, I walked over to Brick Lane via the canal, purchasing a lock and an old rusty screwdriver. Loader's cash donation was running short by now, but this was a priority investment. Back at the flat, I pushed the door with my shoulder, lucky for me the mortice had been left unlocked. Once inside, I replaced the lock, then checked out my new place. Electricity worked, a single bulb in the toilet. No gas or hot water. Rooms were stripped of furniture, left bare by the former inhabitants, even fitted carpets pulled up and carried off. In one tiny kiddie's room, festooned with Micky Mouse and Donald Duck stickers on the walls, a tiny strip of carpet. I thought I'd better camp overnight, despite the whole idea being a gloomy prospect. I went out, bought a Sunday paper, stole some beer and food from a small supermarket, settled in for the long night ahead. When it finally got dark hours later, I crashed out on the carpet strip, a jumper for my pillow, my trusty old lifting overcoat as blanket. When I awoke early morning, for a moment I thought myself to be held in a police cell. Then, clocking Mickey Mouse, I realised I lay in my new residence. Two tasks were to be completed, first of all a visit to the dole office, notify change of address, then off to Mark's, collect the remnants of my possessions. Mark had bunged out most of my stuff, so I shifted everything over to Barnsbury in one go. My entire worldly goods consisted of a battered old radio, a couple of jackets, somewhat frayed, and some tee shirts. As I sat on the carpet, I surveyed the pile that represented everything I'd accumulated over the years. Circumstances had deteriorated considerably.

Over the next few days, I procured myself some furniture. An armchair hauled out from a skip, an old fashioned fridge, dumped on the first floor near the dustbins, a huge model which I walked to the lifts. Not that I had anything to store in it, but a trip down to the supermarket would provide the remedy. Doown the Lane I'd also spent a few pence on a couple of bits of rusty cutlery and chipped plates, swiped glasses from the pub next door. To feed myself I used the old overcoat, timing my expeditions to coincide with rainfall to avoid rousing suspicion. Couldn't afford to get caught, so I operated with extreme caution, going in, looking around and, if the slightest glimmering of a feeling are over me, I'd leave empty handed, off to another one. Diet varied little, cooked food such as those old standbys, pies and chicken plus bottles of wine to wash it down. I'd made sure to invest in a cork-screw

Before my morning constitutional, I heard a knocking at the door, the first visitor since assuming residence. Peeking through the keyhole, fearing officialdom, I was reassured that the hunchback figure outside proved to be Justin. I opened the door to a clean more relaxed person who now looked like he was getting laid on a regular basis. According to Loader, he'd already returned from Asia a month previously. Proof positive in me thinking he'd been getting his end away stood nearby, gazing over the balcony, what I took to be the girlfriend, boyish-looking but, as Justin was quick off the mark to announce, working actress. Justin felt proud of his partner, a bit of class, first bird he'd pulled in years since the bearded lady. I escorted them into the kitchen, showed off my fridge. The rest of the flat though was bare apart from the armchair, radio and discarded newspapers. My bedroom made the girlfriend's nose turn up in disgust, her eyes drawn to the clothes pile crowned on its peak with a plate containing a chicken skeleton, no cutlery in sight. Maybe she thought I'd wolfed it down with bare hands, the empty wine bottle covered in greasy pawprints supplying the evidence. Flies circumnavigated the remains. Justin hustled me aside, taking advantage of her culture shock to slip me a twenty pound note, also promising to lend me an old telly from his flat. A long overdue gesture from this quarter. After they left I went out drinking alone in nearby bars, a boring depressing loser's game, then hit a take-away, finally treating myself to a bottle of whiskey. Once I'd scoffed the take-away, I fell into a deep slumber, leaving the bottle untouched.

Morning, I found myself disturbed by tapping on the door. Mark on his first visit. It didn't take more than a few seconds to guess he was on the earhole, pleading poverty. His excuse this time being that he'd been waiting for money to come through from the sale of the lease. Mark had already blown all the rail money on a drinking bout. What annoyed me about Mark was that this fellow had made me suffer owing to his meanness. Whenever he got a dole cheque, Mark had always, without fail, put on the old disappearing act. With cash in his pocket he wouldn't hang around in our shabby circles, where he'd been poncing drinks and money. To avoid spending and paying back his numerous creditors, Mark would slip off to Soho, mix with his old art school scene. From there followed party invites, him vanishing weekends, me sleeping rough. However, when I got a cheque, Mark clung like a barnacle. I thought I'd have some fun at his expense, remembering the full bottle of whiskey. So before he could put the tap on me for some imagined back rent, I'd get him drunk, see what developed. I poured out Mark quadruple measures, then took the helm, toasting

"Here's to the United States of America! Here's to you selling the flat!"

At my urging, Mark downed all the drinks in one, me roaring him on to greater drinking feats. Ater fifteen minutes, Mark started getting energetic, enthusiastic about everything, living in America, going back, inviting me over. Once he'd gulped another measure, this time a double quadruple, Mark did a wild mad Indian dance around my empty rooms, whooping it up. He bent over double, gasped as blood rushed to his head, even making him look like a Redskin. We went to a local pub once he'd drained the bottle, almost a solo feat, me virtually abstaining. By now, Mark was flaming, walking as if battling a force ten gale. I steered him into a pub, ordering a couple of lagers, myself not too inebriated, setting up balls for a game on the pool table in a side room. Even before we'd broken, Mark puked up over the table, promptly collapsing. I spun my heels, walking past bar staff, outside, over the road. From a vantage point, I saw the doors of the pub fly open, a crimson head emerging, Mark being unceremoniously heaved out by an irate bull terrier of a landlord. The front of Mark's clothing was decorated with liquid vomit. He landed on all fours, tried to rise but slid back into his own puke, floundering. Mark crawled like a wounded dog, producing more runny brown vomit, making horrible noises. And so, with it still only early afternoon, I left the horror show, off for a stroll up West.

A few days later, more morning knocks on the door. A gang of workmen here to do double glazing, rewiring, plumbing. I let them in, within an hour they'd ripped up half the floor, taken out some wiring, removed doors, transforming my place into a building site. I left for breakfast and to mull this one over. Arriving back a bacon sandwich and coffee later, the flat was completely upside down, apart from my little den. Water switched off, even the toilet wasn't flushing. They said this would be a ten day job. I knew that if I resisted, they could have thrown me out easily, change the lock, so I co-operated to the extent of leaving them a key, concealed underneath a mat outside, to leave behind when they quit for the day. They weren't bad geezers and I guessed it would be alright to trust them. Besides, I didn't have anything worth stealing. I'd just have to spend some time away, socialising, then dossing on other people's floors, returning for the odd night or dole cheque delivery. This refurbishment, I felt, might also be a prelude to the council moving in a fresh tenant.

First port of call, Justin, who still lived in the same flat. Once inside, I realised how the tide had turned, such a stark contrast to my own debased living conditions. As Justin was about to spend some time over with his actress, he said I could stay over for a few days, look after his place, even tipping me some spending money. That soon went. I didn't refuse this generous offer, taking the money, agreeing. Although, there and then, I felt grateful, I remembered how Justin behaved in the past and that I'd helped set him up. So it didn't bring on pangs of conscience as I started to fine-tooth his gaff. Plenty of ill-concealed money lying around, proceeds of drug dealing. I skimmed those hidden wads. Evidence of trade was all over the place. Bits of dope on the carpets, next to the bed, on his coffee table. Justin came back after a few days, failing to notice I was wearing a pair of his jeans. He gave me the telly he'd promised, an old black and white portable. I thanked him, heading back to the building site, no plans for the future apart from a plan to track Loader down. Sure enough, key in place under mat. At least some progress had been achieved, double glazing fitted.

With Loader in his weird state, I wondered about seeing him, having a gut feeling something was wrong in his loft area. He stayed with June, who'd taken over the West End flat he'd shared previously when working at the theatre. June answered the door, me asking straight away if Loader were in. She put her index finger on her lip, glanced backwards and I knew instantly that Loader had rekindled his loony trip. June ushered me into the kitchen, brewed a cup of tea, our conversation conducted in hushed whispers.

"How is he?"

"Bad, really, really bad."

"How bad?"

"I've never seen him like this before."

I explained that I had, during our stay in Maastricht. I went then into a small bedroom near their bathroom. Loader sat in a leather upholstered swivel chair he'd once fished out of a skip. He faced a corner of the room away from the window and door, head tilted downward. I spun him around to face me. Loader looked up, gave out a weak grin then stared at his feet again.

"What's the trouble Loader?"

"It's bad."

"How bad?"

"Really bad."

"Oh, I see."

Loader switched off, resumed toe gazing, me spinning him back to his corner.

"Catch you later, Loader."

A weak grunt the only reply. I closed the door quietly, moved back into the kitchen where June sat, chain-smoking. I told her Loader seemed to be far beyond any reclamation effort we could mount, instead, he needed professional assistance. June seemed to think that as I knew what was going on then perhaps I could lend a hand. But I had hassles of my own and besides, the pigeons had well and truly flown the coop. June would have no choice but to phone the hospital. I thought about Loader as I walked downstairs, into the streets where there were more beggars on the beat, homeless people kipping in doorways. Poor old Loader, a sobbing wreck in a half catatonic state. I'd keep in touch, visit him in the bin once June eventually got on to the blower. A couple of ECT hits and he'd be right as rain.

In Camden, I visited a couple of other people I'd nudged elbows with in the past, their place of employment now the local bars. One being Lena, who had a home in the area where she lived with her teenage son. She'd worked behind most of the bars in Camden Town, where I'd provided amusement for her many times and she'd bunged me free drinks whenever the landlord's back was turned. Lena had a touch of glamour, always well turned out despite being past her prime and ageing. The other barmaid, Harriet, came from the country, wealthy folks. Now she lived in the big city, roughing it. Harriet seemed impressed with the weird characters who strayed into bars in this neck of the woods. Harriet herself was a strapping wench, tall, big boned, portly and a good bomber punter, using them as appetite suppressants. Trouble is, with their comedown aftermath, you develop eating urges, then stuff yourself, putting it all back on again. Harriet must have weighed a good fourteen stone, possibly more. She lived in the pub, went out drinking with Lena, then smoked dope back at Lena's gaff, like good buddies. I took note Lena didn't mind me crawling over, staying the odd night.

Even though the building site cleared, I preferred to kip over at Camden. Burglars, probably kids, had broken in, stolen my telly, the only thing of value, not bothering with anything else. So now the only time I'd turn the key would be to change clothes or collect giros. Booze became my major energy source. Waking up mornings at Lena's, I'd need at least a quid to start off the day, just to get that first drink. I drunk around Camden Town more than ever, luck and fmances notwithstanding.

Price of booze had increased to the outrageous sum of a quid a pint, so I saw more of Lena and Harriet. They were always good for a drink or two and I'd lob them the odd scrap of dope or bomber. Harriet got the sack from the pub for insulting customers, me not knowing whether the bombers or her gaining confidence was responsible. Whatever the cause, she had to vacate her room in the pub, problem solved when Lena rented her a room. Harriet now signed on for the first time in her life. She was going through a screwing phase. Whenever I stayed at Lena's, Harriet would have different geezers around after closing time, picked up from pubs, young Northern geezers with Newcastle United tattoos and incomprehensible accents. Come morning, I'd take the mickey but be more conciliatory if they were good for a quid if I didn't have my starter.

As regards Loader, June bowed to the inevitable, having him carted off to a hospital in Muswell Hill, near Highgate Woods. It looked like an old chocks away setting minus airfield, building of a phalanx design, low level, spreading out from a circular centre point. I located Loader's room where he lay in bed, smiling as I entered, telling me how he'd had the shocks. Loader even cracked jokes, demonstrating some of his customary flair of old. I thought he'd made good progress, the shocks certainly seemed to produce results. After an hour I left, confident that he'd soon be out and about once more.

Back at the building site, the place had been re-squatted by two geezers. I didn't argue the point as I'd already decided to up camp, move to Lena's sofa, squat myself a more inhabitable residence. Still on a bender, once in Lena's, I befriended everyone in a bar near her place, carried on well as possible without money. Yet every night I'd arrive back at Lena's well plastered, where her and Harriet would rustle up more drinks. I steamed into the alcohol once again, our boozy conversations aided by blow, lasting well over the midnight hour. As normal, I provided entertainment, utilising my talents of mimicry, sussing out the people we'd encountered that day, taking the mick. Sometimes, should cash be available, we'd take the show on the road.

Cashing my giro, I walked up to Kentish Town, thinking about catching a bus up to Doctor Nico's. So what with it being that time of the month to score bombers, needing fresh air, I decided to take a healthy stroll up there instead. I thought I recognised a familiar grey-haired figure standing motionless in the distance, gazing into a shop window. On closer inspection, it turned out to be Loader with his coat collar turned up. I greeted him, saying how good it as to see him out and about. But Loader just stared into the record shop window, eyes riveted to an album cover on prominent display featuring an empty bedstead floating in the sky. Loader didn't acknowledge my presence beyond a muted emotionless "Hello Dan," staring into the void beyond. Seems the shocks hadn't worked too well this time, Loader back to a state of almost catatonic proportions, me just about squeezing the information from him that he'd walked down from Highgate. He just stood there, saying he'd let everyone down, that he was a bad person. No reasoning with him, pointless to take him to the pub for a swift one, so I bought him a coffee, telling him I'd be up to visit sometime soon. Then, off to Doctor Nico's. Any further attempt at communication with Loader in this state I knew to be worthless.

At Doctor Nico's things were hectic. Young lads in track suits and trainers, junkies and a few punks jostled around the entrance. I waited for an hour, seated amongst the scratching, rheumy-eyed, nodding-off masses. In came junkie couples with lethargic kids, bedraggled nutters. Depressing. I finally got into the surgery where Nico sat behind his desk, arm in a sling, result of an encounter with an irate customer. Another man present to write prescriptions I presumed to be doubling as a bodyguard. I cut out formalities, straight to the point. Durophet please. Doctor Nico looked up, puzzled.

"Do you know where to get them?"

I thought this to be a funny question but paid him the money, collected the script, barging my way through the motley gathering. Into the pharmacy next door, handing over the prescription only to be met by a self-satisfied smile.

"I'm sorry, but the government have ordered us to cease distributing these pills."

Stunned. I'd been on these for four years. Source of entertainment, money, buzzed out a week a month. I pushed my way back into Nico's surgery past protesting deadbeats, demanding my money back. He coughed up, me leaving in a huff.

Being late September, magic mushroom season came upon us. Me, Lena and Harriet plus a couple of their friends, Jiff and his missus, who lived in a squat in the council buildings opposite, were driven by Jiff to Kenwood House, Hampstead Heath, for tea. Over a cuppa, Jiff told me there were empties on the council estate, arousing my interest as I'd been impinging on Lena's hospitality for a shade too long. After tea we went for a stroll on the Heath. Jiff spotted some mushrooms growing, so we were soon scanning lawns, filling up a plastic bag. I had to watch Harriet who, despite being a country girl, picked toadstools by mistake. Later we dried them, dropped them but they weren't very strong. Back at Lena's, her new boyfriend called around. Previously she'd been seeing a Canadian but this latest romance happened to be a Peruvian Indian. Didn't catch his name, calling him Big Chief. Having no humour or not understanding, he shrugged off my remarks. Big Chief hung around with another Latin American, a little fat geezer who spoke virtually no English. I didn't bother questioning Lena's taste in men, it being none of my business, her putting me up on her sofa. No rocking the boat. The five of us spent one evening drinking firewater in Lena's front room, her and Big Chief sneaking off while Harriet retired downstairs leaving me with the little fat geezer. I felt tired, wanted the room to myself, to get my head down on the sofa. So I kidded him up in a half joking manner, suggesting to him that Harriet lay waiting for him downstairs. He didn't appear to understand, so I did it in sign language, indicating a plump body, then raising my arm, bunk-up down below, speaking to him.

"Big woman, downstairs, like you much, Esso Besso."

He gave me an idiot grin, scuttling downstairs hotfoot. I crashed out immediately, knackered but smiling to myself. Morning, when up and dressing, Harriet came in.

"Danny, guess what happened last night? That horrible fat bloke came down when I went to sleep, took off his clothes, got into bed."

She didn't know what was happening until awoken by a hand roaming up and down her vast expanse. She went mad, throwing him out by the scruff of his neck. By now, I'd hit a laughing fit. Harriet then suspected that the incident might be something to do with me, but I stressed my innocence. Why, she only had to look at the language problem.

Harriet soon cheered up when her dole arrived. We went out to cash it then visited Jiff. He seemed together. Apart from running a car, his squat had a colour telly and phone. This impressed Harriet and I soon inspected the outside of that empty flat, entry barred by a solid steel security door. Inside Jiff's place I started looking at the racing page in the paper. For a laugh, I suggested to Harriet that she put her dole money on a favourite, double the the dole in one go. She shrugged it off but when Jiff chimed in, claiming to have pulled that trick coming out richer many the time, she took notice. Later, me and Harriet adjourned to a bar in the nearby North London Polytechnic, where she once worked and knew some of the staff. We started drinking our way through free measures while I pursued those day's runners. I'd already picked her a horse, an even money shot on to a four-timer in a small field. by the time Harriet finished her third pint she'd made up her mind. Fifty quid of her dole on that horse. As it was near to the off, we departed to the bookies, her backing it five-to-four on, not quite even money after taking tax into consideration, but near enough. Confidence increased as the horse came to one-to-three on. Lucky we'd taken the price. Waiting for what seemed an age to Harriet, the race was off, live on the video screen. A couple of furlongs out from the winning post, the horse had yet to be mentioned, even seen, which was disturbing since it only raced against four rivals. Harriet bit her lip, I reassured her.

"Don't worry, he's keeping it for a late run."

But those four runners flashed past the post, with Harriet's selection beaten by a distance. Her mouth dangled.

"What about a steward's enquiry?"

No hope of that, I told her. Now Harriet went pale, into a state of shock. I couldn't help it, nor hold it together, bursting into laughter. Not Harriet. She broke down, tears, her wailing distracting other punters so I had to usher Harriet outside where she sobbed hysterically.

"What am I going to do? I owe Lena rent."

I calmed her down and feeling a twinge of guilt, told Harriet she'd be welcome to come and live with me in that new squat I planned to open. This cheered her up, blubbering ceased. Lena's place was getting a bit uncomfortable what with Big Chief having his moccasin in the door. Harriet didn't like him either. Now all I had to do was gain access to the flat. Besides I didn't want to live by myself, thinking a woman's touch might brighten a place up.

I collected a lock, crowbar and special screwdriver to help nudge the steel door off from the inside. Entry would be gained from the roof. I'd costumed myself, wearing some spare gear a council workman I knew from the pub lent me. The first hurdle I cleared by getting into the block by ringing the tradesmen's bell. Having cracked the intercom system, I got onto the flat roof. Out there, I gazed down to a divided balcony below. Jiff said I'd have to drop on to it in order to gain entry into that flat. I balked at this. Five more stories below – should I miscalculate, I'd be brown bread Lucky for me, courage or judgement wasn't disturbed by barbiturates, instead I was clean as a whistle, not even a hangover. Jumping down would be no good. I could twist an ankle, what with it being a ten foot drop. Down first went the toolbag, followed by me dropping down, almost leaving the skin of my nose on the wall above. The balcony doors opened without having to smash glass.

Once inside, I didn't bother to explore, just went into the corridor to face the door. Opening it, I found myself confronted by the steel monster of a security door. I put on the new lock but just couldn't make any impression on that steel door, giving up when my crowbar buckled. So now I stood there, trapped, cursing. I had to remove the workman's cap, put on a thinking one. No way back up, certainly not down. I noticed the other flat that shared the balcony had its lights on, music playing, laid back stuff. Maybe the inhabitants would be of the understanding variety, so I knocked on the other balcony window, told the young woman who answered that I'd been locked in by my workmates who'd gone off to a café with the key to the metal door. She wanted to know just exactly what we'd been doing in there, so I spun a cock and bull story, claiming new residents might be moving in and there might be some noise as we removed the door. I saw leftist type literature, type of stuff schoolteachers and social workers in 'Revolutionary' groups tried in vain to sell outside Camden tube.

Out on the streets again, I wondered how I could remove that steel brute. I visited Lena, talking so fast that Sitting Bull couldn't understand. She suggested I go see her Canadian ex who was employed in a workshop around the corner, maybe he'd have the correct tools for the job. There, I loaned a matloc from the cowboy. I'd burnt out my welcome everywhere, what with Lena's turning into a reservation, so I worked up my adrenaline, went up again to the roof. Another jump and there I stood once more, gazing at the steel door from the inside. There would be no milk chocolate calling card, this time I'd succeed. Sure enough, the wonder tool worked at the very first attempt. Tremendous noise but no curious neighbours. I walked the door into the flat, tested my lock, becoming the new resident. Removing the council clothes, I headed down to the pub after dropping off the matloc. I even ponced a couple of quid off the cowboy. Hitting the pub, who should be there propping up the bar but Redd, sipping half a pint, pinned.

"Ah! Danny Boy."

I smiled, ordered up a pint which I downed in one.

"I needed that Redd."

He must have thought I'd become a raving alkie. Redd put on a serious face, went into Barney Rubble.

"This habit man, what's the best way you can think of overcoming the problem?"

It transpired that Betty had left him, shacked up with a geezer she'd met in rehab. Redd probably thought that if he gave up gear, he could get her back. I'd heard this story before in different variations, then suggested Narcotics Anonymous.

"What's that? What do they do?"

I gave Redd the lowdown. How you raise your hand in the meeting when you have the urge to speak, tell them your name is Redd and that you're chemically dependent.

"I don't want anyone to know my name."

I didn't bother to explain to Redd what anonymous meant, let alone the God bit and the twelve steps. I drained my second pint.

"Must shoot off now Redd. Don't forget, NA."

Back at the block I followed a couple in through the intercom entrance. Inside the flat, I looked around carefully. Long corridor, bathroom, bog, kitchen, large front room with those shared balconies, further down the corridor, four bedrooms, electric working, along with heating. I turned it on and within quarter of an hour the place was like a greenhouse. But I needed a couple of keys for downstairs, so I knocked up next door, where the woman answered the door. I admitted that I was a squatter, needed a key and wasn't it terrible what the government was doing, or rather was not doing, about homelessness. Even before I'd had time to wheel out some pleasing slogans for her benefit, she'd handed over the key so I could get a duplicate cut.

"Right on sister."

Before she could invite me to attend a meeting, I'd dashed down the stairs, good as in.

I spent my customary first night on the floor at the greenhouse. Morning, Harriet buzzed up on the intercom. She liked the look of the place and the idea it would be me, her, no one else. We went up to see Jiff in his squat in the other block, yet another friend of his, Jock, was in attendance. This urned out to be handy because Jock lent me some bedding, a couple of blankets, sleeping bag, a sheet of foam and a carpet. Then off to Lena's to collect an old leather sofa and a black and white telly she'd promised me. Now we were starting to get set up. It was essential that I had a few bob in my pockct, so thoughts of that Golden Goose came to mind. With Enrico's help, me laying on entertainment, I procured two railfulls, pulling in a cool one hundred and fifty, even having stuff left over. So I rigged out Lena, payment for putting me up and helping me. Harriet liked the dresses but, despite the generous sizes, nothing came close to fitting. Boo failed to see any of the money but didn't seem to mind so I reckoned myself to be in for another couple of rails. We set to decorating the flat, yellow light cream for the living room. I'd found a couple of cans in a skip. Harriet lent a hand and, doing so, told me a bit about herself. She came from a big house in the country which had a long gravel driveway. Facilities for servants, stables for horses. But no servants or horses. Billiard rooms were converted into dining space. Harriet's sister turned out to be the golden girl, successful, academic, married, home in the sticks and physically half the size of Harriet's dimensions. Apple of the parents' eye. Father's trousers could just about be glimpsed through the apron, henpecked. The mother hated Harriet, beating her. Both had money, were academics themselves but, reading between the lines, I figured out they lived on inherited wealth.

CHAPTER SEVENTEEN

Me and Harriet settled in, dole now arriving at our new address. Another rail came through, two fat sackfuls. I laid the dresses out in the front room, Harriet this time passing disparaging remarks about the styles, how she couldn't bear stuff like that. Just because she'd never fit into them. Soon after, Harriet came in depressed, telling me she was pregnant. Second abortion of the year coming up, me thinking it must have been one of the Newcastle geezers with tattoos. I chanted "United! We are the champions!"

I hadn't seen Loader for well over a month, so wondering how he'd progressed, if at all, I jumped on a bus, took a ride up to the bin. Loader seemed half and half, somewhat on that road to recovery. Being a crisp sunny winter's day, I invited Loader to take a trip down to my new flat. He fancied a walk, so off we trekked. As we strolled down to Camden, I noticed Loader's tendency to drift off the topic of conversation, me guessing he just wasn't ready to resume normal transmission. Later, up at the flat, I introduced him to Harriet. He looked ill, not his usual sun-tanned self, medication having given his skin a yellowish tinge. Once I'd showed him around I prepared a coffee, Loader standing out on the balcony, gazing out to the horizon. I brought the coffee out but he simply stood there, back turned, me asking if he felt alright. Loader eased over to face me, tears streaming.

"What's up Loader?" "Nothing."

After coffee I cheered him up, offering the fare back to the bin. He politely declined, heading back under his own steam, watching from the balcony as he started his uphill climb. Loader wasn't better but I had a feeling he'd be back, sooner rather than later.

One Sunday morning, me and Harriet sat in the front room discussing the flat. We'd put shelves here, a carpet there, potted plant here, even rent a colour TV. Apart from her forthcoming trip to the abortion clinic, Harriet seemed happy enough considering, even looking forward to Christmas and New Year. I'd be getting another rail, so we'd have money. The intercom rang. a Welsh woman's voice crackled through.

"Hello Danny."

Cleo, a friend of Ozwald's, a cockney dope dealer from way back during my smack days. I'd heard she'd cleaned her act up, worked earning money at her profession, the oldest one around. I buzzed down, let her in. Once up, I introduced Cleo to Harriet, then we all sat down together. For some reason though, Harriet took instant dislike. Cleo was small or, what they say in the trade, petite, with a rather prominent conk, making her look like something out of a Tolkien fantasy. She had a teenage son who attended a progressive school in the country where the pupils never advanced beyond basket weaving and joint-rolling. Cleo herself also shifted a bit of dope and as a sideline knocked out other drugs. And she always had money. Once we'd rapped awhile, I gave her an introductory tour of the flat, where, in one of the empty bedrooms, she pulled out a two hundred ml bottle of Codeine.

Like nearly everything else, the government had slapped a prohibition but Cleo claimed to know a bent chemist who dispensed it for the usual consideration. I took a long hard swig of the evidence, Cleo then asking if I fancied a drink in the pub. She was obviously thinking about getting together a base for Christmas here in London for dealing and working from a bordello shared with some other women. The three of us went to the pub and by now, the Codeine started to come on. Harriet detached herself from our company, went off to rein in some more prospective one night stands. Cleo staked me to drinks. Soon, I was offering her temporary space in the flat, even a small room for her son Blodwyn. A shrewd operator, Cleo took advantage, snapping up the offer. A few drinks later, she'd made all the arrangements, Cleo talking fast in her singing Welsh tones, me falling in with it all. She'd be down tomorrow with Blodwyn and some belongings. Hours, and many drinks later, I shouted to her as she slipped away.

"See you bright and early tomorrow Cleo!"

Harriet's antenna must have picked up the gist of things because back at the flat, she launched into me.

"I thought you said there'd only be the two of us. I don't mind Loader but I don't like the look of that Cleo. Who is she? What does she do?"

I didn't think Harriet would appreciate the whole truth, so I gave her a manageable fragment, telling her Cleo was okay, together, owned her own house in Swansea, had money, worked sometimes as a pavement artist, wanted to stay over for a couple of weeks during the Christmas period to make some cash. Harriet, more forward than usual due to alcoholic intake, demanded to know why didn't Cleo go back to Swansea, spend Christmas there? I tirelessly explained that all Cleo's Welsh friends were down here in London, that she wanted to spend some time here to make money, here being more profitable to practice pavement artistry, me knowing though it would be more from walking on them than drawing or chalking. Harriet kept droning her objections until I snapped, giving it to her.

"Look, this is a squat. She'll only be down till just after Christmas and it'll be more money in the house. We've got the rooms and it's not as if the flat were ours anyway. Besides, if you don't like it, you can always go elsewhere for a couple of weeks. Your parents' residence in the country for instance."

Harriet absented herself to her own room, where she sat weeping bitterly. Harriet knew she had no choice but to go along with my decision. As far as I was concerned, the matter had been resolved.

First thing next morning, Cleo arrived, making it seem like a traveller's encampment at the door. Rolled up cuts of foam, rucksacks, little Jack Russell on a length of string and Blodwyn, a fourteen year old who towered above his tiny mum. Blodwyn looked like a hippy kid, desert boots, corduroy trousers, shabby old man's jacket with rolling equipment tin in his pocket. He also carried an electric guitar and small amp. Blodwyn wasn't the most communicative of human beings either. Harriet just stood rooted, arms folded, pouting as they moved into their respective rooms, the dog stopping to cock his leg at the radiator. Within half an hour, Cleo fitted in a red lightbulb, incense burning as she sat cross-legged on the foam, Blodwyn by her side, rolling spliff. Over the next few days, Cleo strutted around the flat like she owned the place. The kitchen filled with Marks & Spencers food and Cleo took over the telly and front room. Harriet meanwhile, retreated into her bedroom with another telly she'd borrowed from someone. She wasn't exactly pleased with the new occupants but I felt happy enough as Cleo always had an inexhaustible supply of drugs at the ready. I still drank heavily, hanging around in Camden bars, spending all my money. After a particularly prolonged bout, I rounded an evening off with a fight against two Northern geezers. Coming back to the flat looking the worse for wear, Cleo greeted me with a siren song.

"I'll help you relax Danny, come to my room now."

I plonked myself down on her bedding as she fished out some foil. Then two and two added up. I should have suspected after the Codeine that she was still into smack. Once a junkie. But I didn't issue forth condemnations. So I indulged once again, seeing Harriet before I crashed out, her wanting details on the fight, I felt too far gone to deliver a frontline report, but she failed to understand what my pinned eyes signified, or the scratching and tilted head.

Morning, Cleo woke me up, saying she was off to Swansea, me guessing that she was off to supply her contacts there once she'd collected the drugs in London. Cleo offered to lend me the fare if I fancied coming. Blodwyn would remain with Harriet, who was glad to see the back of Cleo for a while. Harriet herself had been spending more time hanging about with Jiff and his girlfriend in their flat, telling me she was having her dole cheque redirected via their address as she didn't trust Cleo. This annoyed me because Cleo always had money, there being no need or desire to help herself to Harriet's pittance. So we left Blodwyn in his room with an ounce of hash and headed off. I felt glad to get out of London, hadn't left the confines for ages. Maybe I'd have an adventure or two. Being with Cleo, a well respected person by miscreants in that neck of the woods, I'd be guaranteed a good time away from grumpy Harriet and the bars of Camden Town.

We caught the train at Paddington late aftemoon arriving early evening stoned out of our heads. We'd been smoking heavy black on the journey. Cleo's house was situated near the station, a damp two up two down. We soon decamped to the local dreg hangout, a pub nicknamed the Menby. Once inside, crowds of people buzzed around Cleo, who fixed deals amidst the Welsh babble in this crowded smoky place, full of punks, hippies, travellers of various descriptions. The whiff of different hash joints clouded the atmosphere, everyone knew everybody else like a dealer's pub in Camden except all had Welsh accents. I felt a touch whacked after the journey, asking Cleo if she had any sulphate, my standby since the demise of bombers.

"Don't worry Danny."

Cleo slipped me a rolled up cigarette paper, which I swallowed, washing it down with beer. It soon hit the bloodstream, pepping me up. I looked around the pub, all sorts of girls, some very tasty with English accents. I put this down to the university in town. With the buzz coming on, I got into the flow straight away, taking the mickey, cracking one-liners in rapid succession. Cleo introduced me to a friend of hers, Enid, who, judging from the stream of signals transmitted for my benefit, liked me. Enid was another hobbit, same height as Cleo, well into her thirties, fuzzy long hair, big nose and eyes. A benevolent witch. I found her attractive enough, although not my usual type. Soon I was cracking her up and, once the pub finally emptied, we went along with most other patrons to a nearby party. I sat down with Enid, hair standing on end but feeling rusty with the old chat up routine I just kept her amused. I realised that, despite her laughter at the witticisms, she didn't understand half what I was talking about. Maybe the heightened Cockney on speed was confusing for her. Still, at least Enid seemed happy enough with my company. Any reference to telly programmes usually elicited a response, meaning she was probably on the dole, watching the box all the time. I was enchanted by her accent, it sounded exotic, like a smouldering sexy Pakistani voice. Once the party wound down we went back to Cleo's place. She had in the meantime been flying around, doing her dealing, supplying Swansea with dope and other goodies, me now suspecting Cleo had a smack sideline on the go. Cleo certainly looked like she'd been sampling, eyes pinned, but I didn't mind, what with Enid hanging on my arm all lovey-dovey. Cleo drew me aside, giving the nudge.

"She's fond of you now Danny."

Cleo made herself scarce, leaving us alone in front of a gas fire in the living room. Yet another fag, off with the lights, lit a candle and I did something I hadn't been capable of for well over a year. We slept on the sofa afterwards, my sleep not sustained, thanks to the speed. Things raced in my head, confirming recovery back in the libido stakes with a repeat performance morningtime. Cleo was more than delighted when, between yodellings in the kitchen, I told her I'd invited Enid down for Christmas. Cleo had done all her business, was wadded up, ready to go back to London, ply her other trade, generate yet more money. We arrived back at

Paddington, me bending her ear about how much I liked Enid, that she'd done something to me, even declaring myself to be in love, causing Cleo to comment.

"She'll give you a baby if you want."

I was so carried away with myself that I started wondering what it would be like to be a dad.

Almost as soon as we arrived back, the intercom buzzed continuously. Afternoons the flat was being over-run by Welsh hippies and convoy traveller types. Mumbled conversations drifted from Cleo's room. Harriet virtually confined herself to her own room in between visits to Jiff and girlfriend, obviously better types of people. Blodwyn always sat there just rolling joints, looking after the dog. I felt a tiny bit shaded in my own gaff but happy enough with the dope, looking forward to Enid coming down.

Nightime, Cleo's callers changed to a more select bunch, her friends, a shady duo. One, a young gay art student named Matthew, fresh faced with glasses but heavy smack habit. Pete, the other fellow, yet another gay bloke who seemed to be her main supplier of dope and smack. Pete was in his mid-thirties, cool, long hair, beard and Welsh. Cleo hustled them into her room until the smell of joints mingled with chased smack seeped out. I knew the score now so I knocked on the door, waited for my invite, with Pete greeting me.

"Welcome to the opium den Danny."

Harriet hadn't the slightest idea of what was going on and, although Blodwyn stuck by his mother's side rolling joints, he also seemed unaware of what was happening. I felt this to be weird, considering his daddy died of a smack overdose. Harriet pulled me aside one night, failing to comprehend the significance of my pinned eyes.

"Why are those two always here?"

Meaning Matthew and Pete. My bread had been well buttered, so I told her it was of no consequence, what did it matter? Might as well use the flat to entertain while she had it. Harriet resigned herself, under protest. She also had another query, wondering why so many Christmas cards were coming through the post, at a rate of ten a day. I explained that Cleo was a popular person. Look at all those visitors she received. I neglected to mention they were from her Billy Bunters in the skin trade. Apart from dealing, Cleo proved to be a hard working girl, putting in long shifts at the bordello. So she was loaded, never hesitating to bung me the odd tenner. By some miracle she also managed to sign on in Swansea.

The Goose laid a rail before Christmas. Now I was rolling in dough. Enid would be down any day and I wanted to show her the bright lights. Then came good news from the loony bin up the hill. Loader had checked out, sending me a card announcing the tidings, telling me he'd moved back with June in the West End and once he'd regained his bearings I'd be in for a drink. Ozwald came over, more though to see Cleo than me, fixing up deals. Both knew each other well, were sharp characters equally into the secondary market, drugs and landing a dishonest touch. The day before Enid was due over from Swansea, Loader called up. We went for that drink, him one hundred percent again. I told him of the grand romance and he offered us the use of June's flat on Christmas day, which I jumped at. Colour telly, mod cons. This all had the makings of an excellent Christmas. All I wanted now was to see Enid in my wealthy state, full of seasonal cheer and goodwill. I began to construct a love nest in my room, buying comfy cushions from a second-hand shop, putting all my washable materials through the laundry, hoisted a pattern curtain, placed a pink light bulb into the socket, flowers in a vase, cleaned up, lit a scented candle. So I'd set it all up, romantic atmosphere provided, then went down to the bus station to collect her as arranged, six in the evening.

With breathless anticipation I waltzed down to Victoria. The coach from Swansea pulled in and Enid jumped off clutching a bin-liner full of her necessities. I greeted Enid with an effusion of kisses, grabbing her bag like a gentleman, walking her to the bus stop, arm on shoulder. Back home at the squat the place was deserted, everyone out. By now, Cleo had about one hundred Christmas cards blue-tacked up in the front room. As there wasn't anyone to greet us, I took Enid over to Boo's. Here, everything went well, champagne poured, Enrico preparing little delicacies. Later, with me well steamed, Enid told me she was happy, even though she felt strange, nervous even. I understood. The big city, champers flowing, tropically heated flat. Must have been different from the creaking pace of Wales. Later, in the pub, drinks were on me as I showed off Enid. People were glad to see me in such good form. In love, spending, spreading festive cheer. Back home everyone had returned, me introducing Enid to Harriet, who didn't appear all that impressed. Later that night, when we finally retired to the love nest, I learned that my performance in Swansea wasn't just a flash in the pan. Fully functional on all levels again. Morning, laying in bed together, smoking a joint, Enid told me about the alternative lifestyle in Wales. How people squatted on the land in remote valleys, erected teepees, lived like Red Indians. Curious, this evolved into a regular conversation, me wondering how they got their dole delivered. It all sounded idyllic from my bed, a new way of life, the inevitable dreams woven. As I prepared coffee in the kitchen, whistling away like a songbird, Harriet came in. She seemed upset, the sound of lovemaking and pillow talk had possibly kept her awake. Instead, Harriet produced some burnt foil unearthed from the front room.

"Skagheads. I should have guessed."

At last. She'd managed to twig part of it. I was merely blasé

"Well, it's Christmas, innit."

Meanwhile Cleo and Enid blabbered away in high frequency Welsh accents. Off they went together to do the Christmas shopping, thereby relieving me of that tiresome chore. Later that evening in the pub I introduced Enid to Ozwald and a few other people I'd hung about with, the usual collection of loafers, drunks, thieves and pillheads. Like a fool, I started preaching to them about the joys of an alternative lifestyle in the untamed wilds of Wales. Ozwald and the others weren't impressed, taking the piss, calling me Teepee Dan. Being in love, I could live with it. Saturday, I decided to give Enid a real treat, go with Loader to see Arsenal play, last match before Christmas. Loader was back to his old form, silly walks down the road, funny hat, heavy joints honed with lethal black that made the head spin like a tumbler. Inside the ground, we met the pub crowd. Enid had never seen so many people packed nto such a small space. We became separated from the rest in the crush to leave. That didn't matter. Enid though appeared nervous but I soon cheered her up, saying that the next day we'd go down to the West End, see the bright lights, to have a meal in Chinatown, visit Loader and June, show her where we'd be spending a happy romantic Christmas day together. Evening, down to the pub again. Money was starting to run dry, but I'd reserved enough for the Sunday. Enid herself didn't drink all that much.

"I'd have a pint you know, with the boys."

She must have guessed by now that I was a bit of an alkie. All the same, managed to rise to the occasion later that evening. We nattered into the wee hours about tepees, the winter solstice, mystical gobbledygook. I gave her a copy of the newspaper.

"Here Enid, read our horoscopes."

She handed back the paper and, in that irresistible accent, asked me to read them instead. The romantic atmosphere was illuminated by flickering candlelight, me reading out loud, Enid gazing intently into my eyes as I smoked a jay.

Christmas almost upon us, Cleo and Enid got in some last minute shopping. That Cleo certainly paid her way, no question about it. Later, me and Enid headed up West, sunk a few beers then restaurant time, Chinatown. They gave us the menus as we sat at the table, hot Chinese tea poured, me glancing down at the list, picking my selection. Enid appeared to be having trouble, asking her what she fancied, she looked at me confused.

"I can't read Danny."

They must have given her a Chinese language menu in error, so I passed over mine.

"No Danny, I can't read, I said."

"What? Not even the stuff printed in English?"

"No. I never learned to, you see."

This indeed came as a revelation. No wonder she wanted an alternative lifestyle, something that excluded the written word. So I had to go through the painful process of reading the menu out loud, number one to one hundred and thirty seven. Later, as we ate the meal, fortified by a bottle of wine, I started thinking that I could do something that bordered on the useful, teach Enid to read, even though at thirty five she had some years on me. On the way over to Loader's, I asked her why she hadn't learnt to read or write.

"I couldn't be bothered."

Strange reply. Enid must have hated school, bunked off all the time. At Loader's, I introduced her to June, tempted to blurt out the surprising revelation. But I kept it to myself. All seemed fine enough, Enid getting on well with Loader and June. As booze and joints were consumed, bedtime nodded on the horizon, me looking forward to it with confidence, even if Enid was an illiterate, I'd teach her at least to write her address come morning. Loader lent us his bedroom but once tucked into bed, Enid froze on me, refusing to let me touch her. I wasn't bothered by this, aided by the day's excesses, I fell into a deep sleep. Morning, I woke, rolled over for a cuddle. Much to my surprise, Enid had already dressed, demanding to go back to Cleo. On the return journey, she deliberately seated herself opposite on the bus, ignoring me, gazing into the void, out the window. What wrong had I done?

Back at the squat, this silent treatment continued. Enid though, didn't extend the cold shoulder to Cleo. They both jabbered away as I brooded in my room, trying to figure out where I'd gone wrong. Was it me? Something I said? I broached the subject, asking her what the trouble was.

"I want to go back to Swansea."

She'd left it a bit late, this being Christmas Eve. Cleo stuck her nose in, saying it would be best to wait until after Christmas, go back after Boxing Day. I tried every method of communication to reach Enid apart from slipping her a note, a pointless exercise given the circumstances. As I put in strenuous efforts to discover the cause of this big freeze, I began to realise the futility of it all. I'd deluded myself. Now dislike smouldered. Even if Enid couldn't read, I thought, at least she wasn't retarded, she should be capable of expressing herself verbally. Despite further prompting, Enid remained silent. Then I realised that yes indeed, she was probably just an idiot. Maybe I'd been daft myself, building up all this romantic fervour, tepee talk, spending all my dough. Reflecting on the last few days, I calculated that Enid hadn't spent a penny of her money. I'd been led up the garden path by a reactivated libido. Harriet meanwhile decided to spend the holiday with Jiff and girlfriend. I felt guilty now. I'd given Harriet a raw deal, apart from also making a fool of myself. That night, Enid kipped alone in the front room. Now I knew where things stood, this particular rejection didn't bother me. It had all evaporated in the space of a day. All I desired now, to see Christmas go quickly, Enid along with it.

Christmas morning, me and Cleo chased some gear along with her friend Matthew, who'd mysteriously appeared. We all transferred over to Loader's in a cab, complete with Blodwyn, dog, drink and food. Loader let us in, then split with June. I just sat watching telly, pinned, while Blodwyn rolled joints. The others nattered away, ignoring me. I noticed that Matthew, despite being camp English, now spoke in a smacked out Welsh accent. Out of boredom, I tried speaking to Blodwyn, who had the dog by his side. In reality, the beast was probably a superior conversationalist. I ate the pre-cooked food, enduring programmes on telly, just wanting to crawl into a hole, forget about it. At last, Loader arrived back with June, saving me from terminal boredom. I took Loader aside, telling him how I'd been fluffed out. The tribe made their way back without my company as I'd decided to stay over in a more convivial environment. At least Loader was back to his old self, persuading me to do impersonations of the dim Welsh.

Boxing Day, I made my way back to the squat, pockets denuded of cash. Inside the flat they all sat in the front room, including Matthew, watching television, discussing a friend of theirs who wanted to terminate a pregnancy. Enid's voice drifted above the pow wow.

"Juniper berries will do the job."

Blodwyn sat on the floor, still at his joint rolling duty. The intercom rang. Justin. I whipped him straight down to the pub and, me being skint, he did the honours. I gave him a rough outline of my recent troubles as he laid the pints out. After consuming vast amounts, I went back home alone to the flat, flaming drunk, ready for action. Entering the hallway, avoiding contact with the living room, I went straight into Harriet's den.

"Alright Harriet?"

I sat down on the floor, let her have it.

"It's not right, is it Harriet? Here we are, sitting in your room and we should be in the living room. Them Welsh are taking the fucking piss."

I raised myself from the floor.

"Now watch this, Harriet."

She seemed unaware an explosion was imminent. I stormed into the front room where they sat, Blodwyn rolling. The motley crew just perched there, eyes glued, apathetic daze, watching a repeat of a programme they'd seen a couple of days previously.

"Everyone enjoying themselves? Well fuck me, not this old crap again. Let's see what's on the other side."

A Welsh voice rose from the hashish mist.

"Oh no, don't turn over."

I snapped, out of control, shouting, raising the half dead.

"Turn it over! I'll fucking turn it over!"

With that, I tore the plug from its socket, throwing the telly against the wall, then turning to face Cleo, Enid and Matthew huddled together, trembling before my white rage. I grabbed Enid, thrusting her against the wall, same spot as the telly.

"Why don't you go then! Fuck off back to Swansea!"

Valiant Matthew vanished, followed by Cleo. Blodwyn still sat there, half-rolled joint in his lap. I patted him on the head, addressing him gently.

"You too Blodwyn son. On yer bike."

It took a mere five minutes for them to place their valuables into a couple of dustbin liners then decamp, me clapping hands in sheer delight as the ragged despondent exodus departed, wailing like the lost tribe. I walked into the front room, followed by an elated Harriet.

"God Dan, that even scared me."

I summed it up.

"This little episode's over. I'm chucking out all their stuff."

Outside the door, in the passageway, I piled up their crap. Unplayed guitar and amp, clothes, magazines crowned by red light bulb on top. Back into the front room, plucking off the Christmas cards, slinging them into a Marks & Spencers bag. Harriet grinned ironically.

"Pavement artist. Really, Danny."

"Yeah, and juniper berries."

We laughed and next morning the stuff had gone from outside. The hobbits had returned, then departed with the gear, posting my spare key I'd had cut for them through the letterbox.

Just before New Year, a surprise letter, an eviction notice. We had a couple of weeks to vacate the premises but no chance of obtaining a court order restraining bailiffs. With New Year coming up there were other things on my mind. I intended catching up on postponed merrymaking now the love affair had finished. The more-enduring affair with the bottle would be resumed for Hogmanay. I met Ozwald during the day's rounds so we spent the New Year's Eve together, knocking it back, ending up at a Camden junkies pub. Here, despite being skint, I was on cracking form, joking about tepees, drink flowing at a frantic pace, others paying. One particular geezer kept asking me if I wanted to buy some magic mushrooms. I told him confidentially my pockets were empty, that I was hustling drink and if he didn't believe me, then to observe me in operation, moving from table to table, getting treated. After New Year came in, everyone kissed each other, the mushroom seller came over, handing me a packet.

"Here you are mate, you have 'em. You really earn your drinks don't you? Better watch out, these are strong, from Cornwall."

That sounded fine, just as long as they weren't from Wales. Me and Ozwald dropped them, myself taking the lion's share, hanging around the pub until it emptied. The mushrooms started coming on, so we took a walk along the canal to visit a dealer friend who lived a couple of miles away. By now, I was roaring, the booze wore off in the cold as we passed by the TV AM building, all lit up. I was so far gone that another biblical scene presented itself, the temple of Jerusalem, a high budget nativity set. Pause for joint wonderment, then we ducked off later into the side streets, narrow and crooked, empty apart from the sound of voices whooping it up at parties. By the time we reached the main road, my head swam in a blaze of colours. Suddenly, I felt ill, my stomach churning over, telling Ozwald I had to rest a while, I felt like puking. Trying desperately to hold it back, within seconds I realised why they call it a technicolour yawn. All over the wall splashing back onto me. I made horrible heaving gasping noises.

"You alright Dan?"

"No man ... "

Another stomach eruption, causing me to bend and heave but nothing issued forth. Empty. Now I crouched in the classic position, arm leaning on wall, the other on hip, trying to regularise my breathing, wheezing, groaning, rattling through the one unblocked nostril. Then a trumpeting fart. Uncontrollable, a lava flow down the inside of my jeans. I cried out in despair.

"Ozwald! Fuck me! I've shit meself!"

He just burst out laughing then screwed up his face, backing away, doing an unwitting impersonation of Hitler, backward goose-steps, arm raised, finger under nose.

"Blimey Dan, what a pen and ink!"

Well pissed off. I'd have to squelch my way back home, so we departed, me arranging to ring him next day. Returning to the flat, the crap began to freeze, stiffen, as I waddled back for a bath, revellers wishing me a happy new year. Still slightly trippy, I arrived back, diving into the bath and changing clothes. Cleaned up, I decided to visit Jiff and his girlfriend who were putting up a Scottish geezer aptly named Jock who I figured might take hogmanay seriously, have some spare booze around, help me come down off the trip. Calling over, Jock answered the door, hushing me up, guiding me into the kitchen past Jiff and girlfriend asleep in their room. I related the mushroom story asking Jock if he had any booze. He didn't but, understanding my plight, asked me to wait a moment as he went out to the balcony, fiddled behind some wood off-cuts, pulling out a bottle. Unlabled, corked, inside, floating in liquid, a preserved snake, complete with grinning fangs, black little eyes. Jock explained he'd found it in the cupboard of a derelict house, had been contemplating drinking it ever since, the liquid must be pure alcohol. Jock hadn't enjoyed New Year's Eve, being skint and, unlike me, hadn't been out on the earhole. Two glasses produced were soon filled to the brim, us toasting New Year, then back in one. Jock somersaulted on to the floor.

"God man! Don't touch any more, you'll go blind!"

I poured my second helping, telling Jock it felt fine. Down the hatch. This time, my empty stomach lit up like a furnace, the trip legged it. Jock turned green, declared himself ill, crawling off to bed. I took the bottle back to the squat, swigging the evil contents. Having left my keys in the soiled pants, I found myself locked out. Harriet however, alerted by my banging the door, opened up to see me draining the dregs, the snake's head beginning to slither out and dangle. Harriet confiscated the bottle, putting me to bed. Getting up late next day, I remembered what happened, phoned Ozwald, arranged to go see him. On the way over, I bumped into Jiff, enquiring into Jock's health. Jiff told me that my previous night's drinking partner had gone to hospital, his head swollen almost twice its normal size, turned purple and, to top it all, he'd been rendered partially blind. I made my way over to Ozwald's to carry on with our session. Hair of the hound.

Jock recovered after a couple of days, the two of us having a laugh over the whole affair. Harriet underwent her abortion, started seeing a shrink to be treated for depression. Her great pals, Jiff and his girlfriend, had ripped off a month's worth of her dole cheques, then moved to another flat, leaving Jock in charge. Unable to prove anything, Harriet had no recourse but to fluff them out. I spent the time over at Ozwald's, two of us on a right royal bender. With him dealing there was no shortage of cash, me even having a win on the horses, buying a bottle of Bourbon. Back at the squat, we downed it all in a minute, wandering on to the streets like mindless lunatics. Later, I lost Ozwald, him ending up asleep on the stairway outside the flat, some kind Samaritan coming out, wrapping a blanket around him. Morning, he woke up, calling for me, frozen stiff. After a can from the offy we tried to retrace our steps. My win, Bourbon, collapsing in the road. Ozwald couldn't figure out what happened to his car. Once numerous enquiries were made, we discovered it had been towed away. He'd have to cough up sixty quid.

"Danny, I'm gonna give up drinking, get my head together."

I just felt a thirst coming on at the mere mention of booze. Ozwald wasn't the only one who had to get his head together. I was being evicted any day now. Harriet, thanks to letters from her shrink, got placed on the council waiting list as a vulnerable, housed temporarily in a bed and breakfast. Ozwald offered to put me up until I found another squat so I retrieved my stuff, transporting over to his tower-block flat.

CHAPTER EIGHTEEN

From the time I moved to Ozwald's floorspace, not much excitement went down. Both of us were squeezed for cash, Ozwald's dealing enterprises reduced to a trickle thanks to a severe dope famine. Our bender ground to a halt, me having been just a notch above turning into an alkie, there being no ill effects apart from an ever-present craving for a drink. We spent most of the time conjuring meals together, me popping out for the odd lifting expedition, food, the odd bottle of wine down the pants. We sat in at nights watching telly. Something I've always noticed when accepting other people's hospitality, you have no say in determining programmes viewed. If there was a good movie on, the host, if they so desired, would watch a stupid comedy on the other side. You'd have to sit there pretending to be amused by the turgid antics on-screen, making with phoney chuckles now and again to avoid embarrassment. Or sometimes you'd be looking at a programme and the other person would walk into the room and switch channels as though you didn't exist. No choice but to grin and bear it, like being a kid again. When being put up by someone, you are at their mercy, prone to their whims and fancies. No matter how easy-going or benevolent they are, there's no room for disagreements. Usually, an insignificant thing such as an oft-repeated phrase or personality trait that nurtures annoyance is enough to kick off the leaving process. I knew I'd have to get somewhere and quick. Fortunately, I got on well with Ozwald, him coming from the same background as myself, no head start in life and I didn't want to mess up our friendship. Life with Ozwald during this period of repose was just about interesting enough to sustain me.

Sometimes he'd rustle up some money on a small deal, meaning drink and the dough for an odd bet during televised racing, me introducing him to the dubious pleasures of gambling. Ozwald kept magazines on varios subjects that interested him such as antiques, travel, guns, treasure hunting and plenty of comics, something I always enjoyed reading. We weaved dreams about holidays we'd take once one of us struck it rich. Ozwald, apart from being relatively hard-headed, practical when generating finances, was an avid reader of Tarot cards. When he revealed this to me, I was bemused. As we were watching boring television, he asked me if I fancied having mine done. Off went the telly as Ozwald produced a box where his cards were lovingly stored, wiping the table down with a cloth, telling me he took the Tarot seriously, so no taking the piss. I respected his wish, watching him doing a Celtic spread once I'd shuffled the pack. My reading began, kicking off with the past. The Jester. Out on a bender, going nowhere. The present.

Highest I could achieve in the future, an offer. Immediate future, the Hermit. A time of being on my own, reflection, a leaning towards celibacy, finally getting my head together. Coins came up. Ozwald liked these cards. Money. Final result, Ace of Wands. Divine justice, love. Nothing could go wrong. This put me in an upbeat mood, a positive feeling.

Maybe, I thought, I should take up this business of Tarot reading, break into the Hampstead circuit, stage a comeback. Ozwald's trade picked up again, him spending more time shifting drugs. I wasn't exactly getting in the way but knew I'd have to make tracks, move on. It had to be another squat, so I went over to the block where I'd lived with Harriet. Steel doors everywhere, no possibility of gaining access. Eventually, I located an empty in another block, ground floor, no steel door, just a mesh across the windows front and back. I told Ozwald about it and he said go for it Dan. Once I'd gained entry, he'd drive down with my worldly possessions. This time, I'd be squatting on my own.

I went along to the flat armed with the usual complement of locks and tools, breaking in, no trouble, changing locks, turning on electricity. A small corridor led to a bathroom and toilet, the only room lacking window mesh. The kitchen had cupboards, no cooker. The only other room in this tiny flat was the living room cum bedroom. Here, one of the windows had been boarded up, the rest meshed, allowing only a modicum of light to enter this room, which contained some furniture. A couple of hard and soft chairs, old wardrobe, set of drawers and a bed, underneath a trunk full of old woman's clothes, imitation fur coat, funny shoes, a few faded photos. The place had a strange smell to it, like dead skin. Maybe the previous tenant laid here for a while after snuffing it. Despite what may have been laying there, the bed was comfy enough. Ozwald helped move in my gear as promised, but I'd continue to visit him. So here I was, new place, change of address for the dole again. Back to stage one. No money, nothing to look forward to except the odd drink now and again. Once inside my cage I did receive a few visitors but once I'd shown them around the gloom, it would be adjournment to a watering hole. Loader came over buoyant. Off to Thailand again. Pub for fond farewells. As there wasn't any central heating this time, I bought a couple of cheap electric heaters, bar and fan jobs, down the Lane, which I left switched on all the time. The bar heater served for cooking purposes. Lucky I'd retained the lifting coat of old which, although having no shape left, did the job. I cooked cans or cold foods over my upturned bar heater, knowing this to be dangerous owing to dripping fat landing on the element. Soon, the room became strewn with clothes, empty cans, chipbags and newspapers. Days were cold and dark, me huddled in front of the heaters, going to bed early to keep warm. When the sun decided to shine, it reflected diamond shapes through the mesh on the walls adding to my depressing surroundings. It looked like the end of the line but I had a feeling something was about to occur that wasn't to my detriment. Hadn't the Tarot promised something in the offing?

Jock, of snakehead fame, lived nearby with some other people in a squatted flat. After telling him I'd become a devotee of the Tarot he invited me over. I took my newly acquired tackle, a flash pack nicked from a Camden Passage shop, and it didn't take long for me to be weaving magic spells with the pack. Here sat a full complement of willing punters, a young geezer with girlfriend, a man slumped in the corner wearing an expensive leather jacket and Jock, who told them with enthusiasm that I read the Tarot. The girl immediately showed interest so I volunteered an instant reading. Spreading the deck following some hocus pocus formalities, I did the business. As the cards came good, I began to get into the flow of things. So smoothly did it go that, judging from her reaction, I could have pulled her there and then. Next on the agenda, boyfriend. He didn't seem all that interested but soon paid attention when he drew some heavy cards. I managed to ease everything out once I'd detected his anxiety, explaining the situation would mellow out, meanwhile, he'd have to watch his step, show extra caution. Jock followed. This Tarot reading lark certainly proved tiring but the new found novelty of it all carried me through. Taking a leaf out of Ozwald's book, I did a Celtic spread, having Jock on the go from card one. By the time I'd hit the past, had it all worked out, Jock sat in absolute agreement, astonished.

"How did you know that about me, man?"

"It's all in the cards, Jock."

By the time I'd finished, Jock was asking me about the future state of the nation, what would happen over the next few years. Flicking a couple more cards, I didn't have to be a soothsayer to answer that one.

"Things will get a lot worse Jock."

I was about to jack it in for the evening when the geezer in the leather jacket showed signs of life, requesting a reading. Despite being tired and not particularly enamoured of him, I spread the cards again. They weren't favourable. The devil appeared, he sighed.

"That fellow again."

So he'd had a reading done recently. Final verdict came up, bad result. Being honest with the geezer, I told him the cards pointed in only one direction.

"You're fucked mate."

"That's what the other reader told me a couple of weeks ago."

All things considered, he acted philosophically enough, pulling out a large packet of coke, about eight grams. A dealer. We got off our heads, then down to the pub where the others, grateful for services rendered, ordered my night's drinks. This Tarot might prove profitable after all.

Boosted by my abilities with the old Tarot, I embarked on readings for other people. I did Lena's, but this effort wasn't exactly crowned with success, her having a different interpretation of the final outcome. For a few weeks, my latest craze drew me steadily further into the Camden pub scene with its no-hopers. I found myself with a solid backlog of potential punters, all on hold, myself quite astonished how many people were into such things. So after reading books on mystical claptrap, I dabbled in the odd bit of palmistry, concentrating on finger shapes and lifelines. Women, the eternal mugs, mostly went in for this, but occasionally an aggressive drunk thrust a bunch of bananas at me.

"Can you read that, Jimmy?"

Always red hot on the dream weaving, I started thinking of learning all this spook racket stuff, getting a triskelion made up to wear around my neck. I even obtained material to knock up a black cape, a carpetbag for any paraphernalia, useful for housecalls. As the idea took hold, I considered dyeing the sides of my barnet grey in order to look distinguished, so I could aim at the higher end of the market, starting off with people like middle aged actresses, working my way up to richer pickings. Ozwald found my adoption of the Tarot amusing, him saying I'd have gone down a wow in teepeeland, Merlin of the show. As the Tarot hadn't made me any money, financial donations would be the next logical move, but I sure enough was getting drink and drugs laid on. Ozwald thought I could earn a few bob shifting small deals around the bars.

"You know enough people, don't you Dan?"

For the dealing experiment, Ozwald laid some dope on me. The Tarot would provide an excellent cover. I soon discovered selling dope in such surroundings is a full time occupation, profits, if any, consumed in liquid.

During one of these punting excursions, I headed to the market where I did the rail, nipping into a pub for a drink.

"Hello Dan."

A girl who'd attended Kingsway same time as me, named Lucy, who lived a couple of doors away from Boo. I'd seen her around, off and on, over the years. Lucy drank with a friend, both studied, doing an art course together. As Lucy was my age, I kidded her up about being an eternal student. One thing led to another, the final bit of Ozwald's blow traded with a mini cab driver. With this money, we moved on to a late night drinking stop, a Greek place. I fancied Lucy's mate but, on the way home, the three of us got into a drunken argument over some trifle or other, resulting in me making my lonely way back to the cage.

With a couple of quid still left in my pocket, I went over to see Lucy, acting on her invitation. My confidence hadn't stopped soaring. Thanks to the Tarot, I'd had weeks of people eating from my palm. Ringing the bell, a smiling Lucy took me on a tour of the massive house. Once upstairs in her own flat, she made with the body talk, so we started getting off with one another. Just as we were about to reach the conclusion, Lucy broke off.

"You've got to wear a condom."

AIDS week had just finished, putting the frighteners on everyone. I didn't fret over this interuptus, so long as there would be drinking compensation. Down to the pub. Lucy was blonde, lots of people thought her pretty. Not from my vantage point. Slightly goofy teeth, moustache. Wearing heels, she stood as tall as me. Lucy was the same as most girls I'd ever dated. White, middle-class, parent who earned plenty of money in liberal professions or so-called creative arts but in reality living off inherited money. Lucy herself hardly qualified for Brain of Britain, ponderously slow on the uptake and dizzy with it. I could take the piss, make genuinely amusing observations, not even strain myself intellectually, but nine times out of ten she didn't understand a thing. She'd never left home and, even at her age, still lived with a friend, a stupid young actress in that flat upstairs. This particular idiot even used Lucy as a role model. Lucy's voice sounded like that of an inebriated Dowager. Unless I was slightly lubricated myself, it tended to grate on the eardrums. As Lucy waffled on, my mind turned to that place I'd just visited. Boo lived only a couple of doors away in the flat but these people owned the whole house, which itself, although terraced, rose high like the Tower in the Tarot. All rooms were centrally heated, wall to wall carpeting. The basement downstairs contained a giant furnished kitchen dominated by a huge wooden table. This led into another room of equally generous dimensions, which in turn led to a garden that contained a tree several hundred years old. Upstairs, the first floor boasted a library and office, Lucy's mother Rosemary the community architect. This office was crammed with large maps of the area and her trade accoutrements while the library had the usual texts found in such a household, padded out with collections of old encyclopaedias, books handed down, childhood volumes, coffee table stuff, tomes given for Christmas. A cleaner dusted them every week or so but I arrived at the conclusion they were rarely touched, least of all by Lucy. The landing included a front door, draft excluder, push bike with basket belonging to environmentally-conscious Rosemary.

Along passages and stairways leading to split level garden, basement area, shelves were filled with phonebooks, photo albums, kids' stuff left over from schooldays. Walls were decorated with country prints, architectural drawings by Lucy's sister, maps of the county this family originated from. Upstairs, midway on the next floor, bathroom and toilet, while further up three rooms, two full of empty beds for guests. Rosemary's bedroom faced the tree, looked surprisingly modest, almost a hotel room. Climbing upstairs, now getting out of breath, yet another floor, Lucy's flat.

Far from pokey. Large Victorian bathtub, massive kitchen, comfortable living room. One more staircase inside the flat itself led to something that resembled a tower with a small bedroom and tilted roof. The other room was fairly impressive as regards size, having a French window leading to a balcony with turret tops and pillars. Gazing down below from here to the street, small figures strolling made me feel as though I were looking from an office block. I could even see the roofs of buildings on the opposite side of the Crescent.

Anyway, I continued to down booze, listen to the now drunken Lucy, finally taking her back to the cage and the decanted Thunderbird. No fifteen minute guided tour here, she didn't seem perturbed by my mess and disorder. I did her Tarot, keeping it as simple as possible, keeping the limited attention span for an hour. Final result, parenthood. As it started to get dark, I went over to the off-licence, lifted more drink. Lucy stayed the night, AIDS warnings unheeded this time.

Morning, I took Lucy to a café for bacon sandwiches. She had to rush off to art school, me feeling this could be start of a relationship. Loved that house. Over to her flat later that very day. One of Lucy's friends from art college came back with her. Thin, long hair, phoney accent, pouting type of gay just out of the closet, intent on lecturing me on the evils of homophobia. I took an instant dislike, him droning on about gay movies and art, Andy Warhol, all that jazz. I'd covered these things myself years before when at Kingsway. In spite of his incessant prattle, the guy knew next to nothing. So it wasn't long before I steamed into him, imitating his accent, calling him Teapot. Whether or not Lucy twigged the significance of this remark, I couldn't tell. Later, she told me not to be so cruel to him. But in such rarefied surroundings something was bound to blow up sooner or later.

As indeed it did. A couple of days later, Lucy, her flatmate, the stupid actress, her boyfriend and a couple of their drippy mates were indulging in a boozing session, an activity I never refused. I'd already downed a bottle of vodka, having a go at the stupid actress's friends. None of these people, despite their pretensions, could be described as even slightly academic, so I mocked them on a simplistic level. The stupid actress's boyfriend butted in.

"What gives you the right to insult people and put them down the way you do?"

Possibly the squirt thought me to be muscling my way into the flat, taking control of the music, conversations, pouring of drinks. The boyfriend insisted on confrontation.

"What makes you so bloody important?"

Before I could get underway with my response, take another alcoholic gulp, Lucy's mother came into the flat looking distressed. Rosemary was well preserved despite being in her late fifties or early sixties, cushioned from life's brutal realities by piles of money.

"Lucinda! What's going on?"

Rosemary cast her eyes about, fixing on empty bottles. "You're drunk!"

This must have been a regular scene, the flat emptied double quick. Not me though, feeling no desire to leave.

"Look Lucinda, I don't want you hanging about with another nutty boy!"

"But mum ..."

My turn to get a word in edgeways.

"Excuse me missus, but I happen to be sitting here, so kindly address your remarks to me please."

She tried to put me in my place.

"Look. Lucy has a drinking problem. It's getting out of hand and I don't want her keeping company with people that drink."

I could automatically tell she didn't like my accent so I used it to full effect, bringing the mind reading trip into play, telling her straight.

"You're just a lonely old woman, scared of dying or letting your daughter grow up."

This threw her into instant silence. Just to rub it in, I threw in a parting shot.

"And I'm leaving now, you fucking old bag!"

Lucy sat, head buried in her hands. I left the house alone. Lucy however, came running out after me. Back to the cage, where Lucy told me her mother always behaved like that towards blokes she went out with at first but soon enough, she assured me, I'd be tucking into tea and cakes with Rosemary on Sunday, watching the God slot on telly. That didn't sound a bad set up except for the viewing. Maybe I could go one better, live there. I'd been living rough now for years, Lucy's place was full of all the required comforts. The only thing was that this relationship with Lucy wasn't all that important, take it or leave it. No more head over heels for me.

I continued seeing Lucy, she was well into me by now. I saw less of the gloomy cage, more of the home comforts. Two weeks after the flare-up, Lucy held another get together. Stupid actress was in work, starring in her mother's play, so she brought over bottles of tequila, and as an added attraction, a crusty Australian plus the old standby, Teapot. Rosemary stormed up yet again, screeching.

"Lucinda! What's going on? I want everybody to get out!"

Teapot tried to calm her down.

"Look Rosemary, why don't you just sit down and talk everything out?"

Rosemary wasn't having any of it.

"Who are you? Get out!"

I didn't bother hanging around for another re-enactment so it was off over to the pub. As I left with the crusty Australian, I glanced over my shoulder into the hallway where the action unfolded. Lucy's mother slapped her, causing the daughter to tumble over at the foot of the stairs. Stupid actress screamed while Teapot ineffectually tried to intervene. After a drink, I ponced a tenner off the Aussie, parted company, off on a mini bender. Back at the cage, a note from Lucy. She'd come over with stupid actress, I hadn't shown up. Other contents included a poem that a six year old would have felt ashamed of and a message to come over on Saturday as mother was going away for a week to inspect the family properties outside London. Sounded good enough to me. Holiday at Lucy's.

On my way over, walking along Parkway, I spied a shady-looking Redd outside a wine bar, parked up in a motor. The woman opposite dealt smack so I put two and two together."

"Waiting for Beryl, are you Redd?"

Same old Barney Rubble as of old.

"How do you know?"

"I know everything that goes on around here."

Told Redd I squatted in Kentish Town, was going out with Lucy. Redd remembered her from years back, probably also knew about the big house, how much the family was worth, the works. He handed me some change.

"Here Dan, play your cards right, you won't be needing that much longer."

Around then to Lucy's flat. Within a couple of days I'd shifted odd bits and pieces into her flat. We had the whole house to ourselves, spending most of the time in mother's section, watching the big colour TV, availing myself of those kitchen facilities, rustling up pastas and dishes from market veg. As for the romance angle, we laughed a lot, drunk even more. I got Lucy tapping her friends for dough so we could continue what now degenerated into a prolonged drinking bout. Trouble was, I didn't like Lucy when she'd drunk too much, owing to her acting even more ridiculous, singing songs out of key, the voice going posher, slurred until it sounded like royalty. Her eyes went funny and there would be no reasoning between moronic splutterings. But they had all the mod cons here and I liked a touch of comfort. As in days gone by, I systematically fine-toothed the house searching for money. It certainly looked like a gaff that would yield plenty of cash. But there wasn't a red cent, drawers containing useless articles like cotton reels. Cupboards and files were stuffed with architectural journals and charters.

I could now handle Lucy but mother might prove a problem. I'd have to work out a plan if I really were going to move in for keeps. Lucy's half-witted actress flatmate had all but departed to live with boyfriend so theoretically I could move in upstairs. I enjoyed myself to the degree that when the mother arrived back I was still in residence. Now it became keep-the-noise-down from Rosemary, us on the bender upstairs. I knew I'd have to adjourn back to the cage if I didn't want to blow it. Another complaint, so I decided I'd had enough for the time being, telling Lucy I was heading back home. Drunk as she was, Lucy didn't believe me at first, but soon I'd packed up some of my clothes into a bag, on my way. Lucy followed, shouting out my name, urging me back. Having been on a bender with her, arguments now flared up all the time over nothing. I wanted to escape for a while, even if only back to the cage. But Lucy wasn't standing for it. Like a spoilt kid she followed pleading. Even though I told her please go back to mummy, she insisted on remaining with me, coming back to the cage. No point disputing. I turned away, leaving the Crescent. Lucy flung herself at me, howling.

"Don't go Danny! Don't go!"

I pushed her away. She fell back, banging her head on a metallic shutter, slumping down to the pavement, moaning and groaning. Shocked, I dashed back to her, thinking she might be badly injured. Lucy's eyes rolled in her sockets, blinking back into focus. I managed to stand her up, then from nowhere, a policeman and woman were on the scene, the policewoman talking to Lucy.

"Are you alright love? We saw it all, do you want us to charge him?"

The policeman meanwhile, grabbed me. I tried to explain that this happened to be nothing more than a personal domestic dispute. They weren't having any of it but Lucy saved my skin, throwing herself around me.

"No! Leave him alone! I'm with him!"

Within moments both disappeared with a disgusted expression on their faces. So Lucy got her way, back to the cage.

The stupid actress flatmate moved out officially, leaving Lucy the whole flat. I had to make my move soon, since I'd got notice from the council, they intended to repossess the cage. I'd heard on the grapevine that Arlington dosshouse were opening up a new refurbished wing with tiny self-contained cabin-like rooms. I thought this would be a perfect way to get my foot in at Lucy's. Rent paid by housing benefit for Arlington, while in reality I'd stay at Lucy's most of the time, slowly moving in. Meanwhile I could get myself down as a vulnerable on the council waiting-list like Harriet, get re-housed from Arlington as a priority.

As a reminder the past was never too far away, I met Mario's Latino, working in a mobile chip van. She recognised me as I strolled by, calling out my name. I went over to the van, her asking if I fancied a drink, saying she'd pack the van in for half an hour. In the nearest bar, she produced a letter from Mario, sent out from prison. Judging from the contents, you'd think here was a saint in the making. Sorry for what he'd done, he sincerely hoped the two of them could get back together. Apparently, Mario was on remand for taking out a man's eye in a pub with a beerglass. Charming. I told the Latino I'd been getting into the Tarot, anything to distract her from Mario. Now she was all over me, trying to fix up a reading, which I promised to do sometime in the vague future. Then came the question.

"Do you think I should get back with him?"

Couldn't believe my ears. The very thought of Mario now had me making excuses and leaving. She looked at me as I slipped on my coat.

"But I love him."

In a daze, I removed myself, wondering how can anybody be so stupid? Off to Arlington, where an overnight queue formed for morning registration. Before joining the happy campers, I knocked back a few drinks with Lucy. A regular bunged me some Moggies, help see me through the long night as I'd be on the steps outside. Later, Lucy brought me a blanket and a flask. The queue was a mixture of young and old, most of the latter being Irish. Young ones were Northerners, unemployed, even some Londoners. Thanks to the Moggies I sank into a decent half-sleep, awaking in the morning intensely cold and hungry. Eventually we were in through the door to be interviewed in a room by a woman who resembled Lucy's mother, patronising, dogmatic, ignorant, middle-class. She informed me that frankly, I was unsuitable material even for the dosshouse. I'd been creating lots of noise all through the night, playing music on a radio to the annoyance of others. I denied involvement. After all, I'd been crashed out on Moggies. All to no avail.

"I'm sorry, but you can't have a room here and that's it."

I couldn't believe it. Barred from the dosshouse. I wandered out into the street, clutching the blanket. Rosemary pedalled along on her way to work. Seeing me, she drew up, managing a hello. I explained what had just transpired, that I didn't get a place.

"Oh dear!"

After this demonstration of her advanced vocabulary, she pedalled off again. Over to Lucy's for breakfast spending the day complaining about being rejected from the bottom of the lowest pile. Later, we went out, I persuaded Lucy to borrow a tenner from the family newsagent.

"After all Lucy, he's known you since you were eleven."

In the pub, I pointed out dossers from the queue.

"I bet he got one."

This dragged on for hours as people passed by. I stayed over at Lucy's that evening, during which time she went down to Rosemary for a chat about me becoming a tenant upstairs. Over the last couple of days I'd already spun a yarn to Rosemary telling her me and Lucy were giving up drink, that I was going to get a stall together in the market on the Enterprise Allowance Scheme. She seemed to be taken in by this crap, so I half expected a result. Sure enough Lucy came running upstairs breathless. Mother agreed to me staying if I paid rent, shared bills. I'd landed it. On my feet again A dollop of applied psychology and I'd have no trouble dealing with mother and daughter, having already lined up some God raps for Rosemary. As for Lucy, the girl loved me.

"That's really great Lucy."

She wanted to celebrate, go out for a drink. I told her to hold it for a while.

"I've just got to go upstairs for a minute, do something, wait here Lucy."

I climbed up to the large bedroom, walked out of the French windows on to the balcony, grinning to myself as I surveyed the Crescent. Almost next door, Boo's flat. Future rails. In the distance, Arlington's dosshouse lights twinkling. I knew for sure I'd made it back to the Crescent. Back where I belonged, among people who deserved me.

POSTSCRIPT

The author died of a heroin overdose on 15th February 1999 whilst the final proofs of the first edition of this book were being prepared for the printers.